THE PIONEER HISTORIES

EDITED BY V. T. HARLOW, D.LITT., AND J. A. WILLIAMSON, D.LIT.

THE GOLD RUSHES

THE PIONEER HISTORIES

Edited by V. T. Harlow, D.Litt., & J. A. Williamson, D.Lit.

THE EUROPEAN NATIONS IN THE WEST INDIES
ARTHUR PERCIVAL NEWTON, D.LIT.
Rhodes Professor of Imperial History, University of London

ENGLAND'S QUEST OF EASTERN TRADE
SIR WILLIAM FOSTER, C.I.E.
Formerly Historiographer to the India Office

THE PORTUGUESE PIONEERS
EDGAR PRESTAGE, D.LITT.
Camoens Professor of Portuguese Language and History in the University of London

THE EXPLORERS OF NORTH AMERICA
J. BARTLET BREBNER, M.A., PH.D.
Assistant Professor, Department of History, Columbia University

THE GREAT TREK
ERIC A. WALKER, M.A.
Harmsworth Professor of Imperial and Naval History in the University of Cambridge

THE EXPLORATION OF THE PACIFIC
J. C. BEAGLEHOLE, M.A., PH.D.

THE SPANISH CONQUISTADORES
F. A. KIRKPATRICK, M.A.
Emeritus Reader in Spanish, University of Cambridge

THE INVASION OF CHINA BY THE WESTERN WORLD
E. R. HUGHES, M.A.

THE AGE OF DRAKE
J. A. WILLIAMSON, M.A., D.LIT.

THE GOLD RUSHES
W. P. MORRELL, M.A., D.PHIL.

In Preparation
THE DISCOVERERS OF AMERICA
J. N. L. BAKER, M.A., B.LITT.

THE GOLD RUSHES

by

W. P. MORRELL

M.A., D.PHIL.

READER IN HISTORY IN THE UNIVERSITY OF LONDON

ADAM AND CHARLES BLACK
4, 5 & 6 SOHO SQUARE LONDON W.1
1940

The United States
THE MACMILLAN COMPANY, NEW YORK

Australia and New Zealand
THE OXFORD UNIVERSITY PRESS, MELBOURNE

Canada
THE MACMILLAN COMPANY OF CANADA, TORONTO

South Africa
THE OXFORD UNIVERSITY PRESS, CAPE TOWN

India and Burma
MACMILLAN AND COMPANY LIMITED
BOMBAY CALCUTTA MADRAS

MADE IN GREAT BRITAIN
PRINTED BY R. & R. CLARK, LIMITED, EDINBURGH

EDITORS' SECOND PREFACE
TO THE SERIES

SEVEN years ago the publication of the Pioneer Histories began, and since that date ten volumes have been issued. They deal with a variety of manifestations of one great branch of human energy, the expansion of European enterprise over the world. In their first preface the editors felt it necessary to suggest to the general reader that current controversies were the fruits of past activities. To-day there is little need to re-state such a connection; for there are few now who do not recognise that the problems of war and peace can be illuminated by a knowledge of history.

It may, however, be usefully repeated that each volume of the Series takes for its subject the history of some important movement and deals with it as completely as possible; that each is by an author familiar with the subject and is designed to embody the results of the most recent studies in it; and that some deal with subjects of which no full treatment has hitherto been accessible in English.

The Pioneer Histories have in the past appealed to a world-wide public. In addition to sales of the English editions in the British Commonwealth and the United States, volumes of the Series have been translated into

French, Spanish, German, Polish and Czecho-
Slovakian, a list of which the greater part is now
temporarily suspended, but which will perhaps be
restored and extended as the light spreads once more
over darkened Europe.

V. T. HARLOW

J. A. WILLIAMSON

August 1940

AUTHOR'S PREFACE

THE gold rushes of the last century produced much writing; but, though mining engineers have written books upon the gold mines of the world, there seems to be no book in any language attempting a synthesis of all the gold rushes as an aspect of the expansion of the European peoples. An individual can do no more than scratch the surface of this rich deposit of historical material and hope that others may be encouraged to work it more deeply.

I should like to have visited the scene of many of the rushes, but must confess that I know only one. My interest in gold rushes was first stimulated by the anecdotes of the Central Otago goldfields told by a valued and lifelong friend, Mr. Robert Gilkison, and by visits to the mine worked by another old friend, Mr. R. T. Symes. I have, however, had the benefit of the first-hand knowledge of Western Australia possessed by the Hon. Sir John W. Kirwan; and Sir Henry A. Miers very kindly put at my disposal private papers connected with his visit to the Klondike. To both these gentlemen I wish to express my gratitude. I should also like to thank for their valuable help Mr. Ronald Syme, who gave me various clues about ancient gold production to follow up; Mr. J. W. Blake, who put at my service his knowledge of West African history ; Dr. S. P. Turin, who read my Siberian chapter in draft and gave me access to an important Russian book by making notes

vii

on it for me; Professor H. Hale Bellot, who read my American chapters and made very helpful criticisms of them; Professor Eric A. Walker, who gave similar assistance with my South African chapter; and many others who have spared time to answer queries on special points. I am grateful to Mrs. M. H. Potter for the help which she has given me on this, as on other occasions, with indexing. From the staffs of the British Museum, the Royal Empire Society Library, Rhodes House Library and the London Library I have received the courteous help which readers in those libraries know they can expect. Nor must I omit to say that the years this book has been in the making must have imposed a strain upon the patience of my editors and publishers. I take this opportunity of acknowledging their consideration.

This book has been completed in war-time. It is a tale, however inadequately told, of adventure, enterprise and endurance in which the common man of British and American stock showed the mettle of which he was made. At a time which makes demands on all the energies and the endurance of which those peoples are capable it may not, it is hoped, be wholly inappropriate reading.

W. P. MORRELL

July 1940

CONTENTS

MAPS

THE GOLD RUSHES

CHAPTER I

BEFORE THE GOLD RUSHES

MANY forces have contributed to the spread of the human race over the surface of the earth—climatic change, economic necessity, desire for conquest, a *wanderlust* that defies analysis. Among these forces the thirst for gold has from time immemorial had a place, but until quite recent times it has been a subsidiary place. Men have traded for gold and fought for it: the hoarded treasure of powerful monarchs, accumulated by trade and tribute, has changed hands as a result of war. But only in modern times has this thirst for gold inspired vigorous peoples to seek it out by hard labour in the waste places of the earth. Gold is a metal that has for long ages had a peculiar power over the imagination of mankind, but the gold rush is a modern phenomenon.

In ancient and medieval times we know something about the working, but little or nothing about the actual discovery of gold. Discoveries may occasionally have produced an influx of concession-hunters or miners, but social and economic conditions hardly permitted the movements of population which could entitle these to the name of rushes, and the amounts of gold in question must have been small, for the greatest yields of ancient times came from large-scale exploitation of particular workings, not, it seems clear, from the rapid spread of small workings characteristic of a rush.

Man attained a respectable level of civilisation before

3

he knew the use of metals, but gold was in all prob-
ability the first metal that he knew. It is chemically
inert: its simpler compounds are formed with difficulty
and readily decomposed: and it is therefore found in
nature chiefly in the metallic form. In small quantities,
it is widely diffused in the sands and gravels of rivers
and streams, and there it must have caught the eye of
primitive man. Its lustre, fine colour and malleability
caused it to be valued for ornament, and the small scales
or pellets or rounded grains of these surface deposits
could be picked up without more ado. Curiosity, however, would prompt man to explore the deposits further
by digging with sharpened flints and washing: thus, no
doubt, the first gold workings began.

Gold was known over a fairly wide area in the Near
East as early as 5000 B.C.; but the first people to use it
on a considerable scale were probably the Egyptians.
It came into use in the pre-dynastic period, and in the
early dynastic age it was being extracted by systematic
mining in the granite mountains east of Coptos and
farther south in Nubia, between the Nile and the Red
Sea. Moreover in rings of fixed weight it circulated as
a standard of value; in short, it was used as money.

Peoples which could find no gold within their
borders, like those of Sumer and Babylon, were already
seeking it by trade. The 'beaker people' who spread
from Spain to other parts of Western Europe, probably
in the later part of the third millennium B.C., certainly
sought gold among other things, and found it, in particular, in Ireland. Other civilisations, like those of
Minoan Crete, seem to have got gold from Asia Minor.
In the first half of the first millennium B.C. Asia Minor
was a famous gold-producing region. The golden sands
of the Pactolus and the wealth of the Lydian kings

4

Gyges (*circa* 700 B.C.) and Croesus (560–546) became proverbial among the Greeks. About the same time the ancient workings still to be found in the Ural Mountains and the Altai were probably supplying gold to the Scythians of South Russia and to the great kings of Persia. But the very fact that gold had been one of the hallmarks of the wealthy civilisations of the Near East, which must have accumulated from a wide area amounts considerable by any but nineteenth or twentieth century standards, had the consequence that the readily accessible gold deposits of the Eastern Mediterranean lands had passed their best by Hellenistic times.

Rome was able to bring a large part of Western and Central Europe as well as the whole Mediterranean world under control; and new gold-producing regions could thus be exploited by the most advanced mining technique of the day. Spain, which even before the Carthaginian conquest had an important metal industry, attained far greater productivity after the Roman conquest in the Second Punic War, which was followed by an influx of Italian adventurers. The gold workings were particularly important in the north-west. In the dividing range between Asturias and Leon, especially in the Sil valley, the results obtained by the discharge of water from a height are impressive even to-day. 'Each mine', says a modern scholar who has visited the spot, 'had one or sometimes two canals leading to it. . . . At Las Medulas . . . the denudation was carried out down to the schist and backwards until the cliff became 800 feet high; thus the old workings resemble a huge amphitheatre in which pillars of harder gravel were left owing to the lack of powerful hydraulic machinery to cut them away.'[1] Pliny, writing well on

[1] O. Davies, *Roman Mines in Europe* (Oxford, 1935), p. 102.

in the first century of the Christian era, estimates the
annual yield of North Western Spain and Portugal at
20,000 pounds of gold—216,000 ounces troy. Afterwards the Spanish yield began to decline; but the
provinces in the Balkans to some extent took its place.
The mines of Macedonia and Thrace, the alluvial
deposits of the Vrbas and other valleys in the Bosnian
mountains were productive; and Trajan conquered the
ancient gold-producing land of Dacia and, as most of
the native miners had been killed or expelled, introduced a tribe from Northern Albania experienced in
mining, the Pirustae. Dacian gold-mining, however,
was interrupted later in the second century by the
Marcomannic wars, and in the third century Roman
gold-mining was definitely on the decline.

The Romans do not appear to have been active as
discoverers: such work may have been left to the gold-
working tribes or to the nomadic gold-washers of whom
we hear in the Balkan peninsula at any rate. But their
mining was on a scale that can be reckoned large even
by modern standards. The most potent instrument it
possessed was water, the use of which in 'hushing' or
breaking down the softer alluvial deposits we have
already mentioned. By the aid of picks for soft rock,
gads and hammers for hard, and especially by fire-
setting, the Romans could moreover sink shafts and
drive tunnels into the rock. Lighting was provided
by oil-lamps; haulage by relays of porters with leather
baskets; drainage was attempted by baling with large
buckets, later by *cochleae*—screw-vanes of wood or
copper set on wooden cores and encased in barrels—
and water-wheels. In the days of the Republic and early
Empire the large labour force required seems to have
been frequently supplied by slave-owning lessee com-

panies, though there were also small working mine-lessees. In the later Empire slaves were less numerous, and convicts, Christians for example, were employed instead; but the status of the free working miner worsened, and finally in 424 'the profession and domicile of *metallarii* were made hereditary'.[1] This State control of miners and the appearance of a corps of imperial mining officials were an attempt to counteract the decline of gold-mining. But though systematic Roman exploitation must have added considerably to the world's store of gold, it was fighting a losing battle against the gradual exhaustion of the deposits workable by its methods within the Roman Empire.

There was no serious recovery in European gold production until in the thirteenth and fourteenth centuries German miners began to exploit regions which had never formed part of the Roman Empire. The mountains of the Bohemian Forest, in addition to their wealth in silver, produced gold: so did Silesia, with its rivers running northwards from the Sudeten mountains to the Oder. There was a revival also of the output of gold, and even more markedly of silver, from Bosnia and Serbia, Eastern Hungary and Transylvania —where the former interruption had been due to political rather than economic causes. This mining advance was the work of free miners, taking part in the great eastward migration of the Germans in the Middle Ages. According to the customs of Iglau, codified by Wenceslas II in 1300, unoccupied areas were free to citizen-prospectors, who could hold and transmit their claims subject to continuous working and payment of dues. Mining became more capitalistic in the fifteenth

[1] O. Davies, *op. cit.* p. 7. Cf. also U. Täckholm, *Studien über den Bergbau der römischen Kaiserzeit* (Uppsala, 1937).

century, but it remained free, and it was technically progressive also, largely no doubt because it was free. The great work of Georgius Agricola, *De re metallica*, published in 1556, is a monument erected to the ingenuity and inventiveness of these German miners.[1] Silver and base metals were more important in this late medieval mining industry than gold; but gold benefited notably by the invention, in the late fifteenth or early sixteenth century, of the crushing-mill with iron-shod stamps. The only serious weakness in the industry according to the standards of its own day was in fact the relatively short supply of gold. If Europe was to increase its gold supply it must look beyond its own borders.

It was indeed already getting gold from West Africa. From the tenth century Sahara caravans had brought gold to Barbary, whence some of it reached the northern Mediterranean lands, from the Western Sudan, first from the kingdom of Ghana, afterwards from Mali, afterwards again from the empire of Songhai. These kingdoms did not actually produce the gold. It was derived by silent barter from the negroes of a region known as Wangara, now generally believed to have been the basin of the Faleme, a tributary of the Senegal, where the gold was washed down from the highlands and worked after the floods for four months each year.

One of the motives of the Portuguese voyages inspired by Henry the Navigator was certainly to tap this source of gold. They may have done so to some extent by way of the Gambia. When they reached Samma, on what is still called the Gold Coast, in 1472, an important gold trade soon developed: ten years later

[1] This is available in a fine modern edition in English, the work of H. C. and L. H. Hoover (London, 1912).

8

the castle of São Jorge da Mina (Elmina) was built to strengthen the Portuguese hold on the coast against the Castilians and other European intruders. The export of gold is said to have amounted to 170,000 *dobras* (270,000 ounces) annually. Probably the gold came from Bitu (Bonduku) and Lobi on the Black Volta—which one modern scholar at least identifies as Wangara. It seems that the Portuguese did little or no mining for gold themselves.[1] The actual gold-washers, behind their barriers of distance and interested silence, were hardly capable of intensive exploitation, and indeed as the sixteenth century wore on, though French, English and Dutch competed with the Portuguese for the gold trade, the output seems to have diminished.

The results were even more disappointing elsewhere in Africa. From at least the early tenth century, and quite possibly earlier, gold had found its way down to the south-east coast at Sofala, a town of Arab foundation, and had been traded for the most part to India. Over the highlands between the Zambesi and the Limpopo, and even farther south, are scattered ancient gold workings, the remains of 'quartz mining with regular pits and galleries which were only abandoned when the waters rose upon the miners.'[2] There is no evidence acceptable to the modern investigator of occupation of the great temple-fortress of Zimbabwe, which it is natural to associate with these workings, by any non-Bantu people. The best conclusion seems to be that the mining, under initial stimulus from India

[1] J. W. Blake, *European Beginnings in West Africa, 1454–1578* (London, 1937), p. 81. Mr. J. T. Furley, answering a private enquiry, surmised that the Portuguese might have worked some mines by native labour, but said he had found no actual evidence.

[2] E. A. Walker, *History of South Africa* (London, 1928), pp. 3 ff. Cf. also G. Caton-Thompson, *The Zimbabwe Culture* (Oxford, 1931).

perhaps, was carried on by the Bantu. The gold trade to and from the coast was carried on by Arabs. With the capture of Sofala in 1505 the Portuguese supplanted the Arabs; but they devoted less energy to the trade, and in any case tribal wars seem to have led to a decline in gold production about this time. Later the Portuguese sought to establish themselves in the gold country, but it was not so rich as they expected: 'the natives with much difficulty gathered but little in a long time'.[1] At the beginning of the seventeenth century the chief of the gold country, the Monomotapa, allowed the Portuguese control of the mines in return for support, but it proved an unsatisfactory bargain. Portuguese power, organising capacity and technical knowledge were in fact unequal to the task of mastering this remote country and exploiting its resources in gold. That remained to be done by another people in the late nineteenth and early twentieth centuries.

Asia proved equally unsatisfactory as a source of gold for European adventurers. Though the glitter of the gold of India and China, seen from afar, was one of the stimuli that initiated the European age of discovery, those great civilisations absorbed more gold than they produced; and they were too strong to plunder. Japan may have produced 25,000 ounces a year at the end of the sixteenth century; but the Shoguns, unlike the Chinese Emperors, coined it, and though some was exported by Portuguese, and later by Dutch, traders, the amount cannot have been large.[2] Gold did not in fact play a very important part in the European trade with the East. Some was got from Pegu, from Pahang

[1] M. de Faria y Sousa, *The Portuguese Asia* (trans. Stevens) (London, 1695), i, 355.

[2] On this matter see Y. Takekoshi, *Economic Aspects of the History of the Civilization of Japan* (London, 1930).

in the Malay Peninsula, from Macassar in Celebes, from Cambodia, from the Philippines. But the natural conditions were unfavourable to exploitation by Europeans, and they were not strong enough to enforce native exploitation on a really large scale. It seems clear that they merely happened upon, or at most developed, workings that had been initiated by the native peoples or by Indians or Chinese; and that the quantity of gold secured was limited.

It is hardly necessary to labour the point that the greatest discoveries of the precious metals in the Age of Discovery were made in America. Whatever the objectives of Columbus precisely were, there is no doubt that the finding of gold was prominent among them. In his first conversations with the Bahama islanders he 'was attentive and laboured to know if they had gold', and on leaving this first island he 'resolved to go to the south-west, to seek the gold and precious stones'.[1] His preoccupation with gold constantly appears in the journal of this voyage, and if he found little more than a few ornaments he believed that the mines of Cibao of which he heard would yield a great quantity. From about 1499 the exploitation of this gold in the mountain streams, by gangs of natives under the supervision apparently of experienced miners from Spain, seems to have absorbed much of the energy of the Spaniards in Española. The yield may for a short time have reached 60,000 ounces annually. On the discovery of gold in 1513 about the middle of the island of Cuba, Spaniards swarmed over from Española, but Cuba turned out to be less productive. The output of both islands sharply declined after about twenty years.

[1] *The Voyages of Christopher Columbus* (trans. and edited by Cecil Jane) (London, 1930), p. 150.

These minor gold rushes have paled into insignificance beside the brilliant episodes of the conquest of the mainland. Yet the gold of Montezuma's treasure —'the fruit of long and careful hoarding'—did not according to modern estimates amount to much more than a score of thousand ounces. The Incas of Peru were the great gold-hoarders of America. Though they did not use gold in commerce, they gathered it systematically from the alluvial deposits of the streams and mined it too, for instance in the Curimayo valley, north-east of Cajamarca. Thus Atahualpa was able to offer his captors a ransom, collected from ornaments and temple decorations, which the most recent and conservative estimates reckon at two or three hundred thousand ounces. A further treasure passed into the Spaniards' hands at Cuzco later in the same year, 1533.[1] A few years later, in 1536–38, another conquistador, Quesada, worthy to be named alongside Cortes and Pizarro, discovered a third gold-hoarding civilisation, that of the Chibchas, on the plateau of Bogotá, though the bulk of the king's treasure was successfully hidden by his subjects.

The excitement consequent on these discoveries can be readily imagined. The hoards, representing the production of uncounted years, were not really enormous; but the Spaniards were few. They were loth to admit that the last of the gold-hoarding civilisations had been found. On a report which reached them from Indian sources of the existence of a gilded man—a chief who in a ritual observance covered himself with gold dust before bathing in a lake—they reared an immense structure of speculation. *El hombre dorado*, the man, became *El Dorado*, a city rich in gold and standing

---

[1] For details see another volume in this series, F. A. Kirkpatrick, *The Spanish Conquistadores* (London, 1934).

by a lake. This story blended with another to the effect that refugees from Peru had founded a new Inca empire across the Andes. Many expeditions, some in the region of the Bogotá plateau, others in the upper Amazon basin, others later in the century in the Cordillera separating the Orinoco basin from the Amazon, sought this will-o'-the-wisp.[1]

But after 1540 the results of the treasure-hunts, in which men were content to look for monarchs to plunder or graves to loot, ceased to be important. The Spaniards began to get upon the track of the precious metals in their native deposits, and a new period of discovery began, nearly as exciting for the participants as the treasure-hunts and with more concentration of effort and more substantial results. Had gold been discovered in large quantities, great gold rushes would certainly have occurred; but the silver quite eclipsed the gold. The discovery of Potosí in Upper Peru or Bolivia, early in 1545, produced a great silver rush: Spaniards flocked there with their Indian dependants from all over the country, and within eighteen months this barren, mountainous region contained 14,000 people. In Mexico the silver districts of Zacatecas, San Luis Potosí and Guanajuato were opened up in 1546–58 and were soon 'dotted over with mushroom mining settlements'.[2] All were in a hurry to exploit the mines, and there was much extravagance and disorder; but the silver rushes laid the foundation of a great mining industry which by the end of the century was sending seven or eight million ounces annually to Spain.

[1] V. T. Harlow, Introduction to Ralegh's *Discoverie of the large and bewtiful Empire of Guiana* (London, 1928).

[2] A. S. Aiton, *Antonio de Mendoza* (Durham, N.C., 1927), p. 75. Cf. also J. Lloyd Mecham, *Francis de Ibarra and Nueva Vizcaya* (Durham, N.C., 1927).

Though gold was mined too, it was on a far smaller scale. Chile was most important at first, though Soetbeer's estimate of 64,000 ounces annually in 1545–1560 may be too high. The gold came chiefly from shallow alluvial deposits, at first in the Copiapó region, then from near Valdivia, and, when production there was interrupted by the Araucanian Indians, from near Coquimbo. But the gold industry of New Granada, the province of Quesada's discovery, proved to have more staying power. There was no great rush, rather a series of small ones, Spanish masters and Indian servants moving on as the gold was worked out. The main gold regions were along the Cauca and its tributaries, especially near Antioquia, Anserma to the west of Bogotá and, higher up, near Popayan.

The Spanish Government did not attempt to prevent the rushes. In 1504 all Spaniards had been given permission to seek and operate gold and silver mines. But its policy was not calculated to derive the maximum of benefit from them but rather, by strict control of exploitation, to confine the benefit as far as possible to Spain. It required all bullion to be brought to the royal assay offices, convoyed it to Spain, and forbade its export. But although Spanish industry was at first stimulated by the new American market, the rise in prices which resulted—the more inexorably because of the attempt to retain the bullion—hampered the export of its products to other countries.[1] The illusion of material prosperity was greater than the reality, fostering extravagance and the tendency to think commerce and industry employments unworthy of a Castilian, and probably also encouraging the ambitious foreign

[1] Earl J. Hamilton, *American Treasure and the Price Revolution in Spain, 1501–1650* (Cambridge, Mass., 1934).

policies of Charles V and Philip II, which proved in the end to be beyond their strength. Nor was Spanish exclusivism likely to bring to bear upon the mining industry the best technique of the day. In the seventeenth century the output of the silver mines declined, owing apparently to an increase in taxation and working expenses and a loss of labour through overwork as well as decreasing productivity.

The migratory gold industry of New Granada, being less intensive, was less affected. New districts were opened up near the Porce. A new labour supply was imported in the shape of negro slaves. In the second half of the century the miners invaded the thickly forested region of Chocó, whose fierce Indians had been somewhat tamed by Jesuit missionaries, and found rich alluvial deposits. In 1680 the richest gold mine yet discovered in America, the Espiritu Santo at Santa Cruz de Cana, was opened up in the coastal province of Darien. Its working was interrupted by buccaneers and was closed in 1727 by an Indian rising, but at its height Restrepo thinks it may have yielded over 1,500,000 pesos (150,000 ounces, say) a year.[1] But by this time Spanish America had lost its primacy in the gold industry to Brazil. It recovered it temporarily later: the trend of gold production in the later eighteenth century was upward both in New Granada and Chile, and in 1771 new alluvial deposits were opened up in the Mexican province of Sonora and yielded well despite the lack of water. At the beginning of the nineteenth century Humboldt estimated the total gold production of Spanish America at about 330,000 ounces annually. There were no new gold rushes, however. There never

[1] V. Restrepo, *Estudio sobre las minas de oro y plata de Colombia* (Bogotá, 1884), pp. 238-42.

had been any comparable in importance with those of
Brazil. After 1810 the industry was sharply interrupted
by the Spanish American Revolution, and in the great
age of gold rushes which was about to open Spanish
America played only a very minor part. Its miners had
a certain skill, but had made no important contribution
to technical progress: they were too dependent upon
cheap slave or Indian labour, and they had had no share
in the great revolution which was transforming industry
everywhere and would ere long transform the mining
of gold and silver.

CHAPTER II

BRAZIL

WHILST the Spanish conquistadors were win-
ning Mexico, Peru and New Granada for
Spain, the Portuguese were beginning to colonise
Brazil. Portugal had produced some men with the stuff
of conquerors in them, but their task had been to open
up and organise a trading empire in the East. What was
there to conquer in Brazil? No gold-hoarding civilisation like those of the Aztecs and the Incas and the
Chibchas of New Granada: merely a vast expanse
peopled by native tribes which had not even words for
the precious metals. The first export was of dye-woods:
the first flourishing industry was the planting of sugar,
from about 1560, particularly in the captaincy of
Pernambuco in the north: the first occupation followed
inland, for instance in the basin of the Rio São Francisco, was the rearing of cattle for the sugar plantations.
But the impetus to expansion came above all from the
settlement of São Paulo, founded by the Jesuits on the
cool, misty plateau of Piratininga. The Paulistas soon
developed a marked individuality. They were not men
of wealth like the planters of the north: their characteristics were vigour, enterprise, and a roving disposition which doubtless owed something to an Indian
strain in their blood. They sought primarily for Indians
to work their land, for they could not afford negro
slaves like the sugar planters and they did not intend to

17   2

be mere peasants. They took little heed of the restraining influence of the Jesuits or of the royal authority to which the Jesuits appealed. As their slave-raids depopulated the regions near São Paulo they ranged farther afield. A *bandeira* of men, women and children would set out from São Paulo, along Indian paths through the forests of the coastal zone and down the inland rivers, taking with them Indian servants and baggage animals, and would vanish into the wilderness for years. In the first instance the expeditions of the *bandeirantes* took a westward direction, towards the Paraná: it was not until the last quarter of the seventeenth century that they turned northwards and opened up the richest gold regions of Brazil.

Gold had actually been discovered much earlier, in 1560, and in the province of São Paulo: the exact locality is doubtful. An Englishman, John Whithall, writing from Santos in 1578 to a friend in England, mentions that 'certaine mines of silver and gold' have been discovered and await development, but does not say where.[1] Two Paulistas, the Sardinhas, father and son, made further discoveries in 1589–97 in the same region: in 1598 there was the first sign of official interest, which culminated on 15 August 1603 in the issue by Philip III of the first code of mining regulations for Brazil. But though no doubt they enriched a few individuals, these gold workings can only have produced a few thousand ounces and were of merely local importance.

In 1674 royal encouragement was given to the search for gold in Brazil. The Crown of Portugal, again independent of Spain, had now only this one important

---

[1] Hakluyt, *Principal Navigations of the English Nation* (ed. Masefield, London, 1927), viii, 16.

overseas possession left to it: Brazil alone had been able to shake off the attacks of the Dutch, who in the middle of the century appeared to have established a firm hold over the north. But with the spread of sugar cultivation to the West Indian islands, the foundations of the prosperity of Pernambuco and Bahia had been undermined: another profitable industry was necessary if the colony was to be developed and swell the revenues of the Crown. Moreover, appreciative though it might be of the enterprise of the Paulistas, the natural leaders in the development of the interior, the Crown was anxious to divert their energies to some other object than slave-raiding. Gold was not the only magnet that might draw men into the interior: reported discoveries of emeralds and silver at first attracted more attention: but the predominance of gold arose from the course of events. Some gold-seekers turned southwards and were rewarded by discoveries at Paranaguá, Corityba and elsewhere in 1678–80, but the more difficult enterprise of exploration to the northward was ultimately the more successful. Behind the great coastal range of the Serra do Mar, in the upper basin of the great Rio São Francisco, lay a mountainous region, cut off from the coast by steep cliffs, roaring torrents, and almost impenetrable forests, and not very easy of access even from the plateau of São Paulo in the south-west. It seems probable that gold had been found in this region, though not in the richest part of it, in 1567 or 1568; though then and for some time afterwards emeralds were the principal object of the search. Even now the most thorough exploration of the region, by a *bandeira* which remained there, planting crops for its sustenance, from 1674 to 1681, was made in search of emeralds. But at last, in 1693, two distinct expeditions brought

back specimens of gold. One of these was led by a
priest, the other and more important by a member of
a leading Paulista family, Antonio Rodrigues Arzão,
who had entered the region by way of the Rio Doce,
with a party of fifty men. He was led to prospect by the
similarity of the country to the new gold-producing
districts of São Paulo, but the exact locality of his discovery is uncertain. Arzão succumbed to the hardships
he had endured before he could follow up his discovery,
but he left the necessary directions to his brother-in-law
Bartolomeu Bueno de Siqueira, who with the assistance
of a rich Paulista, Carlos Pedroso da Silveira, returned
to the wilds in 1694. Before reaching the spot indicated
by Arzão this party found gold at Itavevera, near the
headwaters of the Rio das Velhas, an important tributary of the Rio São Francisco. They planted crops,
making evident their intention to stay and work the
gold. Whilst they were away in search of game, another
bandeira, on slave-hunting bent, discovered their workings, and it was this second party that brought back
further specimens to the town of Taubaté in 1695.
Pedroso, who had financed the expedition, was rewarded
by the governor with the office of *capitão mór*, and
Bartolomeu Bueno was appointed registrar of the mines.
Orders were given to erect a smelting-house at Taubaté,
and this must have had, as Southey says, 'the same effect
as a proclamation of Government would have had,
announcing that there was gold in the land and inviting
all persons to search for it'.[1]

None of these preliminary discoveries was sur-
passingly rich, but there were later and richer finds in
the same region, the most important being perhaps that
of 'steel-coloured gold' in 1696, which gave a name to

[1] *History of Brazil* (London, 1810–19), iii, 51.

the mining camp of Ouro Preto, above a remarkable defile of the Rio do Carmo. By 1697, though the outlines are only dimly discernible, there was in progress from São Paulo, from Rio de Janeiro, from the northern captaincies which contained about 70 per cent. of the free inhabitants of Brazil, a movement of population which undoubtedly deserves the name of a gold rush. Farms were abandoned. Negro slaves were bought in the sugar districts to work the mines: the white employees of the sugar-mills all left to make their fortunes. The Governor of Rio de Janeiro, visiting the mines in 1697 on the order of the king, engaged in the same pursuit as the rest and did not return, according to Southey, until he had enriched himself thereby. The news of the discoveries spread to the mother country and, says von Eschwege, there were not ships enough to carry the Portuguese who wished to go to the mines.[1] So intent were all upon gold, such was the neglect of supply and local cultivation, that in 1701 there was famine at the mines, and many had to be abandoned.

The chief object of the mining regulations hitherto in force in Brazil had been to ensure payment of the fifth due to the Crown. Though the size of claims was regulated, it is probable that the wealthier and more powerful of the miners had done more or less as they pleased. This seems to be implied in the new code of 19 April 1702, issued, one may take it, in the light of experience gained in the rush. The normal claim was to be about seventy-two yards square, worked by twelve slaves; but those who had fewer than twelve slaves might receive smaller claims, and if there was more

---

[1] Eventually, in 1720, the Government of Portugal sought to confine emigration to Brazil to those appointed to office.

than enough ground on this basis, further allotments were to be made to those with more than twelve. After the discoverer had chosen the first and third and the Crown the second claim, the order of location was to be determined by lot. No second claim was to be allotted to any person until he had worked the first; and grantees were not allowed to sell their claims for the purpose of obtaining others in better situations, though they might do so if unable to work them for want of slaves. If a claim remained unworked for forty days without good cause, one-third was forfeit to the informer, two-thirds to the Crown. Crown claims were to be leased at auction or (a modification introduced a few months later) worked by private individuals of conscience and credit in consideration of half the produce. Private claims paid the now traditional fifth to the Crown at the smelting-houses to which all gold had to be taken for assay and stamping.

The processes of an industry dependent on slave labour were likely to be simple, though according to von Eschwege the slaves themselves, acquainted with gold-washing in their West African home, introduced the *bateia* in place of the small vessels, the tin plates for instance which every traveller carried for use at meals, in which the first gold-washing was done. The *bateia* was a round wooden shallow funnel-shaped vessel, from eighteen inches to two feet or more in diameter: it was shaken from side to side in running water until the earth was washed away and the metallic particles had sunk to the bottom. It was somehow discovered that precipitation could be hastened by addition of the sap of certain trees. In poorer workings, or where operations were on too great a scale for the *bateia* alone to cope with them, the gold-bearing sand was first concentrated by the use of a gently sloping washing-floor (*canôa*) lined with raw hide or flannel. Streams were diverted or dammed and the gold-bearing gravel carried away in *carumbes*, timber boxes of truncated pyramidal shape. Stream-beds were dragged by a sort of long-handled sharp iron scoop. Sometimes even divers descended to the bottom with a *bateia* in their hand. But it was not long before it was discovered that the *taboleiros* or terraces on the banks of the streams also contained gold. The first method of exploiting these was to dig a square pit or *cata* down to the *cascalho*, 'a stratum of rounded pebbles and gravel immediately incumbent on the solid rock'. Quite early, however, perhaps as a result of the despatch of mining experts from Portugal in 1700, the miners learnt how to make water do some of their work. Mawe, writing early in the nineteenth century, saw and described one process which had long been in use. 'Where water of sufficiently high level can be commanded, the ground is cut in steps, each 20 or 30 feet wide, two or three broad, and about one deep. Near the bottom a trench is cut to the depth of two or three feet. On each step stand six or eight negroes, who, as the water flows gently from above, keep the earth continually in motion with shovels, until the whole is reduced to liquid mud and washed below. The particles of gold contained in this earth descend to the trench, where, by reason of their specific gravity, they quickly precipitate. Workmen are continually employed at the trench to remove the stones, and clear away the surface.' After five days' washing, the precipitation in the trench was carried to a convenient stream and washed with the *bateia*.[1] Elaborate as these processes were, however, they had

[1] J. Mawe, *Travels in the Interior of Brazil* (London, 1823), p. 108.

by no means reached the technical level of the sixteenth-century miners of Germany.

Such were the processes of the gold industry and the framework of regulations within which it worked. But the mines in their early years were far from being the scene of regular, law-abiding industry. Customs houses were placed on the roads to São Paulo, Rio de Janeiro, Bahia and Pernambuco in an effort to prevent the traffic in unstamped gold. Attempts were made, with the same object, to prohibit all trade with Bahia except in cattle. All goldsmiths were excluded from the mines. But there was more serious trouble than mere defrauding of the revenue to cope with. The Paulistas were the discoverers of the mines, and regarded themselves as their rightful lords: but they were soon swamped by the inrush of *forasteiros* or strangers, whom they nicknamed *emboabas*—a Tupi Indian word meaning birds with feathered feet—because they wore boots or leggings whereas the Paulistas apparently went barefoot. It is not quite clear how the trouble came to a head. But in 1708 the *emboabas* assembled in arms and elected a certain Manoel Nunes Vianna as captain of the mines to curb the insolence of the Paulistas: a clash occurred at the Rio das Mortes and a number of Paulistas were killed. Manoel Nunes Vianna was obviously a strong man who used his supremacy to maintain order and not merely to avenge himself upon his opponents. But São Paulo was smarting at the defeat and eager to wipe it out, and the Governor of Rio had also to be reckoned with. Manoel Nunes, perhaps by a show of force, induced him to abandon his first journey to the mines, assuring him that he would in due course resign his captaincy to the regular authorities. The more extreme element among the

miners appear to have thought that they could hold out
for eight or ten years, enrich themselves, and if refused
pardon retire with their treasure into the Spanish
colonies. It never came to that. A new governor, Affonso
de Albuquerque, approached the task of pacification
with moderation and skill. It appears that he attempted
to dissuade the Paulistas from their projected attack on
the mines and, failing, warned the *mineiros* of their
danger. The Paulista attack, in the later part of 1709,
was repulsed. On the other hand, according to von
Eschwege, dissensions had broken out between the
Portuguese under Manoel Nunes and the native-born
Brazilians. However that may be, Albuquerque was
well received at Caete, one of the mining camps, and
granted an amnesty; but Manoel Nunes was not
received with favour. Although in November 1709 São
Paulo and 'Minas Geraes' were erected into a separate
captaincy-general, Paulista ascendancy at the mines was
at an end, and the completion of a road from Rio de
Janeiro to the mines in 1710 weakened the economic
connection with São Paulo.

Albuquerque, who had made the royal authority a
reality and shown himself able to manage the *mineiros*,
was appointed to the new governorship, which in view
of the strictly limited authority of the Governor-General
at Bahia was in virtually direct dependence on the
Crown. A series of governmental acts show an intention
not merely of regulating the industry but of moulding
the society of the mining regions. In 1711 many of the
chief mining camps—notably Ouro Preto, which
received the name of Villa Rica—were given regular
municipal institutions. At the same time, all monks and
priests not holding a cure—whose activities according
to von Eschwege's account had caused the *emboaba*

war—all merchants, tavern-keepers and foreigners were forbidden to enter the mining district; and the authorities were given power to expel any undesirable person. Gambling was forbidden; restrictions were placed upon liquor-stills. A regular militia was organised, and limitations were imposed upon the carrying of arms.

The first task the Government had set itself remained, however, the most troublesome. The royal fifth was obnoxious to the *mineiros*, and was no doubt difficult to collect. Accordingly in 1714 the governor accepted an offer to commute it for 30 *arrobas*—rather more than 14,000 ounces—annually. At first the king was not satisfied and ordered him to accept an alternative proposal for a tax upon all negroes employed at the mines; but a year later this system was abandoned for the other. The difference, however, was not very substantial, for it appears that the commutation was assessed by the *camaras* of the municipalities according to the number of negroes employed, and as a stationary revenue from an increasing gold yield was not satisfactory to Government, it was supplemented by duties on imports entering the mining districts. An attempt in 1719 to revert to the fifths provoked a serious riot at Villa Rica; and the Governor, to pacify the people, granted a year's delay. The Crown however was insistent, and would not accept an increased commutation; and after the way had been prepared by consultations with magistrates, officials and leading *mineiros*, the fifth was duly introduced on 1 February 1725 and smelting-houses were reopened. Enforcement, however, remained as difficult as ever. Goldsmiths made trinkets, crosses, rosaries out of 'unquinted' gold until in 1730 they were excluded from the mines. Illicit assayers cast ingots identical with those of the smelting-houses. In the hope

of reducing evasion the rate was reduced in 1730 to
12 per cent., but still finality had not been reached. In
1732 Government decided to try a poll-tax on slaves
instead. The *camaras* thought this would be a change
for the worse: the burden would be equally heavy upon
successful and unsuccessful miners: they suggested a
guaranteed minimum of 100 *arrobas* of gold a year.
But in vain. The capitation was introduced on 1 July
1735. Slaves born in Minas Geraes and under fourteen
years of age, and those in the service of the Governor,
the clergy, military officers or civil officials were exempt.
All manual workers were subjected to the same tax;
and a shop tax was likewise imposed. The Government
had found a tax that was easier to collect, though it too
was evaded; but revenue had triumphed over equity.

But in spite of these endless financial contests the
mines had been developing, as the increasing amount
of the commutation offered for the fifth plainly showed.
New districts were opened up in Minas Geraes—Villa
do Principe about 1715, Itabira about 1720, Paulistas
being in each case the discoverers. Attention was
directed to deposits on the hills or *morros*. This entailed
often large-scale water operations: elaborate stone
reservoirs, *mondeus*, divided into compartments, were
erected in the valleys to concentrate the mud washed
down. It also entailed disputes about water rights, first
regulated in 1720. But it clearly gave a fillip to gold
production. Moreover the Paulistas were stung by the
loss of their predominance in Minas Geraes into new
prospecting expeditions westward. Travelling for the
most part along the rivers, they reached the district of
Cuyabá, and there, in a land of warlike Indians, they
found gold in 1718. They chose a certain Pascal
Moreira Cabral as their captain and sent a messenger

to São Paulo announcing their discovery. Rich new finds were made in this region in the years following, though it appears that the old strife between the jealous Paulistas and the *forasteiros* flared up again. Moreover the desire of an enterprising Paulista, Bartolomeu Paes de Abreu, to open up a land route to Cuyabá owing to the dangers of the river route during the monsoon period, led to a new and even more important discovery. In 1682 Bartolomeu Bueno, one of the Minas Geraes discoverers, had brought back rich samples of gold from the land of the Guayas. His son, a boy of twelve, had accompanied him on the expedition, and joined Bartolomeu Paes in a prospecting expedition to this region even though the road scheme was dropped by a new governor. After three years in the wilderness the expedition encountered Indians who led Bueno and his companions to their destination, the Arrayal do Ferreiro on the Rio Vermelho, which flows into the Araguaya. The Governor of São Paulo notified the king of the discovery in a letter of 27 October 1725 and rewarded the discoverers with office at the mines, lands and tolls of the crossings of the rivers. Thus the rich mining district of Goyaz was opened up, and remote though it was, miners came in such numbers to it as to cause a famine in 1730. When Cuyabá had passed its best, yet another region to the west of it was found to be gold-producing in 1734, when two brothers, Fernando and Artur Paes de Barros, found gold on the banks of the Sarare, a tributary of the Rio Guapore.

Another discovery may be mentioned, although it falls outside the special province of this book. In 1723, a diamond was discovered in the Serro do Frio in Minas Geraes. A rush followed a few years later, marked by scenes of anarchy like those in the gold rush twenty

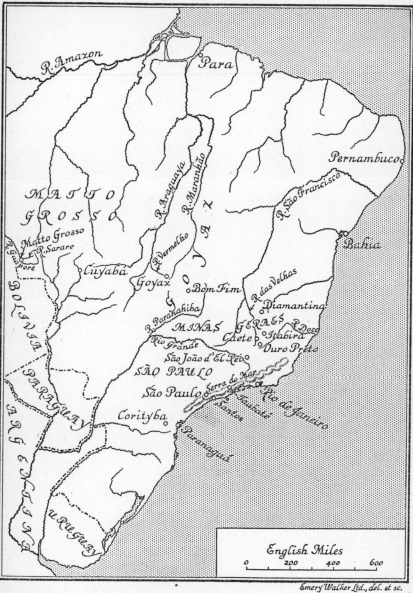

BRAZIL

years before, and the output was so great that the price
of diamonds fell from eight to two *milreis* a carat in two
years. The Government took alarm. A first attempt
to reserve the diamond district failed in the face of
local opposition; but in October 1733 a royal letter
strictly limited the extraction of the precious stones.
Later the Crown resorted to a system of monopoly—
farmed out to contractors in 1740–71 and then taken
under its direct control—and coped as best it could
with the activities of unlicensed diamond-seekers or
garimpeiros.

This succession of discoveries explains the long continuance in the mining districts of Brazil of something
of the atmosphere of a rush. The multitudes that
flocked to new discoveries in Minas Geraes at any rate
made application of the mining regulations difficult. In
1728, on a rush to a *morro* on the Rio das Pedras, it was
proclaimed that no grants would be made, but that the
ground should be open to all, though a certain distance
was to be left between pits. The population continued
turbulent and restless. The use or abuse of water rights
provoked conflict between the owners of such rights
and the general body of miners. Distance, the risk of
famine, of Indian attack, of fever from the swamps near
the Rio Guapore or Matto Grosso field, did not deter
men from venturing out into the *sertão* (backwoods),
though in 1730 a royal letter forbade persons to go
prospecting at great distances from existing mines
without the king's special permission. Southey tells us
that the miners were often misled by false reports and
'abandoned sure profit for the hope of a richer con-
tingency'.[1] Legislation in 1728 and 1734 against
drinking-houses and booths, in which slaves were de-

[1] *Op. cit.*, iii, 262.

bauched and tempted to spend the gold collected for their masters, suggests the riotous life of the mining camp: so perhaps does an edict of 1730 that no women should go to Brazil without the King of Portugal's permission, except wives accompanying their husbands. Of the well-established town of Villa Rica or Ouro Preto, Professor Percy Alvin Martin remarks that 'the wealth and extravagance of its citizens are attested by the palaces, stately churches, and imposing public buildings which invest the present moribund city with such a romantic charm'.[1] The municipal institutions that were bestowed upon the chief camps of Cuyabá, Goyaz and Matto Grosso indicated a certain faith in the permanence of the goldfields but not necessarily a settled existence: in 1755 the Guayás, whom Bartolomeu Bueno had kept on good terms but his successors had antagonised, attacked Villa Bôa (the present Cidade de Goyaz) itself: and in Matto Grosso also the miners were disputing the terrain with the warlike Payaguás and Guaycurús. Yet 'the finest silks which were imported into Brazil found their way to this new establishment in the centre of the continent, where the miners purchased them with characteristic prodigality'.[2]

The capitation returns show a slave population in Minas Geraes remaining more or less stable from 1735 to 1743 at about 100,000. The general population is estimated about the middle of the century at some 240,000. To these figures must be added an uncertain but much smaller number for Goyaz, Cuyabá and Matto Grosso. Although new and rich discoveries continued to be made, at any rate until the middle of the century,

[1] P. A. Martin, 'Minas Geraes and California' (*Revista do Instituto Historico e Geographico Brasileiro*, Tomo Especial, 1922, p. 266).

[2] Southey, *op. cit.*, iii, 310.

in these remoter fields, the peak of gold production in Brazil had now been attained. According to Calogeras, who bases himself on the capitation yield and makes an allowance of 20 per cent. for evasion, the total production from 1736 to 1751 was probably 12,000 *arrobas*— which would mean about 350,000 ounces a year—in Minas Geraes; and the allowance for Goyaz and Matto Grosso, then in their heyday, might bring the total for Brazil to half a million ounces in its best years: this would also tally with Soetbeer's figures. It may be significant in this connection that in 1750 the Government agreed to abandon the capitation and return to the system of fifths, the people of Minas Geraes guaranteeing a minimum return of 100 *arrobas*. The change is usually associated with the death of John V and the advent of King Joseph and his minister Pombal; but it is worthy of note that the guaranteed minimum had been offered and refused sixteen years before. With the fifths the elaborate regulations returned. Travellers on entering Minas Geraes exchanged their coin for gold dust, the only circulating medium allowed. Goldsmiths were prohibited not only at the mines, but in the ports.

In most of the years before 1762, the produce of the fifths exceeded the 100 *arrobas* that the *mineiros* had guaranteed: then it gradually became evident that a decline had set in. It may seem superfluous to look for causes, beyond the exhaustion that sooner or later awaits all gold deposits: indeed, in comparison with most of the nineteenth-century gold rushes, the remarkable feature of Brazilian gold had been the length of time before the yield declined. No doubt the sheer difficulty of prospecting in the *sertão* had delayed the extension of the goldfields: no doubt, too, the number of miners capable of prospecting was relatively small:

the *bandeirante* was a rover rather than a skilled prospector, and the *faiscadores* who worked for themselves on a small scale were mostly negroes and mulattoes quite incapable of organised expeditions which the vast distances and the Indian danger entailed. However it is generally agreed that the decline of the gold industry was hastened by specific weaknesses. Von Eschwege, who was called to Brazil to report on this very subject, held that the proper working of the reefs, which usually follow the alluvial phase of a gold rush, required technical knowledge that the Brazilians lacked and greater capital expenditure than they could afford; that they devoted all their energies to securing the greatest immediate return; and that they adhered to individual working on a comparatively small scale when they should have combined in companies to extend the scale of their operations. Instead of combining they would borrow money and buy more slaves until they ruined themselves, when they would move off to the *sertão* down the Rio São Francisco or between the Paranahiba and the Rio Grande and betake themselves to agriculture or pastoral pursuits. But if there were shortcomings on the part of the *mineiros*, there were also mistakes in Government policy. Far from seeking to remedy the technical backwardness of the industry through foreign experts, Portugal jealously kept it a national preserve, doubtless in the fear that some nation would appropriate its Brazilian El Dorado as the Dutch and English had taken its trading empire in the East: in 1730 it was even decreed that no Portuguese leaving to take up an official appointment in Brazil might take other than Portuguese servants. Not until John VI called in von Eschwege in 1811 was this exclusive policy reversed. The financial policy pursued was not calculated to encourage long-range development, and the capitation put a premium on the production of a maximum of gold in a minimum of time and thus on hasty and superficial exploitation which spoiled the sites for scientific mining. Seeking to encourage the *mineiros* to raise capital in 1752, the Government re-introduced an old regulation of Philip III and exempted from seizure for debt the slaves of miners employing more than thirty. But this measure rather discouraged lenders than helped the miners to raise money. More-over the Government of Portugal, though not always deaf to advice from Brazil, was too rigid and left too little discretion to its Captains-General, who were some-times, though not always, able men with a real grasp of the problems of the mines. In the minor posts, the Government was none too well served: in the early days of the rushes there was a tendency to give office to the actual discoverers, who were at any rate men of initi-ative and vigorous personality, but as time went on the *guardas-mor* were, it appears, sometimes absentees, some-times corrupt, and the judges, who profited by the fees, had no scruple in prolonging litigation and thus holding up the working of claims. A vigorous, turbulent society which needed some guidance from an enlightened government received a rather spasmodic and not very effective control, which sometimes verged on exploitation.

Moreover the immense geographical distances of Brazil were obstacles in the way of a permanent gold industry, which must depend upon increasing technical efficiency in the working of less and less rich deposits. It was difficult before the days of railways to transport machinery even to Minas Geraes, let alone Goyaz or Matto Grosso. It was not merely lack of technical skill that was responsible for the failure of Minas Geraes to rise above such simple machines as chain-pumps and such like: iron (likewise gunpowder for blasting) was dear. Goyaz from about 1740 could perhaps feed itself but could hardly supply itself cheaply with any other commodities. As for Matto Grosso, it suffices to say that owing to Indian attacks, it was worth while to communicate with it by a ten months' voyage from Para up the Amazon and its tributaries. Under such conditions only rich deposits could pay, and no gold industry has ever flourished for long upon rich deposits.

Efforts were made from time to time to check the decline of the gold mines. Governors and private individuals sent expeditions to reported new gold districts, and some discoveries were made: in 1782, for example, there were, according to von Eschwege, 12,000 working on the Rio Maranhão in Goyaz, though their numbers were thinned, first by an epidemic and then by lack of capital. Some large-scale water operations were planned, but often they were not carried through. From about 1766 the fifths in Minas Geraes began to fall further and further below the guaranteed minimum of 100 *arrobas*, and though before long the guarantee was not enforced, the obligation was not remitted. Moreover the administration was oppressive, suspecting fraud where there was merely declining yield. The revolutionary conspiracy of José da Silva Xavier Tiradentes in 1789 was partly based on a rumour that the arrears were going to be collected, and the programme of remission of debts due to the Crown, throwing open of the forbidden diamond district, and freeing of gold and diamonds from duties throws light upon the state of affairs in Minas Geraes, though the means of the conspirators were pitifully inadequate for their political aim of an independent republic.

It was not until the regency of John VI that the Government of Portugal showed much inclination to grapple with the fundamental causes of the decline of the mines. The best experts in Brazil were then invited to report upon the measures needed, and on 13 May 1803 there followed a royal charter which sought to encourage the formation of companies, granting larger claims and reducing the royal dues from a fifth to a tenth, and to promote discovery; it also set up a Mining and Mint Council for Minas Geraes. Even this statement of policy remained largely ineffective, however, until the Prince Regent moved his court to Brazil and in 1811 brought the German geologist and mining expert, Baron von Eschwege, to the country. Von Eschwege remained there ten years, and it was he who introduced Brazilians to the wet-crushing stamp battery and to systematic underground mining, by exhortation and by the example of his own mine of Passagem near Ouro Preto, acquired in 1819. A Brazilian mine-owner declared that these machines with two slaves in two days did more work than eighty men in eight days. But the new industry that now arose was one of a few successful mines, producing no more than perhaps 50,000 ounces a year, not the occupation of a whole province: and its most successful mines were carried on henceforward by foreign capital. The *mineiros* themselves had exhausted their means. The population of Minas Geraes in 1821 was 514,000, about a quarter of these being whites; but, in Southey's words, 'the miners, from being the most opulent, had become the most indigent class'.[1] About 10,000 slaves were employed in the industry in 1812–13, and there

---

[1] *Op. cit.*, iii, 826: the figures are not Southey's, but those of von Eschwege, *Pluto Brasiliensis* (Berlin, 1833), pp. 441, 595.

were also some 5000 *faiscadores* (one is tempted to call them fossickers) earning probably a bare subsistence or little more. The two types of exploitation were perhaps tending to shade off into one another: at any rate at Bom Fim, in Goyaz, Ste. Hilaire in 1819 found some of the inhabitants sending their slaves to wash gold on a sort of weekly contract, requiring them to bring in 900 or 1000 *reis* and to subsist on the rest of their presumed takings. Such signs of prosperity as existed were generally due to other factors than gold—the capital and military station at Villa Rica, agriculture and the raising of cattle and pigs for the Rio de Janeiro market at São João d'El Rei. At Itabira Ste. Hilaire found a few large and flourishing mines; but von Eschwege's verdict on the captaincy as a whole was that the smelting-houses simply owed their survival to jobbery. The state of Goyaz, a vast province with only 60,000 inhabitants, was worse, for it was too remote from the coast for profitable agriculture. Many families, Ste. Hilaire tells us, had simply retired into the wilderness and lost the very elements of civilisation. At Cuyabá in Matto Grosso, the number employed in mining had fallen to a few hundred.

The gold rushes, in short, had not succeeded in founding flourishing industrial provinces in the interior of Brazil. Indeed the early nineteenth-century writers remark that the *mineiro* appeared to have lost the enterprising spirit of his ancestors and that those who prospered in agricultural pursuits generally belonged to a new generation. The keynote of life at the mines, says Oliveira Lima, had been luxury without comfort; but so it was in other gold rushes which were more fortunate in their sequel. No doubt the truth was that though the slave-raiding *bandeirantes* had the

courage, persistence, and hardihood and perhaps the
'eye for country' of later prospectors, the slave-owning
mineiros worked too much by habit and rule of thumb,
as slave-owners are apt to do. Moreover, owing to their
lack of technical skill and enterprise, the gap between
the gold rush period and the period of systematic exploitation became a chasm in which they were all en-
gulfed. Nevertheless the effects of the gold rushes on
Brazil were lasting and important. The coastal cities,
and Rio de Janeiro in particular, grew rich through the
supply of the spendthrift *mineiros*: the centre of gravity
of Brazil shifted to the south and the seat of government
was moved from Bahia to Rio in 1763. The mines were
largely responsible for the increase of the population of
Brazil from perhaps 300,000 at the beginning to over
two and a half millions at the end of the eighteenth
century, for they had led to an influx of immigrants from
Portugal and an importation of hundreds of thousands
of slaves from Africa—thereby however confirming the
dependence of the Brazilian economy upon slave labour.
They probably contributed much to the growth of an
independent spirit in Brazil, for the ties of the interior
captaincies with the mother country were not close as
were those of the coast. Nor must it be forgotten that
the gold-miners consolidated the claims staked out by
the *bandeirantes* from São Paulo in the vast hinterland
which Spain recognised by the treaties of 1750, 1777
and 1801 as belonging to Brazil.

The Portuguese Government sought to derive as
much advantage as it could from the gold of Brazil: we
have already seen that revenue considerations played
an important part in its policy. Brazilian gold did
not avail to save Portugal from economic distress
and financial stringency at the time of the Spanish

Succession War, but no doubt contributed much to the improvement which set in from about 1730. It has frequently been said that under John V (1706–50) the wealth of the Crown was poured out upon buildings such as the palace-monastery of Mafra and upon the institution, by permission from the Pope, of a patriarchate and a sacred college of prelates. But the amount so spent has often been exaggerated; and the fact that John was able to convert State loans and free himself from dependence on votes of the Cortes shows there was some method in his financial policy. He was no doubt fortunate in dying before the decline of the gold mines had begun. Pombal, the great minister of King Joseph (1750–77), found his attempts to encourage agriculture, viticulture and manufactures hampered not only by the great Lisbon earthquake of 1755 but by the decline of the Brazilian revenues. In any case, if the effects of the Brazilian gold on Portugal were to be permanently beneficial there must be productive investment of the proceeds. Pombal perhaps perceived this, but his economic projects did not meet with much success. The profits of the trade with Brazil mainly went to enterprising foreigners, and above all to the English with the privileged position they enjoyed under the Methuen Treaty of 1703. Lisbon was not much more than an *entrepôt*: the goods sent to Portugal were largely English; credit was provided by English merchants. The African slaves, imported partly from Portuguese possessions, were also acquired from the English and Dutch. In face of this economic dependence it was futile for Portuguese Governments to prohibit the exportation of gold bullion: it was indeed exported to England without interference, so long as its removal was not too open, by the Falmouth packet or by a man-of-war, not liable to seizure. As the mint ratio of silver to gold in England during the greater part of the eighteenth century was more favourable to gold than the market rate or the mint ratio of most other countries, it seems a fair inference that much of the gold of Minas Geraes found its way into the English coinage. At any rate, in despite of Portuguese prohibitions, it helped to provide the currency basis for the expanding commerce and manufactures of England.

Authorities

The best modern account of the Brazilian gold mines is in the first volume of J. Pandiá Calogeras, *As Minas do Brasil e Sua Legislação* (Rio de Janeiro, 1904); but though it deals in scholarly fashion with the discoveries, methods of working and Government policy, it is not precisely a history. The fullest account in English is in Robert Southey's *History of Brazil* (3 vols., London, 1810–19): it is based upon official documents, so far as then available, and upon an extensive collection of books and manuscripts made by Southey's uncle, who lived in Lisbon for many years. Another very valuable work is Baron W. L. von Eschwege's *Pluto Brasiliensis* (Berlin, 1833), written in German despite its title. His knowledge was gained on the spot: he had clearly made a systematic study of the history of the mines, and speaks with authority on technical matters. Without access to the sources the divergent accounts of Southey and von Eschwege are, however, sometimes hard to reconcile. Unfortunately there appear to be no travellers' accounts of the mines until the early nineteenth century, when J. Luccock, *Notes on Rio de Janeiro and the Southern Parts of Brazil* (London, 1820), J. Mawe, *Travels in the Interior of Brazil* (London, 1823) and especially A. Prouvensal de Ste. Hilaire, *Voyages dans l'intérieur du Brésil* (8 vols. in 6, Paris, 1830–51), give interesting descriptions. Some illuminating remarks and comparisons are made in P. A. Martin's 'Minas Geraes and California', a paper published in 1922 in a special number of the *Revista do Instituto Historico e*

Geographico Brasileiro. Works on Brazilian history which contain useful material on the mines are H. Handelmann, *Geschichte von Brasilien* (Berlin, 1860); M. de Oliveira Lima, *Formation historique de la nationalité brésilienne* (Paris, 1911); and Roberto C. Simonsen, *Historia Económica do Brasil, 1500–1820* (2 vols., São Paulo, 1937). On the effects of the mines in Portugal and the export of bullion to England there is interesting material in J. Lucio de Azevedo, *Epocas de Portugal Económico* (Lisbon, 1929); V. M. Shillington and A. B. Wallis Chapman, *Commercial Relations of England and Portugal* (London [1907]); and Lucy S. Sutherland, *A London Merchant, 1695–1774* (London, 1933).

CHAPTER III

SIBERIA

IN Siberia, as in Brazil, the discovery of gold came at a comparatively late stage in the occupation of the country. The ancient workings to be found in the Urals and the Altai had long been forgotten when towards the end of the sixteenth century the Russian conquest of Siberia began. The Russian peasant was by this time losing the right to move which he had possessed and used in earlier days, but beyond the frontiers of the Muscovite State there was a fringe of Cossacks and hunters virtually beyond control. It was a band of Cossacks, under the auspices of the powerful commercial family of Strogonoff and the leadership of the bold Yermak, which first undertook the conquest. As the wealth of these vast lands in furs was revealed, independent hunters and trading venturers ranged far afield over them until in the middle of the seventeenth century the progress of conquest, exploration and trade carried the Russians to the shores of the Pacific Ocean. But there was no legendary El Dorado, no actual mine of Potosí, to direct the energies of these enterprising men to a search for the precious metals: they had no skill in prospecting: and though their range was immense, their numbers were few. There was no great advance of colonisation in their wake: as the great Russian historian Kluchevsky points out, the development of internal freedom in Russia was in inverse

43

proportion to her territorial expansion; and in any case the full exploitation of Siberian resources at this time was quite beyond the strength of Russia's economic system.

According to their lights, however, the Russians began in the second half of the seventeenth century to acquire some systematic knowledge of Siberia; and Peter the Great, in particular, sought to encourage mining. He introduced, in this, as in so many other fields, technical experts from abroad. He abolished the imperial monopoly of exploitation of mines. With the iron of the Urals he had some success, signalised by the foundation of Ekaterinburg. But the search for gold and silver, begun before his time and carried on by him, especially in Turkestan and the Altai region, was hardly scientific and was in any case fruitless. The first noteworthy discovery of gold, in a quartz outcrop at Berezovsk in a hilly spruce-forest region some ten miles north-east of Ekaterinburg, was made in 1744, probably by chance. At any rate Hermann, writing some fifty years later, mentions a report that the peasants collected a considerable quantity of the gold before its existence became known. The mine was not left to the great magnates of the Urals, the Demidov family, to develop, but was taken over by the Crown, which began regular working a few years later. In Hermann's time there were over a thousand workers at the mine: the quartz was crushed by stamps—which suggests a German expert—the gold extracted by careful and repeated washing, and the yield in forty years had been about 84,000 ounces. Most of the employees were 'ascribed' peasants, and though Hermann records some technical progress, the labour seems to have been unwilling and was probably not highly skilled. Though the yield of Berezovsk was increasing, there was actually more gold produced as a by-product by the silver mines of Kolywan in the Altai and Nerchinsk in Transbaikalia. Various attempts had been made to encourage private enterprise in the discovery and development of gold mines, but it must again be said that they bore little fruit. From time to time after 1774, however, there were minor discoveries of alluvial gold, and in 1814 an official at Berezovsk began working an alluvial deposit in that neighbourhood.[1] Its success—and the permission granted to proprietors in 1812 to work gold on their own lands—seemingly gave a new impetus to the search in the Ural region. Alexander I, stimulated perhaps by his new finance minister Kankrin, who wished to improve the finances by the development of trade and industry, appointed in 1823 a commission of heads of districts to take charge of the search for gold and draw up regulations for the exploitation of the deposits discovered. In that year the yield of alluvial gold in the Ural region was some 50,000 ounces, much the highest yet recorded; by 1830 it had reached 175,000 ounces. A large number of the streams on the western flank of the Ural range were in fact found to yield payable gold: there were for example in 1829 over forty alluvial workings near Nijni-Tagilsk, about ninety miles north-north-west of Ekaterinburg, which had produced about 132,000 ounces since their discovery in 1823; and Humboldt and Rose found thirty-three placers being worked and others not yet worked a hundred and twenty miles or

[1] My authority, Gustav Rose, *Mineralogisch-geognostische Reise nach dem Ural, dem Altai und dem kaspischen Meere*, Band I (Berlin, 1837), says 1714; but it is clear that 1814 is meant. Rose, a distinguished scientist, made his journey with Alexander von Humboldt in 1829. A. Striedter in an article in the *Russische Revue* in 1883 declares that the really important event was a rich alluvial discovery in 1818.

so south of Ekaterinburg, near Miassk. In some of these districts copper or iron workings were abandoned because it was more profitable to work the gold. On the other hand explorations in 1828–29 to the southward and in 1830–32 to the northward appeared to set limits to the expansion of the alluvial goldfields of the Urals.

These finds were made within a region which had already, though not always in these particular localities, been the scene of mining operations. Some of them were worked by the Crown, some by great private proprietors on whose lands they occurred. One rich, though apparently not extensive, deposit was worked by an Englishman named Major, who had been brought to the Urals apparently by the Tsar Paul to construct steam-engines: he was in the end murdered for his gold, which he kept each season in an iron box in his lonely house in the forest.[1] But in general the workings seem to have been extensive—Rose mentions one about half a mile long and 50-100 feet wide—and the manual labour was done by serfs, occasionally by criminals. For the most part the deposits were shallow and the workings 'open cuts'. The peasants 'ascribed' to the mines had to put in 200 days' work annually; but they clearly had little or no specialised skill in their work. Another drawback of employing serfs was illustrated by the fact that a sentry stood guard at the sheds where the final stages of the washing were carried out. In spite of this supervision all agree that gold was stolen and smuggled away to the Tartars of the Kirghiz steppe. Alexander von Humboldt, a man of wide experience in

[1] Rose, *op. cit.*, mentions the man, whom he calls Medscher. The story of his murder is in T. W. Atkinson, *Oriental and Western Siberia* (London, 1858), pp. 129 ff.

mining matters, told Kankrin he would like to see free
workmen settled in the region and employed in the
gold workings. But whereas the serfs of Siberia were
little if at all superior to the Brazilian slaves, Humboldt
thought well of the mining officials, many of whom
were of German descent, though by this time assimilated
to the Russian population. In any case the Ural alluvial
goldfields were from the first a regular industry, with
available labour and an established, though not very
advanced, method of exploitation. Ekaterinburg remained the centre of the region: there were alluvial
fields in its near neighbourhood: to it all the gold was
required to be sent for assay before despatch twice a
year to the mint at St. Petersburg. Alluvial gold was
a new and valuable asset to the Ural region but did not
radically change the character of its life and activities.

Far to the east, among the northern and north-
western outliers of the great mountain mass of the Altai,
lay the silver mines before mentioned, which were by
this time producing more silver than any other region
of the Old World. They had incidentally yielded some
hundreds of thousands of ounces of gold. But a new
infusion of enterprise was needed if gold was to be discovered in these ill-explored regions. It was provided
in two ways, though the energetic Kankrin probably
deserves some of the credit for both. In 1826 it was
decided to license private individuals, in defined governments, to search for and work gold on the lands of the
Crown. Various merchant capitalists took advantage of
this permission. It appears that a certain worker in the
Ural mines, condemned to penal servitude for surrep-
titious disposal of gold, escaped to an uninhabited
region of the Altai and there discovered and worked
an alluvial gold deposit. Rumours of this percolated

through to Ekaterinburg and two merchants, Popov and Riazanov, determined to follow them to their source. The fugitive was dead, but from indications given by his widow Popov discovered and exploited the deposit, on the river Birikul in the district of Tomsk, in 1828.[1] It was not particularly rich. In 1830, however, a certain Colonel Begger, who had been in charge of the gold-producing district of Bogoslovsk in the Middle Urals, was transferred to the charge of the silver mines of the Altai, which were at the same time handed over by the imperial 'Cabinet' which managed Crown lands and mines to the management of the Ministry of Finance. Begger was instructed to put forth his best efforts to find gold, and in October, in the Salair mountains separating the valleys of the Ob and the Tom, a district resembling the eastern slopes of the Urals, he made a rich alluvial discovery. The effect was a further stimulus to prospecting by private individuals; and the Crown made a demarcation of spheres, virtually leaving all the district eastward of its new discovery to private prospecting and exploitation. In 1832 the richest discovery yet was made by Riazanov on a stream which was a tributary at one or two removes of the Chulym:[2] he appears to have agreed to share his interest with Astaschev, a retired official of Tomsk and an associate of Popov, who died in this year. The partners pursued their enterprise farther afield, into the great Yenisei basin, and in 1836 made rich discoveries

[1] This story is in N. Tarassenko-Otreschkov, *De l'or et de l'argent* (Paris, 1855). C. H. Cottrell, *Recollections of Siberia* (London, 1842), speaks of a military deserter, and replaces the widow by a daughter. As Tarassenko-Otreschkov was a high official of the Bureau of Mines, one may perhaps call his the official version; but Cottrell speaks as if his source was Astaschev, the associate of Popov.

[2] The product of 1840 was about 135,000 ounces.

in wild and inaccessible places on the Birjussa. In 1839 Riazanov and after him others turned north, and in 1840–41 unprecedently rich placers were discovered between the Upper and Stony Tunguska, great affluents of the Yenisei. The search for gold in Eastern Siberia had, allowing for the peculiarities of Siberian geography and Russian economic and social life, acquired something of the momentum of a rush.

The prospecting parties were small.[1] But their organisation involved long preliminary work—authorisation by the Ministry of Finance, the finding of suitable overseers and of guides with at least a general acquaintance with the region, recruitment of men often from widely separated towns and villages, equipment with food and even clothing for several weeks or months. For the virgin forest of Siberia, the *taiga*, could not be entered lightly. It was uninhabited except by a few nomad tribes and their haunts were unknown except to an occasional Russian fur trader. It was wet and marshy and broken; pasture for horses was rare. Whereas we have no literary description of prospecting in the Brazilian *sertão*, the mining engineer Hofmann gives a vivid description of a journey through the *taiga* to the Birjussa field in 1843: 'Up and down the mountain leads a small, often hardly perceptible path through marsh in which the horses generally sink to the knee and which is as bad on the heights as in the valleys. The effort of movement affects the animals and tires their riders hardly less. On the second or third day the songs of the grooms, the neighing of the horses cease, the men curse the path, the horses groan. No song of

---

[1] The size of these parties is not mentioned; but at a later period, when the Lena and Amur *taigas* were prospected by similar methods, from eight to fourteen seems to have been the usual size.

bird, not even the croak of a raven resounds in the
deserted forest; only the voice of the wind is to be heard
in the tops of the trees, only the charming striped
squirrel, running up the slender cedar trunks and
gazing down with wise eyes upon the passers-by,
reminds the party that they are not the only living
beings in the *taiga*. . . . The eternal monotony of
the path, with the mountain-tops above, the trunks of
larches and cedars around, only rarely allowing a free
view over the country, is as tiring to the mind as the
path is to the body.' [1] What is to be said of the work of
prospecting before even these paths were made? The
prospecting proper, the digging of prospect holes, was
hampered by the marshy ground. Often winter expeditions were sent out, dragging their own sledges, to
make a fuller trial, breaking their way into the frozen
soil, thawing the gravel at the fire and then washing it
for gold with warm water. They would pass their nights
on the snow in huts constructed of pine branches. 'One
must', remarks Hofmann, 'have the iron constitution
of the inhabitant of Siberia to bear such fatigue and
privations; but even of them many succumb.'

The gold having been thus proved, a detailed description had to be sent to the district tribunal and a petition
for the delimitation of a concession was in due course
submitted to the Governor-General, who after enquiry
would assign to the claimant a concession not more
than three miles long and not more than 700 feet broad.
Two contiguous concessions could not be granted to
the same individual or company.

Armed with his concession, the proprietor would
make preparations to exploit, and these too must

[1] E. Hofmann, *Reise nach den Goldwäschen Ostsibiriens* (St. Petersburg,
1847), pp. 55-6.

necessarily be elaborate. Flour could be procured from the villages, but stock would have to be brought from the Kirghiz steppe, tools and machinery probably from the Urals, and transported to the spot by sledge—a far cheaper means of transport than the summer alternative, the pack-horse. Ordinarily the first summer would be spent in preparation: in the second the working of the gold could at last begin.

With such extensive preparations for the search, with the risk that it would nevertheless be unremunerative, with the long delay in any case before the returns came in, it was obvious that alluvial gold-mining in Siberia was destined from the first to be a large-scale capitalistic industry. In view of what individuals or small parties of prospectors accomplished later in the Yukon region it may perhaps be doubted whether Siberian geographical conditions made small-scale prospecting and exploitation impossible; but in any case the whole administration of the gold industry in Siberia proceeded on the assumption that it must be carried on by a few proprietors with a mass of labourers —in this case, however, not ascribed peasants but wage-earners hired for the season. Regulations of 1838 dealt with the conditions of labour. Working hours were fixed at a maximum of fifteen—from 5 A.M. to 8 P.M. —and work at night, on Sundays, and on the most important saints' days was prohibited. Passports, contracts, *staratel* or overtime work, medical assistance were provided for. The workmen's right to form self-governing gangs or *artels* was recognised. Food and goods were to be supplied to workmen at fixed prices. Flogging of workmen at the discretion of masters was prohibited.

Such was the legal framework within which the proprietors operated; and the activity displayed by them, in the early 'forties particularly, was considerable. In 1842 the Governor-General of Eastern Siberia reported that there were 58 alluvial deposits being worked; 273 concessions granted but not yet worked; 1500 applications not yet granted; and the yield of alluvial gold in his government was 350,000 ounces, nearly three times what it had been in the previous year. In particular, discoveries were being made and the yield was rapidly increasing in the region between the Upper and the Stony Tunguska, especially in the valleys of the Uderei, the Pit, and their numerous affluents. It may be assumed that the regulations, though they included safeguards for their workmen, were not viewed as distasteful by the *entrepreneurs*.

Recruitment of workmen was for the summer only, for work was required to stop on 10 September. Agents of the proprietors went round the towns and villages, ratifying engagements by a payment of 'hand-money' and securing a passport as guarantee. Without hand-money no engagement could be made. Sometimes free peasants would hire themselves for a season: but most of the workers were exiles, sent to Siberia as colonists in punishment for minor offences. They were not merely paid wages but given supplies—meat, fish on fast-days, cabbage, groats, rye-bread and *kvass*, the two latter apparently in unlimited quantities. Vodka was not allowed within about forty miles of the gold workings, on the ground that it would make any sort of order impossible. The wages were very low but were given for an allotted task which, according to Hofmann, could be finished by midday or at latest by three o'clock; and the men were paid extra for work done after hours or on Sundays and holidays, with a bonus for all gold won in this extra time, which they brought to the office every evening. This *starateli* system was characteristic of the Siberian goldfields: it was in one sense overtime work but in another sense a mitigation of the wage system by a measure of profit-sharing. Workers not directly connected with the gold working were at any rate occasionally allowed to take part in it. It provided a certain check, too, upon the theft of gold in ordinary working hours. It was no doubt an attraction to the workers, and if the ground was poor and they gained little by their *staratel* work they tended to abscond from the field. The tasks were regulated by individual contracts. In relation to supplies and other matters the workmen were represented by the heads of the *artels*. Hofmann speaks of log or earth huts: later barracks were common as lodging. There was a hospital and pharmacy in case of illness, and two or three neighbouring establishments would often combine together to maintain a doctor. At this early period—though Hofmann does mention one incipient labour dispute—order seems on the whole to have been easily maintained by the police with a picket of Cossacks, perhaps, as a check on desertions. No doubt the workmen regarded the secret police as part of the order of nature: they knew that they were watched—and the watchers were watched in their turn. With his earnings the worker set out at the end of the summer for his town or village, but by all accounts he spent most of them in the vodka shops on the way and returned, if he returned at all, needing rather than bringing money, waiting for next season's hand-money to begin the round again.

These goldfields establishments were the Siberian equivalent of the mining camps of other countries, but whereas other camps grew quickly into towns, they remained camps only. In the short summer season, with a population which might run into thousands, and situated perhaps hundreds of miles from the nearest settlements, they needed artisans of every kind; but with the coming of snow the population drained away, leaving only care and maintenance parties behind. The management took up its headquarters at a 'residence' on the fringe of civilisation: but the proprietors no doubt often spent the winter in luxurious living in the larger towns—Tomsk, perhaps, or Krasnoyarsk—and what happened to the workers we have seen.

In spite of their heavy expenses, rich deposits were no doubt extremely profitable to the proprietors—many of whom were interested in several concessions. All accounts speak of their lavish, luxurious expenditure. 'The Kalmyk in his felt cap', says the naturalist Tchihatchev, 'brought one on a plate of Japanese porcelain oranges imported from Marseilles or from Messina, whilst after a meal in which the delicacies of all climates had been brought under contribution, not forgetting the grape of Malaga, the Rhine, and Bordeaux, came the aromatic nectar of Arabia along with excellent Havana cigars.'[1] For once the allusive language seems appropriate. He adds that the proprietors were often men without ancestry, education,[2] or even inclination towards commerce and industry. But champagne was the particular weakness of the gold concession-owners: they drank it even at the mining camps. 'If', says Hofmann, 'there is around the *taiga* a raging ocean of vodka in which the returning workmen are overwhelmed, in the *taiga* there are

[1] P. Tchihatchev, *Voyage scientifique dans l'Altai oriental* (Paris, 1845), p. 218. The 'aromatic nectar of Arabia' is, of course, coffee.

[2] Hofmann notes that there was not a single bookshop in Krasnoyarsk.

inexhaustible springs of champagne which refresh the masters.'

We have already mentioned the Government regulation of relations between the proprietors and their workmen; but they had further duties to perform in a system as rigid in its way as that of Portugal or Spain. The management at the gold camps was under close supervision by the department of mines, whose officials received weekly reports and had the right to inspect the books in which the daily yield was entered. At the end—and sometimes, it seems, during the season—the gold was taken to Barnaul, the headquarters of the Altai mines, on a waggon in charge of a couple of peasants and a couple of Cossack guards, armed indeed but probably smoking their pipes in peace. It appears that the larger proprietors sometimes bought and took charge of the gold of the smaller. At Barnaul it was weighed in the presence of the proprietor or his representative, and an advance payment of a third of the value was made. The balance was paid when the results were checked by the Mint at St. Petersburg, but the cost of transport and coinage was deducted. There was moreover a gold tax, which tended to increase from 10 or 15 to 20 or 30 per cent., with an additional percentage levied for the maintenance of order on the goldfields.[1] Moreover if Cottrell, one of the few writers without official connections, is correct, unofficial dues had to be paid to the officers of the mining service: large annual presents were customary. A further sign that the proprietors were not the unchallenged masters of the gold industry is that in the early 'forties concessions for an indefinite period were replaced by twelve years' leases. They might be potentates in Tomsk or Krasnoyarsk

[1] The tax levied varied in different governments.

but they did not count for much as yet in far St. Petersburg.

Economically speaking, Siberia before the gold discoveries had consisted in effect of a military road, carrying a certain trade with China also through the mart at Kyakhta, a mining industry in the foothills of the Altai and farther east at Nerchinsk, a fur trade ranging far afield in the *taiga*, and agriculture and stockraising at various points along the road supplying food for those engaged in other activities but mainly self-sufficient: in some parts at least the peasants, though quite comfortably off, found money hard to come by. In a country so little organised economically, the chief effects of the growth of the gold industry were local. Prices rose enormously at Krasnoyarsk, the chief base of the gold workings in the Yenisei system, and at towns in the government of Tomsk. Tchihatchev estimated the general increase at Krasnoyarsk at 500 per cent. in the years 1837–42. The stimulating effect of higher prices on agriculture must have been counteracted to a large extent by the shortage of labour, for the exiles who formed the bulk of the workers in the gold industry had previously been available for farms. On the other hand the turnover of shops, especially in luxury or semi-luxury articles, increased enormously, and there was much building. Farther afield the government of Irkutsk, which had drawn its stock, meat and butter largely from the Yenisei valley, felt the effects in a rise of prices of these and similar products of about 100 per cent., whereas on the other hand an active trade in cattle developed between the gold region and the Kirghiz steppes, so much so that according to one account the Tartars' herds were seriously depleted. At the great fair at Irbit east of the Urals it is said that the

average turnover increased from thirty million silver
roubles in 1825–30 to sixty or seventy millions in the
two decades after 1840. The effects were felt in the
tanneries of the Tyumen district and in the great fair
of Nijni-Novgorod itself. Moreover as time went on
the peasants of the gold region seem to have accommodated themselves to the new circumstances and
drawn benefit from them, retaining some labour by
large increases in wages and improving their own
standards of living. Their level of housing, dress and
general comfort was higher, according to Skaryatin,
than the peasant of European Russia dreamt of. The
means of communication also improved, though they
were still primitive by Western European standards.
In short the evidence, though not so full or so precise
as one would wish, seems to justify the conclusion that
the increase of gold production exerted a beneficial
effect in Siberia generally in spite of some unfortunate
local reactions. Considering that the number employed
is never at this period put higher than 30,000 in a
population of perhaps two millions, the effects were far-
reaching, no doubt because so much of that population
was engaged in self-sufficient agriculture. But it was
hardly a factor of first-rate importance in the economic
life of Russia itself. Though there were distinct signs
of pressure of population in the central provinces of
Russia, emigration to Siberia was not open to the serfs
unless they committed some crime, and in any case the
economic opportunities that Siberia presented probably never reached their ears. *Pro tanto*, this profitable
gold industry must have benefited the finances of the
Government and the national economy, but when
Kankrin carried out his currency reform of 1839 he put
Russia upon a silver, not a gold basis; its finances

remained in a somewhat unhappy condition and its economy was hardly able to stand the strain of the Crimean War.

The peak of the steady rise in Siberian gold production came in 1847, when it reached 962,300 ounces, of which about 735,000 ounces came from Eastern Siberia: there followed a decline to 742,500 ounces in 1852, the decline in East Siberian production more than accounting for the difference. There were various contributing causes. The steady succession of discoveries in the Tunguska or Yenisei region, which had been mainly responsible for the increase in production, had come to an end. Government expeditions in 1849–1851 to the eastern Kirghiz steppe, to the north of the Tarbagatai Mountains, where private enterprise had since 1834 produced a few thousand ounces with Kirghiz labour, made no noteworthy find. Prospecting of the valleys running down from the Yablonoi Mountains to the Schilka in 1850–51 was followed by an increased production from the Nerchinsk region: but it was still only in the neighbourhood of 35,000 ounces, and if Atkinson is to be believed, this result had only been attained by gross exploitation of convict labourers. About the same time there are discoveries reported in the upper tributaries of the Olekma, but the district was remote even by Siberian standards. The proprietors of the placers of the Tunguska region had themselves, moreover, contributed to their early decline by too rapid and careless exploitation—a fault not peculiar to Russian alluvial mining, though less necessary in so far as it was committed by men with some command of capital.[1] In the Ural region private proprietors and

---

[1] It will be seen below (p. 67) that a French critic in the 'nineties saw serious defects in the organisation of the capitalists.

Crown officials were managing to counteract the decline in the average gold content of the gravel by more intensive working and extension to gravel previously thought too poor to work—though even in the Urals the use of horse or water power to economise labour seems to have been still far from general, and the use of steam-engines quite exceptional. In the remoter regions of Siberia there is no indication that such devices were yet employed. The proprietors for their part complained that the taxes were still rising: in 1849 the tax on gold was made progressive to over 32 per cent. on a production of 50 poods (26,350 ounces) per annum. They did secure a readjustment in 1854 which, as the maximum was 20 per cent. on 10 poods or more per annum, lightened the burden on the larger proprietors, and a further reduction in 1858 to a maximum rate of about 15 per cent. From 1853 the Siberian gold yield began to increase again, and it seems a fair inference that the reduction of taxation came as a stimulus.

Still the main cause of the revival of the middle 'fifties must have been new discovery. The production of the Yenisei fields remained more or less stable, but there was at least one new discovery there. A new field was opened up in the rugged Barguzin district to the east of Lake Baikal in 1854. A more important discovery opened up the goldfields of the Lena, destined, though their development was slow, to become eventually the most important in Siberia. Hitherto the country had been uninhabited except by the indigenous Yakuts and Tunguzes. Details of the prospecting are not available. But the first finds, it appears, were in 1850 on the Great and Little Patom; the richest on the Tschara, a tributary of the Olekma, and its tributaries, especially the Tschuya, and the Mama and other tributaries of the

Vitim. Most of the placers were in a roughly quadrilateral plateau enclosed on three sides by the Vitim and the sharply bending Lena. The region was one of rounded hills and gentle slopes, covered for the most part with birch and larch; but access from the great rivers was made difficult by deep gorges, and the great rivers themselves were remote from the regions of settlement. Moreover although the Lena was the obvious means of communication with the settled region round Irkutsk, it was not ice-free until the end of May.

This situation was met by a development of the 'residence' system which had been used on the Yenisei goldfields. Barges—and steamers in later years— brought supplies such as flour, groats, butter, salt meat and fish, and tools from Katschuga, near Irkutsk, in the summer: they were warehoused at the 'residence', and in the autumn Yakuts and Tunguzes appeared and took the supplies up on pack-horses or sledges drawn by reindeer to the goldfields for consumption the following summer. Cattle formed a special case: they were generally driven up from the Yakutsk region and slaughtered on the fields.

The methods of working the gold remained, in these earlier years, what they had been on the first alluvial fields in the Urals. 'The whole surface is laid bare and all the earth is carted to and thrown in at one end of a large iron cylinder, resembling a coffee-roaster with holes all round it, which is rotated by a water-wheel or steam-engine, the large stones and pebbles being . . . thrown out at one end by the rotation, and the earth and small pebbles passing through the holes, fall into a sluice from which it is washed on to an inclined platform, where the gold is retained by cross-pieces, while the earth is washed by water falling on the platform, and constantly moved to and fro with a wooden hoe.'[1] The steam-engine was a sign of progress: there had been none on the Siberian gold workings in 1860. But in general the processes were dependent still on un-skilled manual labour. The workings were unusually deep—seventy feet in some cases, and in ground that was frozen all the year—and no doubt this was one reason why the undertakings were large and the de-velopment was slow.

Labour was still organised, if with a little more elaboration, as it had been in the rush to the Yenisei fields. The hand-money was given to the worker in the presence of a representative of his commune. He was provided with clothing for the journey or with the money equivalent, though whichever he was given he was apparently apt to come to the assembly point without it. Most of the men apparently made their way to the 'residence' on foot in parties of fifteen or twenty, travelling perhaps a thousand miles with pack and staff; but some came down on the Lena barges. Exiles were still in the majority, though not as predominant as in former years, but there were many poor peasants who engaged to pay their taxes or their debts. The *artels* still provided an element of self-government. In the later 'sixties, a new element in the goldfields—political offenders—appeared, and a better educated type of subordinate officials made possible a new development of social life. 'Music, dancing, lectures, even dramatic representations brought a change in the life of the wilderness, and revels of cards and gambling became rarer'—though the high officials of the old school

[1] C. Mitchell Grant, *The Gold Mines of Oriental Siberia* (reprinted from *The Mining Magazine and Review*, London, 1872).

viewed the change with doubt and spoke of a loosening of discipline.[1]

The season still closed on 10 September and the workmen made their way down to the 'residence', where they were paid off. Maydell observed the exodus in 1868 and gives a vivid account of it. On the opposite bank of the Lena from the important 'residence' of Matscha lay a little village of eight or ten houses, hardly visited except by a few travellers. 'In the autumn, however, this changes: already at the beginning of September one sees the river-bank come to life, a row of boats, large and small, draws up on the strand and their owners busy themselves with the erection of all sorts of dwellings. Some build entire houses of a flimsy kind, others put up tents, still others content themselves simply with planting fir-trunks in the ground and thus marking out an enclosed space. All these are temporary inns, erected with the sole purpose of offering sustenance and refreshments to the workers leaving the goldfields. On the right bank of the Lena, as belonging to the goldfields, by law no such inns, no vodka-shops that is to say, are allowed. . . . Now within a space of about fourteen days a crowd of several thousand workers arrive together at the station, with the sole purpose of finding compensation in wild orgies for the long months of strenuous work which they have just successfully endured, and the majority of these men consist moreover of people who are not necessarily inclined to respect the property or even the health and life of their comrades: so it is absolutely necessary during this exodus of workers to keep a sharp lookout and strong police control. . . . At this time therefore the head of the

[1] 'Skizzen über die Goldwäscherei in Sibirien' (*Russische Revue*, Band XV: St. Petersburg, 1879).

Olekminsk district always comes to the station.' About thirty peasants are enrolled as special constables and paid from a tax on the temporary inns: and all women who are not permanent residents are sent away. At last the first of the boats, kept ready for the workmen when they have been paid off at the 'residence' across the Lena, appears. 'With a loud hurrah the men spring ashore, and their first action is to pull off and throw away their caps and provide themselves at once with new headgear. Those whose means permit let the rest of their clothing follow their caps and step forth, externally at least, new men. . . . Hardly is the new headgear bought when the whole company betakes itself to the friendly beckoning inns to fortify itself.' Police patrols were continuous throughout the night. 'Although it had the whole day for its arrangements and for passing judgment, a sitting of the court would take place at six in the morning, when all arrested for drunkenness would be tried and all locked up at night sentenced. That was always a considerable number, so that the sitting had to be held in the open and indeed before a large public, for as far as possible the whole crowd present on the spot did not fail to attend these proceedings. First came those imprisoned for drunkenness. These had no further punishment to expect; but the patrols have the strictest orders to bring away everyone they see lying drunk, empty his pockets and deliver up the contents. In our official premises the largest room was filled with the greatest possible number of tables, and on these the individual purse-finds were laid in separate heaps and kept under lock and key. . . . After the drunkards had been sent off the real criminals came up: for the most part it is pocket-picking, often also fighting, rarely on the whole robbery and homicide.

Only the two latter categories are taken seriously and the guilty handed over to the investigating judge: all the rest is investigated on the spot, sentence passed and the sentence, invariably consisting of corporal punishment, carried out.'[1] If they have drunk away all their money, Maydell adds, the workmen re-cross the river and re-engage for the following year: but common report says that those who engage summer after summer and beg their way through the winter as best they can cannot stand more than six years.

In the late 'sixties yet another goldfield began to develop in the Amur region, of which Russia only took possession in the early 'fifties—possession being recognised by China in a treaty of 1860. The territory was sparsely populated, and settlers were brought in from the province of Irkutsk and Transbaikalia; but it was natural to expect that gold would be discovered and in 1865 private prospecting was permitted. In the following year a rich find was made on the Djalinda, a tributary of the Ur, which is itself a tributary of the Zeya, one of the main affluents of the Amur: this began to be worked in 1868, and in that year further discoveries were made on tributaries of the Amgun, which joins the Amur not far from its mouth.

In 1870, when the development of the Amur fields was just beginning and that of the Lena fields was actively proceeding, the Siberian gold industry was given a new organisation by an imperial law. The 'sixties were a decade of profound change in Russia. The greatest of the reforms, the emancipation of the serfs in 1861, affected only the older mines in the Urals and the Altai, where ascribed peasants were employed.

[1] G. Maydell, *Reisen und Forschungen im Jakutskischen Gebiet Ostsibiriens* (St. Petersburg, 1893), pp. 494-8.

There attempts were made to retain labour by freeing only those who had long service in the mines and by offering to skilled labourers long-term contracts with exemption from Army service; but there was a serious exodus of workmen. More generally, however, change was in the air, and the development of Russian commerce and industry on Western lines was making progress. In spite of the upward trend of gold production in the Lena region and in Transbaikalia, the Yenisei region was going downhill, and the larger proprietors and companies were complaining of the high taxation and reducing their establishments. The law of 1870 was partly the result of their representations, partly of the influence of the *laissez-faire* economist Vernadsky. All Russian citizens and foreigners also were henceforth permitted to seek for gold, on receipt of a certificate from the Minister of Finance or a Governor-General, in all parts of the Russian Empire except on certain Crown lands where special permission was still required. Additional formalities were imposed in that claims had to be actually staked, registered, and inspected by a Government surveyor before action was taken by the mining administration. A more serious change was that the law omitted the limitation of the working day and in other ways weakened the position of the workmen in relation to the proprietors.

There was an increase in gold production in the 'seventies to higher levels than ever before: the maximum, in 1880, was 1,392,000 ounces.[1] But this seems to have been due not so much to the new favours to capitalistic enterprise as to the natural development of earlier discoveries. There were such developments in

[1] The Lena region contributed nearly 500,000 ounces—a good deal less than the Yenisei region at its peak in the 'forties.

65

the Lena region: but prospecting seems to have been mainly carried on by those who were already established there and had not to begin by collecting a party in remote towns and villages. There were important new discoveries in the Amur region in 1875 on the Gilyui and Branta, tributaries of the Zeya, on the Bureya, and elsewhere; [1] and the usual mining camp and residence system developed, labour being drawn not from the settlers in the region, whom it was forbidden to engage, but from Transbaikalia and to some extent from China and Korea. The new Government policy was on the other hand responsible for the gradual abandonment of various gold-producing districts in the Urals to private exploitation—Bogoslovsk in 1875, Zlatoust (Miassk) in 1876, Ekaterinburg in 1878—and similarly in the Altai. The effect was a marked increase in production. The policy itself was carried further by a removal of the tax on gold in 1877. But the new law cannot be acquitted of responsibility for the worsening relations between proprietors and workmen. The press, freer than in former times, complained of the exploitation, and it is clear from Semevsky's work that there was foundation for the complaints. Sinelnikov, Governor-General of Eastern Siberia from 1871 to 1874, discouraged the engagement of peasants, attempting to replace them by convicts, and whilst he thus implicitly admitted the demoralising tendencies of the gold industry, he tried to suppress the vodka orgies and the frittering away of workmen's earnings, and suggested that model rules should be drawn up for the employment of workmen; but he had little success, though one writer speaks of his having checked excessive hours of work.

[1] Discoveries in the Amur region were often said to be due to unauthorised prospectors.

In the 'eighties there was a growing feeling that the condition of the gold industry was unsatisfactory. The upward trend of production not only in the Amur region but in the Urals was a hopeful sign: but the trend was downward not only on the Yenisei, now given over to a large number of small enterprises, but on the Lena. Relations with workmen were bad: whilst proprietors for their part complained of rising rates of wages, it appears that the price of provisions rose also so that the workmen hardly benefited: indeed there was a series of strikes and riots provoked, according to Semevsky, by low wages, too onerous daily quotas of work, attempts in certain quarters to prohibit *staratel* work, prolongation of work beyond the traditional 10 September, refusal of holidays, bad quality and incorrect weighing of food, and cruel or harsh treatment by police and Cossacks, administrative and medical personnel. Nor could this pressure on the workmen be seriously justified on the score of economic necessity. The most important study of the industry by a foreigner, made by Levat in the middle 'nineties on behalf of the French Ministry of Public Works and Inspector-General of Mines, was based on first-hand investigation of the Amur and Transbaikalian regions only, but was clearly applicable in essentials to all Siberia; and it insists, as do other observers, on the backwardness of the technical personnel. Prospecting was still a search for rich finds rather than for those which might lend themselves to steadily profitable exploitation by modern methods. Exploitation was still almost everywhere based on manual labour and washing by the old easily erected *tchachka* or iron pan; and according to one writer of the late 'eighties the older technical personnel were suspicious even of the replacement of wheelbarrows and

water power. The *staratel* system of course also made
for concentration on the richer parts of the workings
and made large-scale exploitation of the poorer parts
difficult. In Levat's opinion this backwardness was
largely due to antiquated types of economic organisation. Exploitation was still often in the hands of the
discoverer, his friends and relations or heirs. The basis
of operation was an annual programme to which each
shareholder contributed his quota of the anticipated
expenses and from which he expected to be annually
reimbursed. This system clearly made it difficult to
undertake heavy capital expenditure for machinery,
dams and water schemes of one kind or another. Moreover the associates usually had a right of pre-emption
if any one of them withdrew and a newcomer had
not equal voting rights. 'All these restrictions', Levat
remarks, 'are a relic of the old times in which the gold
industry, the appanage of a very small number of persons, jealous of their ascendancy, remained obstinately
closed and resistant to all foreign admixture.'

In these years attempts were indeed being made to
extricate the gold industry from its difficulties. Enlightened officials were striving to liberalise the regulations of 1870, and after prolonged discussion and
resistance by the proprietors, new regulations in 1895
imposed restrictions on the employment of women and
children, Sunday work, fines, etc., and created a special
board for the settlement of disputes and conditions of
work. These regulations had left hours of work to
agreement between workmen and their employers, but
in 1897 a labour code applying to gold as to other
industries fixed them at eleven and a half hours a day.
Certain large companies on their own account made
both in the Amur and in the Lena region marked tech-

nical improvements, introducing mechanical traction by an endless chain in place of wheelbarrows and one-horse carts and sluicing after the American fashion—even dredging—in place of the *tchachka*: Levat notes them as exceptions to his general statements. From 1889 the Government allowed the free importation of mining machinery. The whole industry was being driven back upon poorer deposits—though of course possibilities of profitable working varied greatly as between the distant Lena and the easily accessible Ural fields—and the more enlightened at any rate were beginning to look to foreign capital and foreign technical assistance as the means of enabling these to be profitably exploited. The Trans-Siberian Railway, begun in 1891, was at least the beginning of an attack upon the immense problem of modern communications in Siberia and foreshadowed an increased importance for Siberia in the fabric of the Russian Empire.

These efforts bore some fruit. The trend of gold production was steadily upwards—in 1907 it was 1,291,000 ounces, in 1914 1,984,000 ounces—and for the first time this upward trend was due to technical progress aided by foreign, especially American, mining engineers rather than to new discovery. Quartz-mining in the Ural region received increased attention: dredging brought about a revival of the gold industry in the Yenisei region: in the Lena region a light railway was built from the Vitim at Bodaibo to the most important centre of the goldfields. The first French and Belgian companies appear to have lost their money, but British capital acquired control of the great Lena mining company, which produced about a quarter of all the gold of Siberia. The industry was indeed passing to an increasing extent into the hands of wealthy companies. But it complained of the lack of roads; the high duties, reimposed in 1909, on mining machinery; the high business tax on gold-mining; and the absence of cheap long-term credit.[1] Moreover, despite further regulations in 1902 as to the housing, food and clothing of the workmen, a great strike on the Lena goldfields in 1912 revealed how these were evaded: the revelations of the exploitation of the workmen, and still more the loss of nearly 200 lives when the troops fired on the striking miners, were an important landmark in the growth of the revolutionary feeling which was to bring down in ruins not the gold industry alone but the whole structure of the Russian Empire.

The Siberian gold industry, in fact, began but never really completed in pre-revolutionary times its evolution from primitive to modern methods. The early investigators like Humboldt and Rose criticise the technique of gold production on the side of labour methods, but it seems clear that the real failure on the technical side was in keeping pace with the industrial revolution in gold production in the two generations following the Californian discoveries. The summer camps in the *taiga*, the recruitment season by season in distant towns and villages, the excavation and washing by low-paid hand labour with the *staratel* method as an inducement to industry, the 'residences' on the rivers had evolved in the 'rush' to the Yenisei–Tunguska region and were well enough adapted to the original exploitation of the placers in the *taiga*; but this system showed no power of self-development over a period of fifty years. It was not that the goldfields as such were incapable of exploitation by modern methods. By an encouragement

[1] See on this *The Times* Russian supplements of 28 March 1913, 27 July 1914 and 26 April 1915.

of scientific prospecting, by a grant of privileges to private gold-seekers and of concessions to co-operative groups, by a greatly increased resort to mechanical and chemical methods, the Soviet Government have since 1933 inaugurated a whole series of new gold rushes which have raised Siberia to the second place in the world's gold production.[1] One is forced to the conclusion that the social and economic structure of the old Russia was incapable of the adaptation which was successfully made in other great gold-producing countries after the rushes.

Limited in its potentialities by its technical backwardness and by an economic and social system ill adapted to progress, the gold industry was limited also in its effects on Siberia and on the Russian Empire as a whole. Count Witte's introduction of the gold standard in Russia in 1896 was no doubt helped by Siberian gold production, but it was mainly carried out through foreign gold loans. Siberia itself made great strides in the twenty years before the Great War, when immigration amounted to four and a half millions, but the main destination of the immigrants was Western Siberia, the main stimulus the railway, which was designed as a connection with the Far East and only incidentally reacted upon the gold industry. The gold rushes opened up remote regions of the *taiga*, but for exploitation of the gold alone, not so as to transform them into regions of permanent settlement. Gold stimulated trade in Irkutsk and Blagoveshchensk, as earlier in Tomsk and Krasnoyarsk: but there is no sign that the wealth made in the gold industry was used to fructify others.

---

[1] *U.S.S.R. Handbook* (London, 1936), pp. 198-9, and especially J. D. Littlepage and D. Bess, *In Search of Soviet Gold* (New York, 1938). According to Littlepage, Stalin's imagination was fired by reading about the California rush.

Siberia remained at the end of it all predominantly a land of peasant settlement.

AUTHORITIES

A bibliography of non-Russian sources to Russian history has self-evident limitations, though my impression, for what it is worth, is that less work has been done, even in Russian, on the Siberian gold industry than might have been expected. The important work of V. I. Semevsky, *Labourers in the Siberian Gold Mining Industry* (St. Petersburg, 1898), has been consulted in summary form through notes made for me by Dr. S. P. Turin. Skaryatin, *Memoirs of a Goldseeker* (St. Petersburg, 1862) was summarised in Erman's *Archiv für wissenschaftliche Kunde von Russland* (Berlin, 1862). There are, however, various publications for the period 1820–50 in foreign languages which have the value of primary sources—and so has, for the earlier period, B. F. J. Hermann, *Mineralogische Reisen in Sibirien, 1783–1796* (St. Petersburg, 1798). The *Annuaire du Journal des Mines de Russie, 1835–1842* (St. Petersburg, 1840–45) is an official translation with a valuable introduction. G. Rose, *Mineralogische geognostische Reise nach dem Ural, dem Altai und dem kaspischen Meere* (Berlin, 1837–42) contains a good deal of general information wedged in among the rocks; E. Hofmann, *Reise nach den Goldwäschen Ostsibiriens* (St. Petersburg, 1847) is written by a mining expert also, but shows some literary talent and some interest in matters social and economic; P. Tchihatchev, *Voyage dans l'Altai oriental* (Paris, 1845) is useful, and so is N. Tarassenko-Otreschkov, *De l'or et de l'argent* (Paris, 1856)—though Tarassenko-Otreschkov's extensive knowledge does not appear to have been gained on the spot. On the Lena fields there is an informative article, based on seven years' service there, entitled 'Skizzen über die Goldwäscherei in Sibirien', in the *Russische Revue*, Band XV (St. Petersburg, 1879): the work of G. Maydell, *Reisen und Forschungen im Jakutskischen Gebiet Ostsibiriens in den Jahren 1861–71* (St. Petersburg, 1893–96), though it has the striking description of the exodus of the gold-miners, deals mainly with other matters. This work and Hofmann's appear in a series *Beiträge zur Kenntniss des russischen Reiches*, of which certain other volumes contain references to the gold industry, as do other volumes of *Erman's Archiv* and of the *Russische Revue* mentioned above. There are numerous passing references to the Siberian gold industry in various volumes of travel, but the goldfields are so remote that they are mostly second-hand. This does not apply to the works of mining engineers, of which E. D. Levat, *L'Or en Sibérie orientale* (2 vols., Paris, 1897) is the fullest on the regions it covers and A. Bordeaux, *Sibérie et Californie* (Paris, 1903) is also worthy of mention.

CHAPTER IV

CALIFORNIA

THE dramatic history of the gold rushes in the
United States of America, which made gold a
factor of greater importance than ever before in the
expansion of the European peoples, was played out, as
all the world knows, in the West. It is not so well known
that the drama had a Southern prologue; that a boy
named Conrad Reed in 1799, one Sunday while his
parents were at church, discovered a gold nugget in
the Appalachian foothills in North Carolina;[1] that the
stream in which it was discovered yielded richly for
many years; and that by the middle 'twenties there was
a small but active gold industry in being in North
Carolina. The German mining engineer Rothe describes
the gold-diggers as working in parties of from two to
five or six, renting land from the owners for one-third
or one-half of the gold. The great majority were the
less prosperous farmers of the neighbourhood, working
in their slack periods. A number merely worked long
enough to get bread and whiskey and spent the rest of
their time 'in lounging from camp to camp, and in
hanging about the whiskey carts or huckster waggons,
of which there are always several on the ground
with cider, spirits, provisions and other articles to

---

[1] J. H. Wheeler, *Historical Sketches of North Carolina* (Philadelphia, 1851),
ii, 63-4; *Dictionary of American Biography*, *s.v.* Reed, John.

sell'.[1] For tools the diggers had a mattock, a shovel, a bucket or water dipper, a 'rocker' and a pan.

Discoveries in other States followed, especially in northern Georgia in 1828–29. A number of mushroom towns sprang up and a heterogeneous, lawless frontier population flocked in. Some of these discoveries were on the Cherokee Indian lands, on which there were perhaps ten thousand intruders by the summer of 1830. The Cherokees protested, the more vigorously because they were actually punished for mining on their own lands. Federal troops were moved in, but later withdrawn at the request of the Governor of Georgia. The Georgian legislature itself did not admit the rights of the intruders, and disposed of the goldfields by lottery in the usual forty-acre lots, excluding those who had dug gold or made settlements illegally. But the Cherokees had to cede their lands, as they eventually did by treaty in December 1835, and in 1838 they were removed. It was impossible to maintain Indian rights in the face of a gold rush.

Meanwhile the placer gold elsewhere in the Appalachians continued to be worked during off seasons or as an adjunct to plantations by farmers and planters, the latter often employing large gangs of slaves and perhaps poor white men and even women as well; and capital, even foreign capital, was attracted to the quartz mines discovered in North Carolina as early as 1826. Stamp mills were erected and the gold was separated by amalgamation. The labour introduced to run the machinery was often foreign, and there were riots, even pitched battles, between Americans and foreigners. The only modern investigator of the subject, Mr. F. M.

---

[1] C. E. Rothe, 'Remarks on the Gold Mines of North Carolina' (*American Journal of Science and Arts*, xiii, 1828).

Green, describes the miners as 'a rough, shiftless, fighting lot'.[1]

Perhaps a slightly more settled if less productive gold industry is discernible in the later 'thirties when the boom was over. The floating population had begun to drift away to Texas and elsewhere, leaving a steadier type of miner behind; and a rise in cotton prices had drawn farmers away from mining. New discoveries in the early 'forties caused a second short boom. The actual production was of secondary importance, averaging perhaps 100,000 ounces a year in the twenty years before the Californian rush. The chief importance of the Appalachian gold rushes lay not in the temporary stimulus they gave to the investment of capital in the region but in the fact that some at least of those who went to California had become acquainted with the art of alluvial gold-mining.

California was first occupied by Europeans in 1769, when an expedition was sent from New Spain to secure it against foreign aggression or Russian infiltration from Alaska. For many decades it remained a land of mission stations and cattle-farmers. It followed Mexico into independence and in 1825 took rank as a territory under the new Mexican constitution. But Mexican neglect caused growing resentment, which Mexico had neither money to appease nor troops to resist. In the 'thirties and 'forties there was a slow infiltration of Americans.

---

[1] Articles in the *North Carolina Historical Review*, xiv, and *Georgia Historical Quarterly*, xix. But Mr. Green's estimates of the amount invested —$100,000,000 in North Carolina, $50,000,000 in Georgia—and of the total production, over $50,000,000 in each State, seem excessive, and the production estimates of Special Commissioner J. W. Taylor n 1867 are safer.

There were some signs of British and French interest, seeming to point to intervention, which the United States felt it could not tolerate. Polk, elected President in 1844 on an expansionist programme, determined that the time had come to annex California. Voluntary cession by Mexico was precluded by the Government's antipathy to the United States and fear of its own public opinion. Voluntary arrangement with the Californians themselves as an allied republic or as a new state of the union seemed possible, but was forestalled first by the proclamation of the 'Bear Flag Republic' by the American settlers of the Sacramento and Napa valleys and then by the outbreak of war between the United States and Mexico. To that there could be only one end, and on 13 January 1847 the Californians surrendered. A military governor, Colonel Mason, was still in control when the epoch-making discovery of gold was made on 24 January 1848.

Gold had been discovered in the Los Angeles region in 1842 and a number of men, chiefly Mexicans, worked at the spot for some years. It is possible that the great discovery was not the first even in the Sacramento valley. But the event proved which was the discovery that mattered, the more conclusively because it was made not by skill or persevering search but by pure chance. J. W. Marshall, a native of New Jersey, was erecting a sawmill for a prosperous Swiss settler, J. A. Sutter, on the American River, some forty miles above its junction with the Sacramento, in a beautiful hollow surrounded by lofty mountains covered with oak, pine, cypress and cedar. He noticed some yellow grains in the tail-race and gradually came to the conclusion that they were gold. More was found by the workers at the mill. On 27 January he rode down to Sutter's residence near the junction. They returned together and found gold all along the river. Fearing to lose his workers, Sutter made them promise to keep silence until the mill was completed. But he also hoped to secure the right to work the gold for Marshall and himself and negotiated with that object with the Indian owners of the land and with Colonel Mason. His emissary to Mason not unnaturally let the secret out, and one of the men informed, who had been a gold-miner in Georgia, returned with his informant to American River and set to work. The news still hung fire for a time. The claims of Sutter and Marshall deterred men to some extent from working on the original spot, and late in March the editor of the *California Star* visited it and expressed the opinion that the gold mines were a sham. Soon afterwards, however, the current of opinion grew too strong to be resisted. Men who had been diverted from the American River by the attitude of Sutter and Marshall found gold elsewhere. Gold-diggers laden with bottles, tins and buckskin bags of gold came to San Francisco and men had only to believe their eyes. Throughout May the reports gathered momentum and the rush begun. The townsmen of San Francisco and Monterey, the settlers of the great valley, the crews of the ships in harbour and even the soldiers flocked to the mines. The Governor of California, the commander of a man-of-war, and the *alcalde* of Monterey had to join forces and cook their own dinners.

Governor Mason in a report of 17 August estimated that upwards of 4000 men were working in the gold district, more than one-half of them being Indians; and as the news spread northward to Oregon, southward to Mexico and oversea to Hawaii an influx began which may have raised the number to 10,000 by the end of the year.[1] The miners gradually worked their way north and south to the other streams flowing down from the Sierra Nevada into the Sacramento and San Joaquin, and found gold in all of them. If one seemed full, or if results fell short of expectations, parties tried another stream: thus Gould Buffum's party of ten made $150 on the first day, $1000 in the first week at Weaver's Creek, but nevertheless decided to move on to the Middle Fork of the American River, where they made $416 (26 ounces) the first day by the pan, and about $400 the second day by the rocker. By about August extension of the goldfields seems to have stopped for the time, and more intensive working of the streams already opened up began. Then in October the heavy rains and increasing cold restricted mining operations: some devoted themselves to preparations for the winter, others made their way to the coast. In this first season there was ground enough and to spare for all, and the average yield, estimated in Bancroft's *California* at an ounce a day per man, was far higher than was ever reached again. This was indeed less remunerative to the miner than might appear at first sight, so high were the prices of transport and supplies. Miners would usually take up supplies with them, but seldom enough to see them through the season. The transport of three barrels of flour, one of pork, and about 200 pounds of small stores for about fifty miles cost Gould Buffum's party $300. On arrival at the mines he paid $1·50 a pound for flour and $2 a pound for pork: coffee, for which he paid $1 a pound, is elsewhere recorded as rising to $3 or $4 later in the season. A breakfast bill for two at

[1] P. H. Burnett in his *Recollections and Opinions of an Old Pioneer* (New York, 1880) estimated that two-thirds of the adult males in Oregon left for California that summer and fall.

the scene of the original discovery in December—
sardines, bread and butter and cheese, and ale—reached
$43. Pick, shovel and pan might cost $10 each, or
more. The wide range of prices quoted in different
sources no doubt was partly due to the uncertainty and
irregularity of the supplies and the shifting population;
but it clearly indicates that much of the season's profits
found its way into the pockets of the storekeepers.
They were moreover able to take advantage of the
miners' frequent inability to pay in anything but gold-
dust, for which they could at first sometimes get only
$4 or $5 and seldom more than $8 or $10 an ounce.
The Indians, who had no idea of its value, were a particular temptation to the honesty of the trader, the more
so because public opinion here exercised no restraining
influence.

The mining operations in 1848 were confined to the
bars of the rivers, and the tributary gulches and dry
ravines. Crevices in the rocks in such ravines would
often be picked by a butcher's knife, but in general the
miner's tools were a pan and a 'rocker'. The pan and
the rocker were probably first used in California by the
Georgian miner who went up to the scene of Marshall's
discovery. The pan was equivalent to the wooden *batea*
used by the Mexicans. It was made of sheet iron or
tin and had a flat bottom ten to fourteen inches across
and sloping sides four to six inches high. In it the earth
was shaken in water with a kind of rotary motion until
it was dissolved or washed away and the particles of
gold settled at the bottom. The rocker was a wooden
box or even a hollowed log—perhaps forty inches long,
twenty inches wide and four inches high—with one
end left open. At the other end a sieve of sheet iron or
even of a raw hide, perforated with holes about half an

inch in diameter, was rested upon the sides. Laterally
across the bottom were nailed three or four 'riffles' or
pieces of board one or two inches thick. A pair of
rockers like those of a child's cradle, and a handle with
which to rock them, completed this simple apparatus.
One man of a party would dig, another shovel earth
into the sieve, a third dip up water and throw it on,
and a fourth rock, though a single man sometimes combined the two latter operations. As the earth was washed
away, the gold was caught in the riffles: from time to
time it was taken out for further washing in a pan, the
last of the heavy black sand being perhaps removed by
blowing after careful drying. These methods were no
more advanced than those employed by the Germans
in the sixteenth century. In the dry diggings the
Mexicans used a method they had no doubt brought
from Sonora: they dexterously tossed the contents of a
batea into the air so that they fell upon an outstretched
hide, repeating the process until the wind had winnowed
out the gold.

Of mining regulations in this first season there were
virtually none. The entire gold district, with the excep-
tion of a few grants made by the Mexican authorities,
was United States land, but the spirit of United States
land policy at this time was favourable to individual
initiative and development, and Colonel Mason pru-
dently decided that as he could not in any case enforce
United States rights he would permit all to work freely.
There was indeed a tendency among the older settlers
to follow the Spanish American method and let the
Indians do the heavy work. Gould Buffum tells us that
Weaver's Creek was first worked by two *rancheros*
employing no fewer than 1000 Indians whom they
supplied with the necessaries of life and the 'little

trinkets that so win an Indian's heart'. But most of the work was done by small parties of American miners. According to Buffum, they recognised a river bar claim as good when the claimant had cleared off the top soil from any portion of the bar. The prevailing feeling was that there was room and gold for all, and this obviated the necessity for disputing claims and was the fundamental reason for the absence of serious crime. Official authority was certainly not obtrusive, recognising that it was in fact powerless, and even public opinion hardly needed at first to assert its power. Bags of gold lay about unguarded.

Such an idyll could not be expected to last; and when action had to be taken, it was short and sharp. Gould Buffum describes a scene in January 1849 when two Frenchmen and a Chilean, caught in the act of robbery, were flogged by the miners and then accused of an earlier crime. 'The unhappy men were removed to a neighbouring house, and being so weak from their punishment as to be unable to stand, were laid stretched upon the floor. As it was not possible for them to attend, they were tried in the open air, in their absence, by a crowd of some two hundred men, who had organised themselves into a jury, and appointed a *pro tempore* judge. The charges against them were well substantiated, but amounted to nothing more than an attempt at robbery and murder; no overt act being alleged. They were known to be bad men, however, and a general sentiment seemed to prevail in the crowd that they ought to be got rid of. At the close of the trial, which lasted some thirty minutes, the judge put to vote the question whether they had been proved guilty. A universal affirmative was the response; and then the question "What punishment shall be inflicted?" was asked. A brutal-looking fellow in the crowd cried out, "Hang them". The proposition was seconded, and met with almost universal approbation. I mounted a stump, and in the name of God, humanity and law, protested against such a course of proceeding; but the crowd, by this time excited by frequent and deep potations of liquor from a neighbouring groggery, would listen to nothing contrary to their brutal desires, and even threatened to hang me if I did not immediately desist from any further remarks. . . . Seeing the utter uselessness of further argument with them, I ceased. . . . Thirty minutes only were allowed the unhappy victims to prepare themselves. . . . Three ropes were procured, and attached to the limb of a tree. The prisoners were marched out, placed upon a wagon, and the ropes put round their necks. . . . They vainly tried to speak, but none of them understanding English, they were obliged to employ their native tongues, which but few of those assembled understood. Vainly they called for an interpreter, for their cries were drowned by the yells of a now infuriated mob. A black handkerchief was bound around the eyes of each; their arms were pinioned, and at a given signal, without priest or prayer-book, the wagon was drawn from under them and they were launched into eternity.' [1] This episode gave the place for a time the distinctive name of Hangtown. It was a foretaste of what was to happen with the coming of the forty-niners.

There was no question of keeping the Californian gold discovery dark or allowing the news to percolate gradually through to the outside world as had happened in the case of the Brazilian and Siberian discoveries. All

---

[1] E. Gould Buffum, *Six Months in the Gold Mines* (Philadelphia, 1850), pp. 83-5. Hangtown was afterwards renamed Placerville.

the resources of mid-nineteenth-century publicity were employed to diffuse the tidings: all available transport was used to bring intending miners to the spot. Men from Oregon, Hawaii and Mexico were there before the end of 1848. The news seems to have reached the Eastern States in September, and excitement culminated in a presidential message to Congress on 5 December. Governor Mason's report of 17 August was published and copied by the principal newspapers throughout the world. The gold rush for which these reports gave the signal carried 81,000 people to California, according to Bancroft's estimate, before the close of 1849.

Of these immigrants 42,000, of whom 33,000 according to the same estimate were Americans, came across the prairies. Trappers and explorers had found convenient routes, and the most popular of the routes to California coincided until its later stages with the 'Oregon Trail' of 1842 and the Mormons' route of 1846 to Salt Lake City, which often was a resting-place for the gold-seekers of 1849. Never before, however, had there been such an assemblage of emigrants with their carts or waggons or ponderous 'prairie schooners' as gathered at St. Joseph or Independence or other points on the Missouri in the spring and early summer of that year. Though the majority were probably farmers or handy-men from western villages, we are told by one of them that there were among them preachers, doctors, lawyers, druggists, pilots, sailors; and they came from many states. In view of the danger from the Plains Indians, in general they organised themselves in companies, sometimes numbering 200, though apparently small companies of about twenty were more successful. Some of these companies had quite elaborate rules, but the essential thing was the choice of a captain to settle such matters as the order of march, starting-time and place of encampment. There was of course no compulsion to remain with the company, and those which were too large for convenience or harmony broke up. 1849 was fortunately a good year for grass on the prairies, but it was a bad year for cholera: the Indians were relatively harmless, but disease and hardship took quite a heavy toll. The main northern trail up the Platte and the Sweetwater to the broad valley of the South Pass was fairly straightforward. Afterwards there were several routes converging at the headwaters of the Humboldt River. The last stages were the worst, for there was a belt of desert after the sink of the Humboldt, and the eastern slopes of the Sierra Nevada were abrupt, broken and heavily timbered and the western slopes extremely difficult to descend with the waggons, which often had to be lowered with ropes. The whole journey took at least a hundred days. The southern routes were many and various, and a number of Americans as well as Mexicans used them, though a minority of the emigration. The most popular were those which converged from Independence and from Fort Smith and Van Buren in Arkansas on Santa Fé, diverging there to meet again on the Gila River from which they crossed the Colorado Desert and eventually reached the southern mines. Other routes led through Texas or through Mexico, some of these leading to Mazatlan and leaving the journey to be completed by boat.

The remainder of the forty-niners came by sea. The Pacific Mail Steamship Company had recently established a service from Panama, and one of its ships brought the first of them into San Francisco Bay on 28 February. But although the Panama route continued to be used, in spite of the transhipment and the fierce competition for places in the Mail Company's steamers, most of the sea immigrants came by Cape Horn. This route had a special appeal to the maritime tradition of New England, from which no doubt the bulk of the 23,000 Americans arriving by sea were derived.[1] They too were largely in organised companies, perhaps proposing to engage in trading and mining after arrival, and sometimes owning the ships in which they sailed. Many men were fitted out by capitalists in return for a share in the gold. The strain on shipping resources was considerable: in the Eastern States many old hulks were refitted for the purpose of the rush, and the ships were frequently ill found. Most of the immigrants complained of their treatment on the voyage.

For all arriving by sea San Francisco was the *entrepôt*. When the first rush to the goldfields occurred, business almost stood still in the little port with its few hundred people; but many returned with their gains and began to speculate in real estate and prepare for the greater rush of 1849. By February 1849 the population was about 2000, and throughout the year San Francisco was a feverishly active, growing town, though composed for the most part of frail wooden shanties, adobe huts and dingy tents. As few intended to stay there was little inducement to build anything substantial. Goods were piled in great heaps in the open air for want of a place to store them. In the harbour were at one time as many as five hundred ships, swinging at anchor, deserted by their crews. Rents were high and meals expensive: Bayard Taylor paid $25 a week for a room with two beds and another $20 for meals: but this was perhaps

---

[1] Bancroft's estimate again: of the remaining 16,000 immigrants by sea, no doubt the bulk came from Europe, including Great Britain.

not extortionate when wages were $1 an hour for ordinary labourers and $12 to $20 a day for skilled men. Commerce, however, was rather precarious, for the fancy prices realised in the winter of 1848–49 led merchants everywhere—but especially in the North Atlantic States, for there was no place nearer that had much to sell—to unload upon California any goods they could lay their hands on, however old and shop-worn, however inappropriate to the conditions. Broadcloth and silk hats, fine linen, costly furniture, women's clothing were a drug upon the market, and when heavy lighterage and storage charges had to be added, agents and consignees were driven to despair. Cargoes were sold at auction; but in the end bales of goods were often used to make side walks or fill in streets, or left to rot.

In any case for most of the motley throng that filled its streets—'Yankees of every possible variety, native Californians in *sarapes* and *sombreros*, Chileans, Sonorians, Kanakas from Hawaii, Chinese with long tails, Malays armed with their everlasting creeses'[1]— San Francisco was only a temporary halting-place. On the road to the mines Sacramento City, which had grown up on the site of the *embarcadero* of Sutter's 'fort', and for the southern mines Stockton on the San Joaquin, a 'vast linen city' where in 1848 there had been a single log-house, served as distributing centres and bases of supply. In the mining region itself the American River remained in 1849 the chief centre of attraction and the numerous bars on its various forks, the river-bed itself where the stream was diverted by flumes, and the dry diggings of neighbouring uplands enabled it to maintain a remarkably rich and regular yield. Farther north the Bear and Yuba rivers and some

[1] Bayard Taylor, *El Dorado* (New York and London, 1850), i, 55.

of their tributaries were very rich, and some miners went farther afield northwestwards to the bars of the Trinity River. In the late summer, it should be noted, the overland immigrants began to arrive directly upon the northern goldfields. There was also a diffusion of miners southwards, though the southern mines had characteristics of their own. The mountains were not so steep, the country not so rough, the camps more accessible. Mining, however, was more speculative, for the placer deposits were more patchy. The population also was distinctive, being less predominantly American. 'There were many villages peopled nearly altogether by Mexicans, others by Frenchmen; in some places there were parties of two or three hundred Chileans forming a community of their own . . . and besides all such distinct colonies of foreigners, every town of the southern mines contained a very large foreign popula-tion.'[1] This quotation refers to 1851, but the main point is noted earlier. Mexicans from Sonora gave that name to the chief camp of the south, near the Stanis-laus. In the spring of 1849 discoveries of rich nuggets on the Stanislaus and other southern rivers caused an excited rush from the northern mines, but on the whole the San Joaquin valley retained only a minority of the miners. The increased gold yield of 1849, estimated by Bancroft at $40,000,000, or two and a half million ounces at the usual reckoning of that time, came partly from an extension of the gold regions but mainly from a more thorough and intensive exploitation of districts already opened up in 1848. The total output was the greatest yet recorded from any goldfield, but the output per man had declined to perhaps half an ounce a day.

[1] J. D. Borthwick, *Three Years in California* (Edinburgh, 1857), p. 306. On the foreign element in the southern mines, see also below, pp. 107-9.

It is not the extension of the goldfields but the development of organisation that gives particular interest to the season of 1849. The Californian mining camps of 1848—and the camps of the Southern Appalachians, so far as a conclusion can be drawn from negative evidence—were formless; in the camps of 1849 there was organised, if rather rudimentary, self-government. It could no longer be assumed that there was ground enough and to spare for all: it was necessary for the sake of peace and equity to determine the areas in which and the title by which it might be held. As the land belonged to the United States this might seem a proper subject for Congressional legislation. Governor Mason had suggested a system of licences; President Polk proposed that Congress either reserve the mineral lands for the United States or sell them in small lots at a fixed price. But no policy other than *laissez-faire* had been possible to the authorities on the spot in 1848, and in fact it was impossible to contemplate the application of any system of regulation alien to the ideas of the frontier in the midst of a gold rush. Congress wisely decided to take no action in 1849. The natural regulating authority in the circumstances was the body of miners, the natural unit in such a widely scattered mining community the mining camp. The predominant American element had been trained up in democratic self-government, and in other circumstances—for instance in the 'claims clubs' of the Old North-West—had revealed their capacity for spontaneous organisation. The extraneous elements made action more necessary, for they complicated the problem of law and order which arose beside and behind the problem of the regulation of mining. Hundreds of mining camps must have organised themselves in 1849,

adopting a system of mining 'claims' but differing
widely in their detailed regulations. The extent and
richness of the locality and the difficulty of working
suggested a variation in the size of claim from ten feet
square at Jackass Gulch, five miles from Sonora, to
fifty or a hundred feet or more along the river elsewhere.
Existing rights to claims larger than the regulation size
were frequently respected. Claims usually had to be
registered, at a small fee, with a recorder chosen by the
camp, and marked.[1] To secure possession, a certain
amount of work had to be done, and absence for a
given number of days during the season entailed forfeiture. At first, holders were as a rule restricted to one
claim. There were also provisions for the settlement of
disputes. The rules on such matters were usually the
work of a committee appointed at a meeting of the
camp, and in many cases the committee also drew up
something in the nature of an elementary code of
criminal law and procedure as well. The two great
categories of offence were theft and murder, and the
two penalties banishment and hanging—though hanging was often the penalty for serious thefts as well as
for murder.[2] In different camps these committees and
the *alcaldes* who were usually chosen as heads of the
camps—sometimes with sheriffs to assist them—had
different degrees of power in relation to the settlement
of disputes and the trial of offences against miners' law.
Sometimes officers were appointed only as occasion

[1] C. H. Shinn in his *Mining Camps* (New York, 1885) mentions that he
had a few years before seen a deserted claim marked: 'NOTIS: To all and every-
body. This is my claim, 50 feet on the gulch, cordin' to Clear Creek District
Law, backed up by shotgun amendments.—Thomas Hall.'

[2] Cf. the laws and regulations of the Jacksonville Camp (Tuolumne R.)
adopted 20 January 1850: Rev. D. B. Woods, *Sixteen Months at the Gold
Diggings* (New York, 1851).

arose: sometimes miners' meetings met at stated intervals of, say, six months, sometimes on summons by the
head of the camp: sometimes the committee was virtually delegated power to settle disputes, sometimes the
sheriff was empowered to summon, and the *alcalde* to
swear a jury. The registration fee amid such a shifting
population provided a certain revenue, and it might also
be provided by special collection or by assessment on
claims. We hear indeed of other fees. 'The *alcalde's*
fee, in all cases,' says Carson, 'was three ounces;
sheriff's two; and each juror one—with the addition of
the price of all the whiskey used by the court, jury and
witnesses during the trial.'[1] But on the whole it was
an inexpensive as well as a simple form of government.
The sanction was public opinion, which, if authority
was challenged, was ready to use force. C. E. Pancoast
secured from a miners' *alcalde* the support of ninety
armed men in turning a party of Missourians off his
claim. If later the courts, and the United States itself,
recognised the customs of the miners as valid, it was
a recognition due to their effective vindication of
authority through the machinery of self-government.
The principles and methods of the American frontier
had been applied, on the whole with remarkable success,
in communities which had a strong cosmopolitan admixture and were not under the effective control of the
United States Government.

Apart, however, from the essentials of law and order,
a remarkable social freedom, individualism and exuber-
ance carried to the point of recklessness characterised
the miners. They developed a dress and appearance of
their own—red or blue open-necked woollen shirts,

[1] J. H. Carson, *Life in California* (Stockton, 1852—reprinted, Tarrytown, 1931), p. 37.

belts garnished with knives and pistols, trousers tucked into high boots, dingy slouched hats covering bronzed, bushy, bearded heads — and sought to differentiate themselves from the traders and parasites in the towns. They found relaxation in drinking and gambling particularly, but also in bull-fighting, cock-fighting, prize-fighting, horse- and foot-racing, theatrical and other entertainments. Sunday was pre-eminently the day of relaxation. It was customary to spend the morning at their tents and huts in washing and mending, and to flock into the main street and the saloons of the camp in the afternoon and evening. The saloon-keeper was something of a local dignitary, a repository of news and a man to whom the possibility of knifing or pistol-shooting in case of quarrels gave an unusual responsibility. A certain code of morality was imposed even on the unruly by the organisation of the camps, but of religious observance there was little or none, though at quite an early stage there were a few preachers able to hold their own with the roughest crowds. Women formed less than 8 per cent. of the whole population of California in the census of 1850, so that there was little family life. In a sense the mining partnership replaced the family as the basic social unit, though such partnerships were perpetually dissolving and re-forming. Certain friendly societies seem also to have existed.

But some at least of the miners were aware that social organisation did not end with the mining partnership and the mining camp. The California that gold had called into being was also organising itself in 1849 as a community, economically through a gradual diversification of occupations among the miners, politically as a State of the American Union. Increasing numbers of men, dimly perceiving the economic truth that one

cause of high prices of goods and transport was insufficient competition, began to turn to trading and
packing. Lawyers began to come to California not to
make their fortunes by digging gold but to practise the
profession of the law. These were steps towards economic maturity; but steps towards political maturity
were not quite so easily taken.

Though the Mexican War was brought to an end by
the Treaty of Guadalupe Hidalgo on 2 February 1848,
the only official authority in California continued to be
that of the military governor and of the *alcaldes* of the
towns subordinate to him.[1] The official view was that
the laws of Mexican California, not being inconsistent
with the laws, constitution and treaties of the United
States, remained in force until changed by competent
authority. This view, almost irrelevant to the situation
at the mines, did not in any case commend itself to the
American population, accustomed to free institutions
and priding themselves on the responsiveness of their
laws to popular sentiment. During the winter of 1848–
1849, when work at the mines was largely suspended,
constitutional agitation against the military régime was
growing. Fortunately Colonel Mason and Brigadier-
General Riley, his successor, used their legal powers
with discretion, and they were not personally unpopular.
But in such a democratic community a firmer basis for
authority was clearly needed. Congress could provide
one, but Congress, distracted by the slavery issue, failed
to give California even territorial status. It was for the
people themselves to act if they thought action necessary. The unsatisfactory basis of existing authority was
illustrated by the position in San Francisco, where the

---

[1] The office of *alcalde* was of course a Mexican one, though now held by
Americans: its powers were rather ill-defined.

alcalde, upheld by the Governor and perhaps by the older residents, was challenged by a 'legislative assembly' supported by the great bulk of the inhabitants. In January there was a movement for the election of a constitutional convention, voiced by meetings in San Francisco, San José and Sacramento. It failed for the moment, but in June General Riley resolved the difficulty by a proclamation summoning such a convention and providing for the election of delegates to it and of local officers. The legislative assembly, satisfied, abandoned the field in San Francisco to the *alcalde*. There was indeed another rival to existing authority rearing its ugly head. A body of Tammany Hall type, first known as the Hounds and later claiming respectability as the Regulators, formed by a disbanded regiment of New York Volunteers, on 15 July attacked the Chilean quarter of San Francisco: the riot was dealt with not by the powerless *alcalde* but by an impromptu military and police patrol, which expelled the leaders and warned them not to return. It was an indication that the formation of a regular government commanding respect and obedience was of more than merely academic importance.

Yet perhaps there was a certain academic character in the proceedings of the constitutional convention of September 1849. The great majority of its members were Americans, though the native-born Californians and foreign-born were also represented. On the problem of slavery, the thorniest of all, which Congress hardly dared to touch, the recent appearance of some Texans with their slaves on the Yuba had shown plainly where the miners stood: though some of the Appalachian mines had been exploited by slave labour, the Californian miners were unmistakably opposed to slavery, and the convention came quite amicably to the same conclusion. But in general the delegates moved in the field of constitutional ideas familiar to them—a sovereign constitution; an elective governor, executive officials and courts (with certain exceptions on the first occasion); an independent elected legislature of two houses meeting annually; a fear of corporations, banks and paper money, finding expression in constitutional restrictions; a liberal social and economic policy, embodied in provision for a homestead law, a common school law, a university. They worked upon the basis of other State constitutions, especially that of Iowa, the most recently admitted Western State. That such provisions would produce an authority which would make itself respected they took for granted. The constitution was signed on 13 October: it was approved by the people, though only about a sixth of the American inhabitants voted, a month later: P. H. Burnett, a gold rush immigrant of 1848 from Oregon, was elected governor, and on 20 December General Riley handed over control to him.

It remained for Congress to ratify this revolutionary procedure, for the Californians, with unofficial encouragement from President Taylor, had passed at one bound through, or rather over, the stages of territorial organisation which normally preceded admission to the Union as a State. There was a bitter sectional struggle in Congress in 1850, but admission was eventually carried as one item in Clay's compromise resolutions for 'the peace, concord and harmony of the Union', and the President gave his assent to the Act on 9 September. Now at least, if not since the end of 1849, California had become in outward form a regularly organised democratic polity. The fact that a democratic constitution could be framed and adopted amidst all the hurry and confusion of the gold rush shows how deeply ingrained was the American habit of self-government. But the Americans who had taken part in the constitutional movement had come to California before the height of the rush: the attitude of the forty-niners, who only began to reach the mines in large numbers in the summer, had been one of general assent rather than of active participation. The constitution was not in fact specially devised, as the mining camp system had been, in response to the peculiar conditions of the Californian gold rush.

1849 was the year of most rapid transformation in California and in that sense marked the climax of the gold rush; but the gold yield continued to increase until 1853 when, accepting Bancroft's estimate and allowing $16 as the value of an ounce, we find it amounted to 4,062,500 ounces. The immigration can moreover still be characterised as a rush, especially in 1850, when Bancroft estimates the influx as greater than in 1849—36,000 by sea and 55,000 overland. The hardships of the overland immigrants seem to have been greater, as the season was worse for grass, the trails generally were in worse condition and the immigrants were unduly optimistic about supplies. Perhaps on this account plains immigration was less after 1850, but sea immigration was still considerable.

San Francisco remained for many years a gold rush town. The over-importation of 1849 could not at once be corrected, for its sources were months away and after all city and state were growing at a rapid and incalculable rate. In September 1850 there was a commercial panic. In these generally unstable and rapidly fluctuating conditions, in the absence of warehouse accommodation and consignees of good standing, auctions were perhaps the most appropriate and were certainly a common method of disposing of cargoes. The adjustment of the outward appearance of the city to these rapid changes was also difficult. The wet winter of 1849–50 compelled attention to such neglected matters as sidewalks and the paving and grading of streets, though there was still much improvidence and bad planning. A series of disastrous fires—the worst in 1851, when on 3–4 May the business part of the city and on 22 June great numbers of its houses were burned—similarly compelled recognition of the necessity of more substantial building and greater precaution against such catastrophes. Within about a year a motley collection of houses 'in the fabrication of which sheet-iron, wood, zinc and canvas seemed to have been employed indiscriminately' and streets 'chiefly covered with bits of broken boxes and casks, fragments of hampers, iron hoops, old tin cases and empty bottles' was replaced by a city with planked streets full of large brick or stone stores and warehouses, not a few of them standing on land reclaimed within the year from the bay.[1]

Meanwhile there were estimated to be 100,000 at the mines, in continual flux and reflux from one place to another. In the early spring of 1850 there was a rush to Mariposa in the south of the mining district: 'every foot of ground on the creek was taken up for three miles': but by the middle of May the valley was nearly deserted. Some miners worked their way farther south, but the Indians were hostile and there was not much to be found. In the main southern mining region streams, flats, gulches and ravines had now often been dug over

[1] J. D. Borthwick, *Three Years in California* (Edinburgh, 1857), pp. 44-54, 281.

two or three times. The northern mines were lasting
better, the 'dry diggings' especially. Nevada City on
the Yuba was the foremost mining camp in 1850, having a population of 12,000 in or near it. Not far off, at
Grass Valley, valuable quartz was found in June,
causing a new excitement. There were new discoveries
on the headwaters of the Sacramento, and disappointment with the Trinity River mines led to a diversion of
interest to other branches of the Klamath. Some miners
sought a new El Dorado, a lake alleged to be lined with
gold; and a report that certain bluffs at the mouth of
the Klamath contained gold attracted shiploads of
adventurers from San Francisco in the winter of 1850–
1851 but gave them no reward. From 1851 onwards
genuine prospectors were forced beyond the borders
of California in search of new gold. Californian miners
had rather to look to a more intensive exploitation of
gold deposits already known.

Already in 1850 mining methods were becoming
more elaborate. The days when men could pick gold
out of crevices in the rocks were gone. The claim-
holders realised the need of planned operations, and
though large-scale exploitation by slaves or Indians was
no longer in question, they combined themselves in
companies numbering perhaps from fifteen to twenty-
five men including hired labourers, often Mexicans.
These companies built dams laying bare the river-beds
—wing-dams dividing the river lengthwise were
especially common. Pumps were built, and water-
wheels to work them. An improved form of rocker came
into use: it had perhaps been developed in Georgia,
though the devices described by Agricola in the sixteenth century embody the same principle. This rocker
had a perforated iron top and three or four riffles covered

with mercury at the bottom. When the mercury had
been squeezed through buckskin and the amalgam
retorted, a high proportion of the gold was saved,
though at first the cost of this 'quicksilver machine'
was high. A 'puddling box' about six feet square was
found useful for dealing with tough clay where water
was scanty: the dirt was stirred for some time in the
same water and the resultant slime run off at intervals
through a plugged hole a few inches from the bottom.
Where water was available from a dam or otherwise,
the 'long-tom', which had been evolved in the placers
of Georgia—though it too does not appear to differ in
principle from some of Agricola's German machines—
came into general use. It was an inclined wooden
trough from ten or twelve to thirty feet in length,
fifteen or eighteen inches wide at the upper and perhaps
double that at the lower end, and perhaps eight inches
deep: at the lower end were perforated sheets of iron
let into the bottom, and under them a shallow flat box
four or five feet long, with riffles to catch the gold.
Earth was shovelled in at the upper end and a continuous stream of water from a hose played upon it:
lower down the dirt was stirred and stones were removed
with shovels or forks. But the Californian miners soon
passed from adaptation to invention. Early in 1850 a
party working near Nevada City, finding that the bed
of the ravine did not give them enough fall, made a long
board trough on the hillside leading down from their
claim to their long-tom and thus originated the 'sluice'
—which however did not come into anything like
general use until the season of 1851 or even later. It
was perhaps two feet wide and a foot deep as a rule,
but might vary in length from 100 to 1000 feet. It was
constructed in sections, each the length of a plank and

narrowed at the lower end so as to dovetail into the next. With a fall of, say, one foot in twenty the water would rush through the sluice like a torrent, carrying down the large stones, dissolving the clay, and washing the gold along the bottom until caught by riffles in a very nearly horizontal section at the lower end—to which a tom was sometimes added, especially if the earth was very clayey. The efficiency of the long tom and the sluice lay not in the high proportion of gold saved— mercury, which was sometimes used in them, was the efficient agent for that purpose—but in the economy of labour in washing the gold-bearing ground. Bancroft estimates that the long tom was four times as cheap as the rocker, the sluice three times as cheap as the tom. In effect these simple devices enabled water to do more of the work. But water could not always be had in sufficient quantity. Tomming and sluicing therefore encouraged, and were in their turn encouraged by the bringing of water from a distance through flumes or aqueducts, ditches and tunnels, sometimes for scores of miles along precipitous cliff faces and across deep ravines. It appears that the first of these ditches was constructed near Nevada City, where in a mountain basin there was rich ground but no permanent water within a mile and a half, in 1850: but the idea caught on, and by 1855 it was officially estimated that there were 4500 miles of these ditches in California, scarring the slopes of the Sierra Nevada and other ranges, and representing an investment of well over $6,000,000. By this time there had been a further development in the use of water in mining. The place of origin was, once again, the neighbourhood of Nevada City: the originator, it appears, a Frenchman. In 1852 it occurred to him that instead of bringing down his water to his sluice in a hose, shovelling the auriferous dirt and gravel into the sluice and then turning the water on, he might turn the hose directly on to the dirt and gravel and sweep it into the sluice. In the following year a miner half a mile away, working like the Frenchman on a gravel bank, attached a metal nozzle to his hose and, directing it upon the bank, found that with a comparatively small head of water he could wash into his sluices more earth than could be dug and shovelled into them by a hundred men. Thus was developed the art of hydraulic mining or 'hydraulicking'. It was not applicable everywhere: but where it was applicable, whole areas of ground to a depth of one or two hundred feet might be undermined, washed away and run through the sluices in a single season at a cost of fewer cents per cubic yard than it would have cost in dollars with the rocker. It had perhaps only one serious disadvantage: whereas the earlier mining methods had pitted and scarred the ground and created unsightly heaps of 'tailings', hydraulicking tended not only to wash whole hills away but to fill the valleys with boulders, gravel, sand and mud.[1]

Whilst these changes took place in alluvial mining, quartz was also being worked with increasing success. The first Californian quartz boom in 1850–51 arose out of the unprecedented richness of numerous lodes: much money was invested in machinery and for a brief period owners of quartz claims regarded their fortunes as made. But inexperience led to results far short of

---

[1] These descriptions of Californian mining processes are mainly based upon H. H. Bancroft, *History of California*, vol. vi; T. H. Hittell, *History of California*, vol. iii; E. S. Capron, *History of California* (Boston, 1854); and J. Ross Browne, *Report on Mineral Resources of the States and Territories west of the Rocky Mountains* (39th Congress, 2nd Session, Executive Document No. 29).

expectations: and at Nevada City a self-confident charlatan secured the erection of a large furnace to secure gold by 'opening the pores' of the quartz, naturally with a negative result. In many places, moreover, the rich pockets which had led to the erection of costly mills gave out. Quartz mining fell out of favour as rapidly as it had come in. On the other hand, some possessors of rich quartz or inexpensive machinery persevered. The Mexicans knew of a very simple contrivance, an *arrastra*, a circular stone-flagged piece of ground, ten or twelve feet in diameter, where quartz already broken into small pieces was crushed by two heavy stones dragged round and round by a mule harnessed to a horizontal beam. Its simplicity no doubt derives from a Spanish peasant's method of threshing, as the winnowing of gold-dust does from the winnowing of corn. 'The Mexicans', Borthwick tells us, 'have a way of ascertaining when the quartz is sufficiently ground, by feeling it between the finger and thumb of one hand, while with the other they feel the lower part of their ear; and when the quartz has the same soft velvety feel, it is considered fine enough, and the gold is then extracted by amalgamation with quicksilver.' [1] But the *arrastra* was not capable of development like the stamp mill or battery, already known of course in many countries, and itself a development of the principle of the pestle and mortar. In 1853 confidence in quartz began to revive, and two years later there were about sixty mills in operation, producing, so Bancroft tells us, some 250,000 ounces of gold. The stamps at this period were still made of timber shod with cast-iron. The quartz slime after crushing was washed on to an inclined riffle-board and thence conveyed into an amal-

[1] J. D. Borthwick, *op. cit.* p. 244.

gamator, a moving wooden box about six feet square and six inches deep containing mercury. The development of this process was much assisted by the fact that there were rich cinnabar mines in California itself: the price of mercury fell from $6 a pound at the time of the gold discovery to 50 cents in 1855.

Such far-reaching technical developments as these naturally reacted upon the life and institutions of the miners. The effects can be summarised by saying that gold-mining, which in 1848 and 1849 had been an adventure, became an industry. There was on the part of the miners a willingness to wait for returns, an investment of capital, which implied a willingness to stay and a belief that the industry would last. Along with this went a new sense of permanency in the mining camps. The miners cut down the timber on the hillsides and built themselves log cabins in situations near their claims and at the same time convenient for water and firewood. The camps themselves developed into towns. The mountains might in places be so steep that there was only room for a single street: it might still be necessary to bring everything but the timber over the mountains on pack-mules: but there might in these places, besides the inevitable saloons and billiard-rooms, be well-finished two-storey houses, some good hotels, two or three French restaurants, a theatre and a daily newspaper. The miner indeed still 'seemed to be trying to find some way to spend all he had': and the gambling halls, showily magnificent with crimson calico, plate-glass mirrors, chandeliers, and a string band on a balcony, with a saloon bar stocked with choice liquors and cigars, were particularly devised to help him do so. $15-20 a night might be spent in the bar-room, particularly if wintry weather kept the miners idle. But prices were far more reasonable after 1850: in Sonora that summer board was $16 a week for two meals a day, next summer much better board with three meals a day cost $8 to $10, and 'plenty of the good things of this world' were to be had. This may have been partly the result of the commercial collapse of September 1850 in San Francisco, but it was certainly in part the result of better communications with and in the mining region. Here again the first improvement was of Mexican origin. Great pack-trains of thirty to fifty mules with four or five Mexicans to tend them went up into the mountains. They were sometimes suspected of exaggerating new finds to get more business. It was in any case a profitable business, for if one camp was found well provided, a supply train could hope to distribute its load at other diggings. The storekeeper's business was also a profitable one, for the risk was less than in earlier and more unsettled days, and the miners were good customers and the Mexicans and Indians, when they had money, even better. Trade developed on the trails themselves. Enos Christman noted in May 1851 that whereas a year ago the wandering gold-hunter had to carry his blanket, his provisions, his frying-pan and his tea-kettle with him, now there were all along the roads trading tents and houses where travellers could be accommodated with good meals and a good clean bed. Later, roads began to be cut in the sides of the mountains—some by private companies, some by local and State authorities—and rivers were bridged. As these roads developed, the American stage-coach appeared by the side of the Mexican pack-mule: from Sacramento, steadily growing in importance as the base of supply of the most flourishing mining districts, a dozen stage-coach lines

were running early in 1853, with from three to twelve
coaches apiece: soon after these amalgamated into a
single company. Besides the stage-coaches there were
the freight waggons, often the 'prairie schooners' of the
immigrants, though they left the steeper and remoter
districts to the mule trains; and from 1853 the telegraph
appeared. But the most characteristic Californian means
of communication was the 'express'. The express business was not of Californian origin but it grew with great
rapidity owing to the inadequacy, injudicious location,
and tardiness of the postal service: the postmasters may
have been in voluntary, and if not were certainly in
involuntary, collusion with the express-men. These,
despite high rates, enjoyed the confidence of the miners
and had agencies in every mining town. They not only
forwarded goods, parcels and letters: they received
deposits, especially of gold-dust, from the miners, they
purchased and remitted gold-dust on their own
account, and they sold drafts on the Atlantic States.
The express messenger, with perhaps another armed
man, would take down from the more inaccessible
camps a mule laden with gold in leathern sacks. The
wicked banker had in fact appeared in the guise of that
fairy godmother of the miners, the express. There were
at first several express houses, but quite early one firm,
Adams & Co., attained indisputable pre-eminence.

The mining camp, however, had been more than a
collection of tents and shanties. It had been a social
unit, and the establishment of regular constitutional
government and of more settled economic and social
conditions raised the question whether as a social unit
it still had a part to play. Though partnerships might
become larger, the mining partnership and the claim
staked out according to the custom of the camp

remained because the system proved adaptable, though
claims became larger and camps coalesced. Some camps
retained forty-foot claims, but Jackass Gulch in 1851
replaced its ten-foot claims by areas 100 feet square.
There must have been many amalgamations, and the
restriction to a single claim was generally relaxed: an
individual was allowed to hold as many as he pleased,
provided he kept a man at work in each. Though the
free miner remained the foundation of the whole system,
some capital was needed for large-scale operations:
lacking it, miners might combine, or they might go
farther afield, but an increasing number preferred a
regular wage of $5 or $6 a day to the uncertain prospects of individual mining. The mining camp system
was thus adaptable enough to essay the regulation of
quartz-mining. Late in 1852 the Nevada City district
laid it down that quartz claims were to be 100 feet on
the ledge or lode, including all its dips, spurs and angles:
twenty days' labour had to be done on a claim within
thirty days, but time was allowed for the organisation
of a company and the erection of a mill. The inadequacy
of such a method of regulation did not appear until later.
The powers which the camps had assumed in matters
of civil and criminal justice were more difficult to
reconcile with the advance of regular government. A
State law of 1850 abolished the office of *alcalde* and
ordered the election of a justice of the peace in every
township. Next year these justices were given power to
hear disputes regarding mining claims and properties
as the miners' own *alcaldes* had done. But the problem
of order in the mining camps could not be treated
simply as a question of creating the necessary legal
offices; and conditions for a while got worse rather than
better. It was harder to make a living by gold-mining,

and this fact increased the temptation to make a living dishonestly or by violence and likewise the temptation to dispossess those who were making an honest living but were not American citizens.

In the cosmopolitan admixture brought by the rush the English, Scots, Irish, Germans and Scandinavians presented no serious problem of assimilation. The French were more inclined to keep themselves to themselves. Their numbers were considerable, being estimated by a French Government agent at the close of 1853 at 25,000-30,000.[1] In 1849 there was a group at any rate of well-educated men: later many were induced to go by the offer of passages to California as prizes by the Parisian *Loterie des lingots d'or* and by the efforts of various bubble companies. They were not particularly successful as miners, lacking the necessary adaptability and enterprise, and found themselves more at home in keeping restaurants and cafés, in domestic service, and in various small trades and industries. There were enough of them to maintain a thrice-weekly and a fortnightly newspaper and two theatres, though these no doubt enjoyed a wider patronage. If the French were difficult to assimilate, the Spanish Americans were thought by the majority, or at any rate the loudest-voiced, of the miners to be unassimilable. Many were willing to employ them as miners, for they possessed some skill in the occupation, but few were willing to allow them to enjoy claims of their own, though they had often acquired such in 1848 before the great rush. In 1849 many were ejected and virtually expelled from the mining camps. The first effect was to concentrate

[1] P. C. de St.-Amant, *Voyages en Californie et dans l'Orégon* (Paris, 1854). Saint-Amant was the envoy in question. But I cannot help thinking the number is an exaggeration.

them in the southern mining districts, where they had always been more numerous, especially in Sonora. Here they could at any rate defy individual hostility. But hostility was now transferred to the communal plane, and the legislature imposed, from May 1850, a licence tax of $20 a month on all foreign miners. There was little question of enforcement except against the Spanish Americans and the Chinese, not numerous as yet. But the rate was virtually prohibitive to the happy-go-lucky Mexican or Chilean, in view of the declining returns to the miner. Thousands had to seek employment on the claims of others or abandon the mines for the towns or for their native country. Sonora resolved to resist the tax, and in July 1850 rising feeling between Mexicans and Americans there nearly resulted in the hanging by American miners of individuals who were afterwards acquitted by the courts of the murder charge brought against them, and did result in a demand that all foreigners not engaged in permanent business and of respectable character should leave the district unless permitted to remain by a committee of American citizens in each camp. The bluster on both sides died down, but Christman notes late in September that three-fourths of the Mexicans had left the neighbourhood. Business in San Francisco and the southern mining regions felt the tax as well as foreign miners, and it was repealed in 1851, having been more deterrent than productive: it was reimposed in 1852, but at a rate of only $3, later $4, a month. There were still occasional molestations of Spanish Americans, and even Frenchmen, in the southern mines.[1] On the other hand it

---

[1] Mrs. Clappe also notes a mêlée followed by expulsion of Spanish (American) miners from the bars of Feather River in July 1852: *Shirley Letters from California Mines in 1851-52* (ed. T. C. Russell, San Francisco, 1922).

seems that the sporadic acts of highway robbery and murder with which the southern mining regions were troubled for many years were due in part at least to the vindictive feeling of some of the Mexican miners against the community that had dispossessed them.

In 1852 and later years, however, the miners' determination to vindicate their Americanism turned mainly against the Chinese. There were a few of these even in 1848, a few hundreds in 1849, but by the beginning of 1852 there were still only 7500: by August there were 18,000. There was an opening for the Chinese in working placers which the white miners had abandoned, and they were quick to take it. It seems that most of the Chinese were introduced under contracts by Chinese companies. They had a traditional skill in mining according to their own methods, though these struck others as slow, ineffective and wasteful of labour: what made them pay, in so far as they did pay, was of course the cheapness of the Chinese labour. They lived in their own camps, supplied themselves from their own stores in San Francisco, and sent all their gold to China. Thus the miners who sometimes drove them off their claims won considerable support from the general community. But the Chinese are the most patient of peoples: though there was an occasional exodus to China in the face of anti-Chinese feeling and legislation, their numbers moved rather irregularly upwards, and as placer mining in the State became less remunerative they acquired an increasing share of what was left. They remained, an unassimilable but persistent element in the Californian community, to vex a later generation.

In a sense these problems were merely aspects of the struggle for order, the effort of the heterogeneous immigrants of the gold rush to make themselves a community in the face of unwanted foreigners and of criminals and parasites. The rapidity of the constitution-making of 1849 had been deceptive. Quite apart from the criminal elements, the gold-rush immigrants generally were hardly ready for constitutional government. Public spirit is the lubricating oil of all constitutional machinery. The miners had a large measure of public spirit so far as concerned their camp: but, intent upon making their fortunes with the least possible delay and returning whence they came, they cared little whom they elected to make or administer the laws of California and were apt to regard the advent even of regular justice as the intrusion of an alien authority. Their apathy conspired with the selfish interests of others. The laws were defective, the administration of justice slow and imperfect, its officers often incompetent or corrupt. It was difficult to enforce the attendance of witnesses and to find trustworthy jurymen. The atmosphere was not one of respect for law. The miners themselves recked little of it in their dealings with Mexican miners: squatters ignored the land grants of the Mexican Government, which were being investigated by a United States commission, and calmly appropriated or killed grantees' cattle, fenced in their springs, raised crops upon their lands: no one paid any heed to the rights of the Indians when reservations were made in compensation for the encroachments of mining upon their hunting ranges.

But in the mining camps there was at any rate a swift, sharp instrument which, though it might be misused by prejudice and passion, inspired some fear in evil-doers.[1] For that very reason rogues tended to concentrate in San Francisco, where the officials were of poor

---

[1] Yet there were, it is said, 4200 murders in California from 1849 to 1854.

calibre and the police inadequate in number and some
of them in league with thieves. In particular there were
a number of ex-convicts from Australia—'Sydney
ducks'—who had come not to dig for gold but to prey
upon the community. The great fire of 4 May 1851
led many to believe that there was a gang in San
Francisco willing to burn it for plunder's sake. A number of business men with a substantial stake in the town
determined to take the law into their own hands, and,
as the records show, many small tradesmen and clerks
were willing to join them. First a volunteer night patrol
was formed to supplement the police. Then on 8 and 9
June a 'committee of vigilance' was organised to punish
thieves, burglars, incendiaries and assassins by speedier
and more drastic means than the lax and uncertain
administration of the law allowed. Members of its
executive committee were constantly in attendance at
its headquarters to receive complaints. They could
summon the full committee if necessary by two strokes
of the alarm bell. The executive committee met almost
every day for three months; the general committee,
numbering about 700, less frequently. The committee
sent a boat to board every vessel from Australia, and
ordered a few suspicious characters back to Sydney.
It patrolled the streets on the occasion of the second
great fire on 22 June. In all, it arrested ninety-one
persons, punishing nineteen, discharging forty-one and
disposing of the rest by handing them over to the
authorities; for, unlike the miners' meetings, it sought
to sustain the ordinary law when it could be sure that
it would be properly administered. Expenses, however,
were heavy; and in September, hoping that its activities,
and particularly the break-up of a Sydney gang disclosed by a prisoner's confession, would be a salutary

warning both to evildoers and to supine officials, it retired into the background. It had unquestionably been supported by a public much wider than its own member-bership; and its methods, less clumsy and less apt to degenerate into mere mob law than the methods of the mining camps, had been imitated that summer in many country and mining towns.

A settled social and political order had not yet, how-ever, been achieved. And commercial stability was equally difficult to attain. The commerce of California was so peculiar in its rapid fluctuations and its depend-ence upon one profitable but speculative industry that American shipbuilders evolved for it a new type of large, fast-sailing clipper ship. At first markets were extraordinarily resilient. 1851 was a year of difficulty, 1852 of recovery; 1853 saw the gold yield attain its highest level, and the general optimism found expression in a building boom in San Francisco. But next year the gold yield fell by some 300,000 ounces. The city paid the penalty of over-building in a sharp fall in rents and loss of confidence. Moreover the gold industry, in becoming more capitalistic, had also over-built. The more individualistic and less fortunate of the miners were being squeezed out. Now the flumes and ditches in which the more fortunate had invested their money had been expensive, for they had been constructed when labour was dear. They were dependent in many cases upon the sale of water at high prices to rich mines: as the smaller, richer placers were exhausted and the miners who worked them departed, the flume and ditch companies found themselves in difficulties. In spite of the development of quartz and of deep hydraulic mining, miners were restless and uneasy and a dry season added to their troubles. In 1854, 2000 sailed for Peru on the strength of unfounded reports of discoveries on the Upper Amazon. That autumn gold was discovered on the Kern River: in the spring of 1855 thousands went south by sea to Los Angeles and thence up-country, only to find that there was not nearly enough gold to go round. Agriculture attracted some in the mining regions and, in spite of the miners' right of entry upon agricultural land under an Act of 1852 [1] and of uncertainties of title due to Mexican land grants, made rapid progress in the State: the yield of wheat and barley rose from 30,000 bushels in 1850 to over 8,000,000 bushels in 1856. But although this agricultural growth made for a better balanced economy, in the short run it meant a great shift in commercial activity—a decline in shipping and in the profits of many consignees, warehousemen and others in San Francisco. Markets in fact were glutted in 1854. Early in 1855 the failure of a St. Louis banking house caused a run on its San Francisco branch and a financial panic was let loose. In particular the great express firm of Adams & Co., with branches in almost every town and mining camp, closed its doors. There were 200 failures that year in San Francisco, a city of only 40,000 inhabitants. There was a good deal of repudiation not only by private individuals, aided by a liberal bankruptcy law, but by the city and the State, and the air reeked of corruption.

The financial crisis had a political sequel. A bold newspaper editor, James King 'of William', attacked official, business and social corruption of every sort.

---

[1] Damage was also done by the debris washed into the streams especially by hydraulic mining operations. At last in 1884 a test case in the courts put an end to the uncontrolled operations of such companies to the prejudice of agriculture.

He was murdered on 14 May 1856 by another editor whose criminal record he had exposed. King had been a member of the Vigilance Committee of 1851, and a new committee was organised by one of the old leaders to avenge his death. With support from other towns, 8000 men were organised on military lines. The State authorities were powerless. The Governor's declaration of a state of insurrection in San Francisco was ignored; his request to the United States commander for arms was declined; and the Vigilance Committee proceeded to execute the murderer and three others likewise, whilst other offenders were deported. The chief justice of the State Supreme Court, who stabbed an officer of the committee, was arrested but let off for prudential reasons. This time the salutary effects of the committee's intervention were more lasting, for it organised a People's Party which controlled the city for many years and gave it the reputation of being the best governed in the United States. By unorthodox methods public opinion in California and in its leading city had shown itself sovereign: those who had in its name asserted themselves against the regularly constituted authorities had been upheld by the people, and order was on a firm basis at last.

California had emerged from the turmoil of the gold rush into smoother waters. The markets became less subject to disastrous fluctuations, for the calculations of merchants were less disturbed by unbounded and unfounded optimism, and with better and cheaper warehousing they could hold larger stocks. The most difficult point of the transition from a concentration on mining to a more diversified agricultural and industrial economy had passed. The trade of San Francisco took new directions: it grew at the expense of the distributing centres and mining towns of the interior, but saw some other coastal ports grow at its expense, as an export of grain and flour developed by the side of the export of gold. Immigration continued, and as time went on an increasing proportion of the immigrants were foreigners, but sometimes departures were in excess of arrivals. On the other hand, though many of the emigrants from 1858 onwards were miners going to new goldfields farther north, San Francisco remained in a sense the metropolis of these and other Rocky Mountain mining industries. It drew revenue from investment in them, such investment often consisting of implements and machinery made in its own foundries, the inventiveness of the Californian miner and mining engineer securing this reward in spite of the relatively high cost of labour and the necessity of importing raw materials. The development of manufactures in California owed not a little to the earlier development of mining. But manufacturing development in other directions was helped by the long distance—in the case of repairs prohibitive —from sources of supply, and the increased risk and cost of transportation during the Civil War gave it additional impetus.

In this changing California gold-mining continued to be an important and a favoured industry, though the yield had fallen below 3,000,000 ounces in 1860 and continued to fall. Energetic miners without command of capital but too independent to rest content with wage labour and too roving and speculative by disposition to settle on the land, left on one or other of the newer mining rushes—sometimes to return, cured of the fever, and settle down on the valleys and flats they had hastily left. In inaccessible districts such as Trinity River placer mining of the old type was still carried on, largely by the Chinese, who were satisfied with a dollar a day. Beyond the Sierra Nevada divide and in the south there were even a few new discoveries in the later 'fifties, though none of any real importance. A State Geological Survey, instituted in 1860, though it furnished much valuable information, made no new discoveries and gave no new direction to the gold industry. This now rested mainly upon hydraulic mining and to a less extent upon quartz. The famous 'blue lead', an ancient river-bed averaging a quarter of a mile in width and three hundred feet in depth, long sustained Nevada City and the neighbouring district. Quartz mining flourished especially in the Grass Valley district, where there were forty steam-driven quartz-mills in 1860 and the stone averaged about four ounces of gold to the ton. At the end of the decade the average yield had decreased but methods had improved and Grass Valley still prospered. But many of the older districts, unable to turn from mining to corn or fruit-growing, had fallen into decline and their mining towns had relapsed into piteous dilapidation.

Gold, though important still, was losing its predominance in the community that the Californian gold rush had created. But the gold rush had done more than lay the foundations of a prosperous California. The Californian miners were free to wander whither they listed, like the *bandeirantes* of the Brazilian *sertão*, and they had, or soon acquired, a greater measure of skill. They ranged in thousands far and wide over the thick forests and inhospitable deserts of the regions between the Rocky Mountains and the sea, examining every promising gulch and panning every stream. The Californian gold rush brought into existence an advancing mining frontier which called into being prosperous mining communities in many parts of the vast region that these men prospected for gold.

Authorities

The most valuable and comprehensive work on California in the goldfields period is still H. H. Bancroft, *History of California*, vols. vi and vii (vols. xxiii and xxiv of the *Works*) (San Francisco, 1888 and 1890). Besides a wealth of printed material, Bancroft and his collaborators were able to use manuscript material, often taken down from dictation, of many participators in the events described. Bancroft himself was a gold rush immigrant of 1852. But these volumes were in reality written for the most part by Mrs. Frances Fuller Victor and the Swede 'William Nemos': they were both practised and scholarly writers, more so indeed than Bancroft himself, who was more the managing editor, planner and publisher. T. H. Hittell's *History of California*, vol. iii (San Francisco, 1897), also covers the period in detail: it is necessarily less comprehensive, but it is based on wide and sometimes on first-hand knowledge. Josiah Royce's *California* (Boston and New York, 1886), a philosophical history of the years 1846–56, is the work of a more distinguished mind than either of the others, prolix perhaps but extremely suggestive. C. H. Shinn's *Mining Camps* (New York, 1885) deals primarily, though not solely, with California: it is a useful foil to Royce, and is likewise fertile in ideas, though somewhat too chary of giving evidence for its statements.

The first-hand contemporary accounts of the California goldfields are very numerous and vary considerably in value. The best and freshest accounts of 1848 are E. Gould Buffum, *Six Months in the Gold Mines* (Philadelphia, 1850), and James H. Carson, *Life in California* (Stockton, 1852: reprinted in Extra Number 164 of the *Magazine of History*, Tarrytown, 1931). One of the best known, J. Tyrwhitt Brooks, *Four Months among the Gold Finders in Alta California* (London, 1849), still often cited in bibliographies, was revealed as a hoax by H. Vizetelly, *Glances back through Seventy Years* (London, 1893). A well-known and well-written account of California in 1849 is

Bayard Taylor's *El Dorado* (New York and London, 1850); but it is worth bearing in mind that Taylor was not a miner, but the special correspondent of a newspaper. Two unadorned but convincing accounts by gold rush immigrants have recently been published, those of Enos Christman, *One Man's Gold* (New York, 1930), and C. E. Pancoast, *A Quaker Forty-Niner* (Philadelphia and London, 1930). The liveliest and perhaps the best of all the early books on the goldfields is J. D. Borthwick's *Three Years in California* (Edinburgh, 1857): Borthwick, however, only arrived in 1851. So did the talented authoress of the *Shirley Letters from California Mines in 1851–52* (ed. T. C. Russell, San Francisco, 1922). Worth mentioning as giving the foreigner's point of view are the works of P. C. de Saint-Amant, *Voyages en Californie et dans l'Orégon* (Paris, 1854), *A Frenchman in the Gold Rush: Journal of Ernest de Massey* (trans. M. E. Wilbur) (San Francisco, 1927), and Carl Meyer, a Swiss forty-niner, afterwards a professor at Basle, *Nach dem Sacramento: Reisebilder eines Heimgekehrten* (Aarau, 1855). W. H. Brewer, *Up and Down California in 1860–64* (New Haven, 1930), gives interesting glimpses of the gold industry in its decline.

Of the many scholarly monographs on various aspects of the subject, the most distinguished is perhaps Mary Floyd Williams, *History of the San Francisco Committee of Vigilance of 1851* (Berkeley, 1921), which is useful beyond the narrow limits of its title; but Cardinal Goodwin, *Establishment of State Government in California* (New York, 1914), Joseph Ellison, *California and the Nation, 1850–1869* (Berkeley, 1927), Octavius T. Howe, *Argonauts of '49: the History of the Emigrant Companies of Massachusetts* (Cambridge, Mass., 1923), and Owen C. Coy, *The Great Trek* (Los Angeles, 1931), are all of some value.

CHAPTER V

BRITISH COLUMBIA AND THE ROCKY MOUNTAIN STATES

§ 1. Fraser River and Cariboo

IT seems to have been in 1851 that prospectors in any numbers first left California behind them. At the end of that year or the very beginning of the next they made a discovery on Jackson Creek in the Rogue River country of Oregon, which for many years yielded about a million dollars worth of gold a year. But it was long before anything was found to justify a gold rush on a major scale. In the interior hostile Indians, who regarded the prospectors, with reason, as the advance guard of white settlement, made their operations dangerous, if not impossible. The Indians were less formidable in the British territory north of the forty-ninth parallel. This still remained a preserve of the fur-traders of the Hudson's Bay Company, confirmed to them by the Oregon Treaty of 1846. Fort Victoria on Vancouver Island had become the headquarters of the region in 1843 and round it an agricultural settlement was struggling into existence. Once a year a Hudson's Bay Company ship arrived from England: this ship, an occasional man-of-war, and a tenuous connection with the Company's Canadian headquarters in Montreal hardly relieved its isolation. Yet it could not remain isolated from the effects of the great gold discoveries to the southward. A number of the Company's

French Canadian servants were seduced by the attractions of California. Everyone was henceforward on the *qui vive* for gold, and the frontier was merely an imaginary line.[1] When gold was discovered, not in any great quantity, in the Fort Colville region just south of the line in 1855, it was certain that the prospectors would cross it. Late in 1857 news was passed from mouth to mouth of discoveries on the Fraser, the greatest of British Columbian rivers, and its great tributary the Thompson; and before next spring events gave these reports all the confirmation that optimistic Californian miners desired. James Douglas, who combined the offices of Governor of Vancouver Island and Chief Factor of the Hudson's Bay Company, sent about 800 ounces of gold, mostly collected by Indians, to the United States Mint at San Francisco; and on the strength of this a small band of prospectors set out in March 1858 and discovered rich gold at Hill's Bar on the Fraser River. Moreover a hare-brained trader named Ballou visited Victoria in the early spring, accompanied by the Governor and other officials of Washington Territory to enquire into the gold reports. He found out all he wanted to know and went straight to San Francisco, consumed with the desire to start an express business from San Francisco to the Fraser River.

San Francisco and the restless element among the Californian miners readily believed all, and more than all, they had been told about the golden bars of the Fraser River. The mining towns and camps were drained of thousands of their population. 'The newspapers of the interior', wrote a correspondent, 'are in

---

[1] In the spring of 1852 five or six vessels laden with miners came up from San Francisco to the Queen Charlotte Islands, where gold was reported to have been discovered; but this rush was a failure and had no sequel.

spasms about the excitement; they reason against it, they pray against, they ridicule it, and some of the editors would be willing to fight against it, if fighting could be of service. . . . In Sacramento and Stockton there is no life except at the stage offices, when the stages arrive, and about the steamboats when they go away. . . . Farms and stores are offered for sale at great sacrifices. . . . Mechanics and miners are demanding higher wages.' [1] In San Francisco, on the other hand, there were compensations. Certain businesses would lose, but shipping would unquestionably gain, and as there was no city of any size nearer the mines, miners might be outfitted for the Fraser just as for any American river. In May, June and July relays of vessels left San Francisco accordingly, carrying perhaps three times the complement allowed by law. At the lowest computation 18,000 people left for British Columbia, and to these must be added some thousands from Oregon, Washington and places farther afield, as far as Hawaii, Central and South America: perhaps 25,000 in all took part in the rush.

The Fraser River rush was much more sudden than the Californian, and British Columbia was much less able to absorb the miners. Victoria was a mere village of 800 inhabitants, and it was on an island. If the miners disembarked there, they must cross sixty miles of strait and then make their way up the fast-flowing Fraser. Only there indeed at first could they get the licence which, as we shall see, the Government required them to take out. That did not deter certain traders and speculators from trying to attract them to Bellingham Bay in Washington Territory, from which a trail was

[1] Quoted by J. S. Hittell, *Mining in the Pacific States of North America* (New York, 1862), p. 30.

begun through dense forest to the mines: it was declared
to be open in the middle of August, but a party took
eight weeks on the trip. By that time it had been discovered that river steamers brought from the Sacramento and San Joaquin could ascend the Fraser as far
as Fort Yale, and that was the end of the mushroom
towns of Washington. Hence the gold rush passed by
way of Victoria—miners, mechanics and small traders
first, then merchants of some standing, finally 'an
indescribable array of Polish Jews, Italian fishermen,
French cooks, jobbers, speculators of every kind, land
agents, auctioneers, hangers-on at auctions, bummers,
bankrupts, and brokers of every description'. The
miners passed on, some by steamer, some, who could
not or would not pay the fare of $20, in canoes and
boats of every description, mostly built by themselves.
The more disreputable elements were the more inclined
to stay, for their object was 'to sell and to speculate, to
sell goods, to sell lands, to sell cities, to buy them and
sell them again to greenhorns, to make money and
begone'.[1] Birds of passage and birds of prey alike found
accommodation in log-houses or shanties in the little
town or in tents on the surrounding open plain, in
ravines near by, or on the shores of the bay. Wooden
houses rose rapidly, lumber being readily obtainable
from the sawmills of Puget Sound. Lots that a few
months ago had gone begging at $5 an acre now
changed hands for thousands of dollars.

But if the congestion at Victoria was at least no worse
than it had been in San Francisco in the days of the
Californian rush, the configuration of the gold region

---

[1] A. Waddington, *The Fraser Mines Vindicated* (Victoria, 1858): quoted
by E. O. S. Scholefield and F. W. Howay, *British Columbia* (Vancouver,
1914), i, 568. I have not been able to see Waddington's pamphlet.

was much more difficult and the gold itself was much less easily to be had. There was gold on most of the bars or sandbanks on the bends of the Fraser from Fort Hope up to the forks of the Thompson and indeed beyond; and yields of half an ounce or an ounce a day seem to have been common. On the whole the yields were better farther up, but all supplies had to be brought up the steep pine-clad canyons of the river; and the Indians, who themselves took part in the mining, were inclined to resent intrusion where they could. By August there was something like a petty war, and this hostility and shortage of supplies seem to have driven in nearly all of the northern miners, one at least of whom had gone up 160 miles above the Thompson forks, upon Yale. There were no ravine diggings as on the Californian rivers. The bars were limited in extent, even with claims of 25 feet along the river. By mid-summer some ditches were made and some sluices in operation near Yale; but in general the less effective rocker was alone practicable. But the most serious obstacle to mining was the height of the river. The early finds had been made before its summer rise and the miners with their Californian experience seem to have expected to be able to work the bars pretty freely by the latter half of July, whereas in fact the northern snows kept the Fraser high for another month. Many did not think the prospects sufficiently promising to wait, or were not prepared to winter in British Columbia. Nature was in fact going to reduce the rush to manageable proportions.

The question how far the Californian invaders would be able to impose their Californian way of living was, however, of real importance. The miners at Hill's Bar in May made regulations in their accustomed fashion,

establishing twenty-five-foot frontage claims and providing for punishment of theft or interference with the
Indians by a committee of miners. But Governor
Douglas intended to make his authority felt; and his
physical strength, decision of character and long
experience gave him confidence that he could handle
the rough, honest miners and keep the troublesome in
order. Mayne relates a story of a blustering American
who was told by Douglas that he must take the oath of
allegiance before he could hold land. ' " Well," said
he, "but suppose we came and squatted?" "You would
be turned off." "But if several hundred came prepared
to resist, what would you do?" "We should cut them
to mincemeat, Mr. ———; we should cut them to
mincemeat." ' [1] Technically Douglas's commission as
Governor did not extend to the mainland, but he boldly
disregarded the limitation. As early as 28 December
1857, affirming the Crown's right to all gold deposits,
he had forbidden all persons to dig for gold except on
licence from the Colonial Government at ten shillings
a month. He tempered his strength, however, with
prudence. Resenting the extrusion of Great Britain from
Oregon and concerned to maintain the Company's
rights, he at first forbade American steamers to enter
the Fraser. Finding this impracticable, he tried to bind
them to carry none but licensed miners and none but
Hudson's Bay Company goods and to pay the Company
a fee on each passenger. But he soon confined himself
to levying fees on all boats and duties on all goods
entering the river and trying to enforce the licence fee,
which had meanwhile been increased from $2 to $5.
At the end of May he visited the mines himself. He

[1] R. C. Mayne, *Four Years in British Columbia and Vancouver Island*
(London, 1862), pp. 54-5.

appointed a collector of revenue, but confirmed the Hill's Bar regulations as to mining claims and took no offence at the others. Towards the end of July he began the construction of a trail to the Upper Fraser by the convenient Harrison–Lillooet route, employing for the purpose some hundreds of miners, who were glad to serve for their keep and free transport up-country. His efforts at conciliation of the Indians did not avert armed conflict: after two Frenchmen had been killed, two successive expeditions of 150-200 miners proceeded up the river and killed about thirty Indians. He then went up again to the mines, with a handful of soldiers and sailors, met and pacified the Indian chiefs, and stringently forbade the sale of liquor to the Indians; and he appointed two justices of the peace. The miners, respecting the man and feeling that he had their interests at heart, did not find it necessary to develop the mining camp organisation of California.

By this time Douglas had the satisfaction of knowing that his strong and resourceful policy was approved in the main by the Colonial Office in London, whose only serious criticism was of his attempt to restrict American trade in the interests of the Hudson's Bay Company. Moreover the Imperial Government and Parliament strengthened and clarified his position by constituting the territory from the mountain divide to the sea a new colony of British Columbia with him as its Governor, terminating the Hudson's Bay monopoly of trade with the Indians within that area, and asking him to sever his connection with the Company. At the same time, drawing on its Australian experience, the Colonial Office urged upon the Governor a wise and liberal policy towards the miners.

The British governmental machinery, aided by cir-

cumstances but above all by the character of its chief
agent, had on the whole worked more promptly and
efficiently in the emergency of the gold rush than had
the American in California. But a large proportion of
the gold-rush immigrants had returned to California
with no very flattering opinion of the country they had
seen. Early in November the population on the Fraser
was perhaps at its maximum, being estimated by
Douglas at 10,600. Their tents and log huts were
scattered along perhaps 200 miles of river, most thickly
near Yale. They were now working with water from
their ditches the benches or terraces as well as the bars
of the river. With the approach of winter mining slowed
down and many left. Douglas estimated the gold output to the end of November at 106,000 ounces.[1]

Meanwhile the organisation of the new colony was
proceeding. Of Douglas's first temporary officials one
was pretty clearly corrupt, others were indiscreet or
undignified. In the middle of winter the justice of the
peace at Hill's Bar sent a posse of twenty men to arrest
the justice at Yale, who had arrested one of his constables, and fined him for contempt. The Yale justice
appealed to the authorities for support, and over a
hundred bluejackets and marines and royal engineers
were sent up, only to find that the affair, which had
seemingly originated in a Californian Vigilance Committee feud, had been taken far too seriously. But the
administration of justice was soon in the vigorous and
capable hands of the new Chief Justice sent out from
England, Matthew Begbie. There was occasional
violence in British Columbia, but Begbie, from the

[1] The usual modern estimate of $700,000 (rather more than 40,000
ounces) seems too low for the number working and the many reported
successes. I therefore prefer Douglas's.

moment early in 1859 when he made his personality felt, had the confidence of the miners. The nature of the country, with few ways out of its rugged mountains, was no doubt a further deterrent to crimes of violence. A detachment of royal engineers was also sent out, not only as a safeguard of order but also to help in the construction of urgent public works. Early in 1859 they began to hew out of the forest a new seat of government on the Lower Fraser at New Westminster. In the summer, Douglas reorganised goldfields administration on Australian lines, replacing the system of monthly licences, which had never been more than partially effective, by an annual licence at £1 or $5, and instituting gold commissioners to administer the gold laws, settle mining disputes, and exercise the authority and jurisdiction of a justice of the peace. Alluvial claims were to be twenty-five feet long, with width varying according to circumstances, quartz claims a hundred feet along the lode: but regulation by elective mining boards might be introduced on petition of a hundred resident and duly registered miners. The gold commissioners, new to Californian miners, seem to have found more favour than the mining boards.

Whilst Douglas was busy with governmental machinery, mining was making technical advance. More flumes and ditches were built; the Fraser was wing-dammed; rockers were replaced by sluices; mercury was used to recover the fine gold. But the rush was over, the population shrinking. In the spring of 1859, though many stayed to work for wages on the more productive claims down below, about 3000 miners went up by boat or overland with their packs to prospect the upper river. But with the high cost of supplies brought up by pack-train a claim needed to produce

more than $5 a day per man to be worth the miner's
while. Not until the Quesnel River was reached late in
the season were there many claims substantially richer.
Victoria was inclined to throw the responsibility for its
mood of depression upon Douglas, and especially to
demand that land should be made available on more
liberal terms to miners wishing to settle; but Douglas
was clearly right in thinking that the first necessity was
to make mining cheaper by improving communications.
In 1860 he set about building a trail northwards from
Yale along the Fraser canyon and began to transform
the Lillooet trail into a waggon road. But his activity
seemed unable to check the decline of the Fraser River
mines, signalised in 1860 by the arrival of about 4000
Chinese to subsist on the leavings of the white miners.

The finds on the Quesnel gave a definite direction to
the prospectors' search for coarse gold in the country
higher up. In 1860 they penetrated into the Cariboo
region, a tumbled irregular mountain mass like 'a
molten sea lashed into gigantic billows, which, at the
very height of the storm, had been suddenly petrified'.[1]
At the very end of the season Rose, an American, and
McDonnell, a Cape Breton Islander, made a really rich
discovery on 'Antler Creek'. Next day, it is said, there
was a foot of snow on the ground. But miners winter-
ing in the Quesnel country lost no time in making their
way across the mountains: late in March 1861, when
the first Gold Commissioner reached Antler Creek, he
found a number living in dug-outs in the snow. That
season the lower districts were almost abandoned by
white miners and at least 1500 came up to Cariboo.
Antler and other creeks yielded perhaps 125,000

[1] M. Macfie, *Vancouver Island and British Columbia* (London, 1865),
pp. 245-6.

ounces: the rich claims reckoned their daily yields in pounds rather than ounces, and few were so poor as to have to reckon in dollars. But towards the end of the season all earlier results were eclipsed by those from fifty or sixty feet below the surface of William's Creek—named after William Dietz, whose own discovery was unluckily at the poorest part of the creek. Douglas, foreseeing a new rush to Cariboo in 1862, set about improving the trail.

The Cariboo rush of 1862 was much smaller than the Fraser rush of 1858; and though many came from California, Oregon and Washington, there were immigrants from farther afield, from Canada, Australia and New Zealand, and about 1200 from Great Britain. A correspondent of *The Times*, who had seen Cariboo through rose-coloured spectacles, caused such excitement in London that £500,000 was subscribed for a British Columbia Overland Transit Co., which proposed to organise land transport, with river and lake steamers to supplement it, across the prairies. The arduous journey across the prairies was actually undertaken by perhaps 200 Canadians. The parties, having reached Fort Garry (Winnipeg) through United States territory, proceeded with wooden 'Red River carts' to Edmonton, and thence over the Rocky Mountain divide with pack-animals, which, however, had to be slaughtered or turned loose for the final stage of the journey down the Fraser or the Thompson in rafts. Some, however, were seduced into prospecting the prairie rivers on the way and very few arrived at Cariboo that season. The main route of the Cariboo rush was from Victoria by water to Yale, thence by rough pack-trails to Quesnel Forks, and the last forty miles on foot. A lively writer describes this last stage. 'The cargo was

made up into packs weighing about 80 lbs. each. . . .
All the sides of the mountains were soaked with the
melting snows and the soft drizzling rain, which seemed
to fall for an average of three days out of four. The
ground itself was a soft spongy mass, and the inferior
vegetation consisted of various mosses growing amongst
the roots of spruce and balsam fir trees. The trail
through this had become trodden into a filthy quagmire,
with fallen trees across it every few feet. . . . The path
was generally very steep, often at an angle of 40 or 50
degrees, and occasionally skirting precipices where a
false step would have sent the wayfarer to destruction.' [1]
A good proportion of the 6000 who perhaps reached
Cariboo did well. The pack-trains, which might number
forty-eight animals and as in California were frequently
in charge of Mexicans, with huge *sombreros, ponchos*
and silver-spangled leggings, had a profitable season.
Victoria boomed again, as in 1858. Criers paraded the
streets, shouting out the departure times and fares of
steamers for the Fraser: useless goods were auctioned
at street corners: miners thronged the streets: and
'groups of dirty and stolid Indians in many-coloured
blankets . . . watched the scene with the air of grand
spectators for whom it had been specially prepared'.[2]
But many of the newcomers—some of them 'clerks,
retired army officers, prodigal sons, and a host of other
romantic nondescripts'—shrank from the journey up-
country and stopped in Victoria.

The best mining in Cariboo was on 'deep leads'.
Shaft-sinking, drifting and tunnelling were the order
of the day. The good results of 1862 lasted into 1863
and 1864, perhaps 200,000 ounces being produced,

[1] R. Byron Johnson, *Very Far West Indeed* (London, 1872), p. 110.
[2] *Ibid.* p. 50.

mainly by William's Creek, in each of those seasons. In 1863 two claims 100 feet square—one held through a foreman, one with a partner—yielded a clear profit of $250,000 to a Canadian, 'Cariboo' Cameron, who then sold out.[1] On their way up late in the season Milton and Cheadle met a bullock-waggon escorted by about twenty armed miners: it carried 630 pounds of gold from Cameron's claims. The Government continued its exertions to make Cariboo more accessible. A steamer, whose machinery and boiler-plates had been brought 200 miles on mule-back, plied in 1863 from the end of the waggon-road to the mouth of the Quesnel, from whence there was a pack-trail. This decreased the cost of living, but Cariboo remained a difficult and expensive field to work. Claim-holders had not only to sink deep; the leads were irregular and hard to follow. Drainage was difficult without pumping machinery which was extremely expensive to install. With the exhaustion of the shallower claims Cariboo ceased to be a 'poor man's diggings': the deep claims were for men like Cameron, who employed eighty miners at wages of $10 to $16 a day.

Nevertheless Cariboo, and William's Creek in particular, had an attractive individuality as a mining camp. It was no place for loafers: idling was too expensive a luxury where food was so dear and acccommodation so rough. The tradition of good order established on the Fraser River was well maintained. Gambling and dancing indeed flourished: but the dancing partners, for the most part Germans, 'hurdy-gurdy girls', or 'hurdies' as they were commonly called, are spoken of with respect. When a little later a public reading-room was opened it was well patronised. Though by the law

[1] It is said he lost his money and eventually came back to die in Cariboo.

and custom of British Columbia mining could be 'laid over' in winter and the claim-holder go to Victoria or San Francisco and spend his season's gains, it was in winter that this remote camp 4000 feet up in the mountains was most truly itself. Snug in their thatched, mud-plastered log-cabins, some hundreds of miners lived sociably together, engaged in debates, recitations, plays and music, and dropped the Californian habit of carrying arms. Luxuries were few and food was still dear, but supplies were ample: 'large numbers of cattle were slaughtered in the fall, and were soon frozen solid and thawed out as required'.[1] There was hardly any family life, and the field proved unprofitable to the churches, but it made some contribution to the art of living. It was a more successful adaptation to the environment of the frozen north than were the summer camps of the Siberian *taiga*. Lessons were learnt which were applied a generation later by the miners of the Yukon.

The Cariboo, unlike the Fraser River rush, did not find the colony unprepared. There were steamers connecting Victoria with the lower Fraser, packers and express agencies operating above the head of navigation. There were banks in Victoria, though one, a branch of the Bank of British North America, left the purchase of gold-dust to the other, an unchartered private bank, and to the express firms. In 1861 and again in 1863 Douglas attempted to establish a Government gold escort, partly no doubt with a view to feeding the Government Assay Office set up in New Westminster in 1860: but the Government would not guarantee safe delivery and the miners preferred the

[1] Victor Ross, *History of the Canadian Bank of Commerce*, vol. i (Toronto, 1920), p. 283.

express. The currency position was difficult for a time, and Douglas toyed with a project for a mint; but relief was found in the introduction of more coin and of the notes of the new Bank of British Columbia, chartered in 1862, the most enduring result of London's interest in the Cariboo rush. The unchartered Macdonald's Bank was robbed in 1864 and failed to meet its liabilities. Much of the gold business was however retained by the expresses. Barnard's, the leading firm, put a line of stage-coaches on the road to William's Creek as it was completed in 1864–65. The bank itself used the coaches, with their burglar-proof safes, for the gold it purchased, and in their first full season they carried over $4,500,000 of gold. The Cariboo rush made British Columbia and Vancouver Island less predominantly American in population and less dependent on California, but their economic life was organised, if less elaborately, very much on Californian lines.

Politically there had from the beginning been a difference. British Columbia had been nominally separate from Vancouver Island, but practically had been ruled by Governor Douglas and the Island officials without the check there imposed by a small representative assembly. Those who settled on the mainland were less and less satisfied with this position and the Cariboo rush reinforced their desire for effective separation and representative government. In 1863, when Douglas retired, separate governors were appointed and a partially representative assembly consisting of five officials, five magistrates and five members informally elected attempted to reconcile the demand for representation with the difficulties presented by a scattered, migratory and still largely alien population.

But before the fledgling colony had really learned to

fly, it began to be aware that the Cariboo mines were declining; and new rushes, to Wild Horse in the Kootenay region in 1864 and to the Big Bend of the Columbia in 1865, failed to bring compensation. In the ensuing depression, reunion of British Columbia and Vancouver Island seemed a necessary measure of retrenchment, and it was effected by an Imperial Act of 1866. But the united colony felt itself overstaffed and overburdened with debt and was inclined to seek a new political remedy for these evils. Some of the islanders advocated joining the United States, with which economic ties were still close; but there was no sign of enthusiasm among the miners. The alternative of admission to the newly forming Canadian Dominion had very little actual economic basis. But it would be a different matter if Canada would build a railway across the prairies to the Pacific. In that hope, and one may presume also from a genuine desire to take part in the building of the new British North America, opinion on the mainland favoured entrance into the confederation. With the sympathy of Sir John Macdonald and of the Imperial Government, the confederationists won the day and British Columbia joined the Dominion in 1871.

It was a long time before British Columbia reaped the expected reward. In the 'seventies she still had to depend mainly on her gold mines. The older placers, mostly worked by Chinese, continued to decline. The capitalistic miners of Cariboo were troubled by water, and hopes of quartz-mining were dashed by the costs of transport of machinery, living and labour. The individual miner found an outlet in prospecting northward. The creeks on the Omineca or south fork of the Finlay River enjoyed brief fame in 1871. The Cassiar country near Dease Lake, best reached from the coast by way of the Stikine, had a summer population of over 1000 from 1874 to 1877, and pointed the way still farther north. In the 'eighties all eyes in British Columbia were fixed upon the railway, completed in 1886. Farming, commercial and industrial, and mining development followed—the latter in the Kootenay region. It was based at first on silver and lead, but there was gold also; and by the end of the century production had again reached the levels of the Cariboo rush. The great quartz output of Rossland, with its English and American capitalistic concerns, did not however make the camp attractive to the individual miner. He had left for the Yukon and would not come back.

The gold rushes had left their mark, however, on British Columbia. Not many of the immigrants of 1858 remained; but the gold transformed a fur-trading outpost into a true colony, which had the vision to perceive that its destiny was Canadian.

§ 2. WASHOE AND THE COMSTOCK LODE

The least attractive part of the journey of the fortyniners to California overland was the long stretch of territory from the Great Salt Lake to the Sierra Nevada. From 1850 this 'great basin' formed part of the territory of Utah controlled by the Mormons of the Great Salt Lake, who sent a few farmers to its habitable western rim. There they met a few prospectors who had climbed over the western rim, the Sierra, and found a little placer gold. 'Few occupations are more monotonous and colourless', remarked a later writer, 'than the work of a scattered colony of placer miners along the line of a creek. The Gold Cañon miners toiled in the usual way with long toms and rockers, washing the sand from the various bars, and when the richest placers were exhausted, carrying sacks and buckets of earth from the neighbouring ravines to the nearest spring or to the creek itself. At nightfall they would return to their huts, cook their simple suppers of bacon and potatoes, with bread and tea, smoke a pipe or two, and then wrap themselves up in their blankets to sleep until daybreak. In summer most of the huts were mere heaps of brush, rather inferior to the Pai-Ute [Indian] lodges. The winter cabins were usually of rough stones, plastered with mud and covered with canvas, boards or sticks, overlaid with earth. Sometimes holes were made in the walls for ventilation, but generally the cracks and open doorways were sufficient. Glass windows were an unthought-of luxury. Some of the better cabins had small iron stoves and funnels, but the majority of the miners were content with stone fireplaces and rude cranes. A nondescript ball was sometimes given at one of the stations, but few of the miners succeeded in varying the staple amusements of gambling and drinking. On Sundays the men . . . washed their clothes and cleaned up their cabins.' [1] There might be 200 miners at this camp on Gold Cañon, a ravine running down to the Carson River, when water was most plentiful. Like the others of the region it regulated its affairs by miners' meeting and paid scant heed to officers appointed by the Mormons. In any case in 1857 all the Mormon settlers in Western Utah were withdrawn by Brigham Young.

By this time Gold Cañon, never very rich, seemed to be a decaying camp. Two brothers Grosch, of more

[1] Eliot Lord, *Comstock Mining and Miners* (Monographs of the U.S. Geological Survey, vol. iv, Washington, 1883), pp. 19-20.

education and experience than the average, had with the aid of a Mexican discovered silver ore but had succumbed, one to a blood-poisoning due to remoteness from medical aid, the other to the hardships of a winter crossing of the Sierra, before they could raise capital to work it. The exhaustion of the placers, however, stimulated further prospecting. Early in 1859 rich gold was found in dark heavy soil on a neighbouring hillside, and in June a solid ledge four feet in width was found by a party of four miners, one of whom had secured admission by controlling a spring necessary to the working of the claims. He was Henry Comstock, and it was by his name that the lode, on which the party in accordance with local rules claimed 1500 feet, was to be recorded in history.[1] The discovery caused some excitement among the miners, prospectors and ranchmen of the neighbourhood; but no one knew what precisely had been discovered. There were thirty or sixty ounces of gold a day for Comstock and each of his partners, and there were masses of 'blue stuff' which they threw aside. A curious farmer took some of this stuff away and not long afterwards a friend of his rode over the ranges with it to Nevada City. The two best assayers in that mining town discovered that it was rich in gold and richer still in silver. The news was not kept secret: before dawn next day a few of the shrewdest men in Nevada City had loaded a pack-mule, saddled their horses and ridden off over the ranges. Hundreds of miners followed them in waggons, on horseback or on foot. It was the beginning of the Washoe rush.

[1] The real discovery was made by two miners who, to judge from their names, were of Irish origin—M'Laughlin and O'Riley. The fourth man's name, Penrod, has a Cornish ring. All four died poor, it is said.

This was in July; but the Ophir Company, which acquired the claims of Comstock and partners and employed ten miners to work them, was able before the end of the season to send thirty-eight tons of ore in sacks and boxes by mule-train to San Francisco and the yield, after crushing and smelting, was $112,000.[1] Another company also sank a shaft about thirty feet and extracted some tons of rich ore. New arrivals numbered perhaps 4000 by the end of the year, and signs of their activity were everywhere. 'The ground was torn up in all directions with shallow cuts and pits; diminutive adits pierced the hillsides like the holes of sand swallows in a mound, and the grey carpet of sage-brush was buried under unsightly heaps of sand and crumbling rocks.' They had also built for themselves a town, with a single street. 'On the line of this street two houses of roughly cemented stone had been built, surrounded by straggling lines of flimsy huts. Tents of dirty, ragged canvas pieced out with tattered clothes covered with grime—hovels of pine boards roughly nailed together and pierced by bent and rusty stove-pipes—heaps of broken rocks with shapeless crevices into which men crawled like lizards—shallow pits partly covered over with boards and earth—and embryo adits, dark slimy holes into which the melting snow dripped with a monotonous plash—these were the winter homes of the citizens.'[2] The life of 'Virginia City' was in its saloons and gambling houses. 'Gold and silver were stacked up on the *monte* tables; dice rattled and cards were shuffled all day and all night. The ragged, greasy, dirt-covered multitude filled the

---

[1] This was both gold and silver. The proportion of gold varied from, say, 42 to 45 per cent. in different mines.

[2] Eliot Lord, *op. cit.* pp. 60, 64.

saloons with loud talk and laughter, except when a
pistol-shot rang out sharply and the crowd swayed into
the street.'[1] Though the district was part of a county
of Utah, authority, apart from irregular miners' courts,
was non-existent.

The winter was severe, and prices were so high that
attempts were made to bring mules over the Sierra
with supplies by leading them over blankets spread
for miles upon the snow. At the earliest possible
moment the army resumed its march to Washoe—
'Irishmen with wheelbarrows; American, French and
German miners with tools and heavy packs; Mexicans
with *burros*; gamblers and confidence men on valuable
thoroughbreds; Missourians struggling through the
mud with their families and household goods in lumber
waggons; drovers with hogs and cattle; organ grinders,
Jew peddlers, "professors" with divining rods and
electric "silver detectors"; women, even, dressed in
men's clothing and usually under some gambler's
protection. One saw youth and strength, illness and
old age, cripples and hunchbacks—"all stark mad for
silver."'[2] 20,000 men came up to Washoe in the rush,
in the belief that the whole district was streaked with
silver lodes.

The whole floating population of California had been
skimmed off by the news from Washoe, and society
in 1860 was chaotic. There was a sharp clash in the
spring with the Pai-Ute Indians to the northward. A
force of cavalry, artillery and militia was sent up from
California, and the miners deserted their tunnels and

---

[1] C. H. Shinn, *The Story of the Mine as illustrated by the Great Comstock
Lode of Nevada* (New York, 1896), p. 64.

[2] J. Ross Browne, 'A Peep at Washoe' (*Harper's Magazine*, xxii),
quoted by Shinn, *op. cit.* p. 56.

prospecting holes to enrol for the fighting. At the end of May a thousand men marched against the Indians and drove them into the desert. Martial law had been declared for the purpose of the war; but it exerted no influence on the state of the mining camps. On the contrary some of the volunteers who had been permitted to make levies of all sorts for the war afterwards swaggered about Virginia City, lording it over peaceful citizens, drinking, gambling, and occasionally shooting or stabbing one another. The federal military authorities looked to defence against Indians and later arrested some obstreperous secessionists, but Congress took no action until early in 1861 when it organised the new territory of Nevada.

The canvas tents and hovels of the winter were replaced that summer by log cabins and wooden buildings, and as the roads were made passable for waggons prices fell to a fraction of their former rates. Prospecting was of course busily proceeding, but the actual yield of the mines was probably only $1,000,000 in 1860. These silver lodes could not be rifled of their treasures as speedily and easily as the bars and gulches of California; and the Californian miners—apart from the Mexicans—knew nothing of silver. At first the ores were sent to San Francisco for crushing, and the best even went to England, perhaps to Swansea, for smelting. The erection of mills capable of dealing with ores on the spot was an obvious objective. The first, which used a process of amalgamation in pans after crushing, was opened by a stamp mill expert from Nevada City in August 1860, and processes and machinery were steadily improved. There was, however, much over-building of mills. At the same time mining was going deeper, and a German with Californian experience devised a system of framing timbers together in square sets which, when filled with waste rock or wooden braces and piled on top of one another, could support the roof in spite of the forty-five feet of ore body requiring to be worked. Thus early mining on the Comstock lode showed itself capable of technical progress. But a more fundamental change was its concentration in the hands of a few great companies which emerged like towering peaks out of the mist of the early years of the 'Washoe'.

The actual locations of claims were largely made by working miners. But they had little idea of their durability or value and were very willing to part with them for a few thousand dollars at most; and there were many buyers. All California could not get rich quick by taking up claims in Washoe, but it hoped to do so by taking up feet or inches of them. In the first speculative fever of the spring of 1860 no one troubled to enquire as to the place of the location, the locators, the title, the character of the rock; and Washoe responded by sending to San Francisco 'mysterious hints of new discoveries that never existed, strikes in mines never located, accounts of sales that never took place'.[1] At a later and more sober stage, towards the end of 1861, the 5000 claims located within thirty miles of Virginia City had reduced themselves to eighty-six working companies, with an aggregate nominal capital of $61,500,000; and in September 1862 the San Francisco Stock and Exchange Board was organised, mainly to deal with silver stocks. Even of these companies only eight or nine actually paid dividends; but they were so remunerative that the habit of speculation formed in San Francisco when

---

[1] Contemporary letter quoted by Shinn, *op. cit.* p. 140.

there was all Washoe to speculate on was merely confirmed when it was virtually reduced to the Comstock lode.

Neither mining laws nor mining morals really passed the test of the Comstock. The mining laws, allowing claims of 300 feet along the lode with all its dips, spurs and angles, had been adopted by and were adapted to a community of small or medium owners of the Californian type. It is said that the first recorder was an uneducated blacksmith and that the transcripts of notices of claim were kept in a saloon and lay on a shelf behind the bar. Moreover the Comstock itself was difficult to reduce to type. 'The Comstock, though called a lode, is really a broad metalliferous belt or ore channel. It contains many narrow lodes, disjointed strata, bunches and chimneys of ore, in distinct clefts, separated from each other by what the miners call "horses" or fragments of rock . . . often a thousand feet long and several hundred feet thick. . . . The whole body, constituting what miners call a vein . . . is lodged in a system of fissures rather than in one great fissure.'[1] Now the question how far the Comstock companies could follow the dips, spurs and angles clearly depended on whether it was a single lode or not. It was a matter on which scientific opinion was doubtful but popular opinion was dogmatic: the more lodes, the more claims. Different judges held different views, as well they might, but in the end the single-lode theory won the day, though a suspicion persisted that the decision had been reached not by weight of evidence but by weight of money-bags. Nor was this the only source of litigation. A situation difficult enough in all conscience was made more difficult by deliberate omissions to record

[1] Shinn, *op. cit.* pp. 92-3.

claims and recordings purposely ambiguous.[1] The mass of litigation absorbed nine or ten million dollars, one-fifth of the product of the 'first bonanza period' of the Comstock, and helped to make a lawyer, W. M. Stewart, its dominant figure.

When the situation began to stabilise itself, a community very different from California after the great rush had come into existence. In place of the restless independent miner of the Californian placers, its typical figures were the skilled wage-earning miner—though he was often a speculative investor into the bargain—the speculative stock-market investor, off stage, and the 'bonanza king'. The typical social and economic units were not the mining camp and the mining partnership but the joint-stock companies. The political confusion had come to an end when the Nevada territorial officials had arrived in July 1861. In October 1864 Nevada was admitted as a State of the Union. The chief reason for the advance in status, apart from the exigencies of Civil War politics, had been the disinclination to invest capital on the strength of doubtful titles interpreted by a corrupt judiciary.[1] Stewart had wrecked the first constitutional project because it made all mining property liable to taxation. After statehood, as before, Nevada politics were dominated by the mine-owners of the Comstock.

The independent miner found consolation, for a time at least, in swarming over Nevada in search of gold and silver, with a small magnifying-glass to examine ores, a pestle and mortar to crush a few ounces, a spoon made from half an ox horn in which to wash them for gold.

[1] In 1866 an Act of Congress confirmed mine-holders in possession acquired under district laws and permitted them to acquire a certified title by patent from the United States. On this see further below, pp. 194-5.

He learnt to test for silver with acids. Late in August
1860 three prospectors discovered silver in the 'Esmer-
alda' mining district, some distance south-east of
Virginia City in a canyon surrounded by barren hills
'with scattered scrubby pines and more scrubby cedars
here and there'. In the course of the next year or
two this unprepossessing spot attracted perhaps 5000
people; the town of Aurora arose; 5000 claims were
recorded and perhaps twenty quartz mills were erected.
Then in the summer of 1862 an express employee,
looking for his ponies in some treeless ranges about
170 miles west of Virginia City, found an outcrop of
bluish-green quartz resembling some quartz he had
seen on the hill above Gold Cañon. Further investigation revealed the presence of rich silver ore; and in the
spring and summer of 1863, 5000 people came to Reese
River and established the town of Austin. Machinery
and supplies were very dear and at first crushing and
amalgamation mills were not very successful, but a
roasting furnace opened in March 1864 produced
better results: San Francisco capital began to be
invested, and in spite of the usual waste and disappointments another silver district had established itself. It
was only a question of time before any silver district
passed from the prospectors to the capitalists; but for
those who preferred gold there were from 1861 to
1865 continuously developing rushes to Idaho and
Montana and a rush on a smaller scale to Central
Arizona.

For years the feverish excitement on the fringe of the
established mines of the Comstock continued. Truth
was not sober in Virginia City in 1862–63, and Mark
Twain, who was a reporter on the local newspaper,
gives a description in *Roughing It* which has the ring

of truth: 'New claims were taken up daily, and it was the friendly custom to run straight to the newspaper offices, give the reporter 40 or 50 "feet", and get them to go and examine the mine and publish a notice of it. They did not care a fig what you said about the property so you said something. Consequently we generally said a word or two to the effect that the "indications" were good, or that the ledge was "six feet wide", or that the rock "resembled the Comstock". . . . If the rock was moderately promising we followed the custom of the country, used strong adjectives, and frothed at the mouth, as if a very marvel in silver discoveries had transpired. If the mine was a "developed" one and had no pay ore to show . . . we praised the tunnel. . . . We would squander half a column of adulation on a shaft, or a new wire rope, or a dressed pine windlass, or a fascinating force pump, and close with a burst of admiration of the "gentlemanly and efficient superintendent" of the mine—but never utter a whisper about the rock. And these people were always pleased, always satisfied. Occasionally we patched up and varnished our reputation for discrimination and stern undeviating accuracy by giving some old abandoned claim a blast that ought to have made its dry bones rattle—and then somebody would seize it and sell it on the fleeting notoriety thus conferred upon it. There was *nothing* in the shape of a mining claim that was not saleable. . . . Every man had his pockets full of stock, and it was the actual *custom* of the country to part with small quantities of it to friends without the asking.' There was still much of the atmosphere of a rush. The population, variously estimated at from 16,000 to 24,000, was still not settled. But solid progress was being made. Order was better maintained. Mining was on the way to becoming a regular industry. Transport had already become one, employing twelve or fifteen thousand draught animals, largely owned by men who had had ranches in the mountains before the rush, and two or three thousand men. Roads across the mountains had been much improved, mainly by private enterprise, which recouped itself by tolls. There were three flourishing stage-coach lines. There was the inevitable Wells, Fargo express.

The 'bonanzas', however, were unlikely to last for ever. In 1864 the rich ore chutes near the surface approached exhaustion and depression descended on the Comstock. The yield that year was $16,000,000, the highest yet recorded; but to carry on work at deeper levels new assessments on stockholders would be required. Stocks therefore fell to a fraction of their former values, and the 'wildcat' speculations collapsed completely. Retrenchment was the order of the day even in the productive mines, and wages were reduced, after strenuous resistance from a Miners' League, from the hitherto customary rate of $4 a day to $3.50. Numbers of the floating population left Virginia City, and hundreds of prominent men were ruined.

The shocks of 1864 made for better co-ordination and more businesslike working of the Comstock mines. William Sharon, who had come to Virginia City in March 1864 as manager of the Bank of California, made himself in these duller times the master first of a group of mills, finally of many mines also, and became king of the Comstock in place of Stewart, who had become and for many years remained one of the United States Senators for Nevada. Another able business man, Adolph Sutro, embarked on a great scheme for draining all the Comstock mines to a depth of 1600 feet by a tunnel three miles long, though his methods did not

commend themselves to Sharon and his associates. But
the trend of the yield of the Comstock was downward,
and perhaps for that reason mine-owners resorted to
dubious devices for concealing their operations. If a new
level in the lode was beginning to be explored, they
would confine the miners engaged upon the work for
days below the surface, securing their acquiescence by
liberal extra pay. The mystery would send the mine
shares up, and if profit was made on the stock market,
a reported strike might be nearly as remunerative as a
genuine discovery. Sharon was thinking on sounder
lines, but he was probably mainly concerned with reducing costs, his great coup being the building of a
railway (by Chinese labour) in a few months in 1869–70
to connect Virginia City with the Central Pacific Railroad. Ore could now be sent for milling to Carson City
for $2 per ton instead of $3·50, when it had gone 'by
lumbering ore-carts, dragged by plodding files of mules
on steep, muddy and at times impassable roads'. It may
well have been calculation of costs as well as jealousy of
an independent influence that caused him to oppose
Sutro's tunnel scheme.

There was in these years one new rush that seemed
for a time likely to compensate for the decline of the
Comstock lode. Some 120 miles south-east of Austin,
in a range covered with white pine timber, silver was
discovered by a party of prospectors in 1865: in the
winter of 1867–68 an Indian discovered a richer mine
and then a chloride deposit was found which yielded
thousands of dollars to the ton. As this news spread,
miners and prospectors hastened to White Pine. Four
or five thousand were there, 9000 feet 'up in the frozen
clouds', in the midst of the winter of 1868–69. Next
year the numbers rose to 10,000 or more: the output

amounted to $4,000,000: quartz mills and roasting furnaces were erected farther down: the Bank of California tried to acquire a dominant interest in the mines, but in vain. Yet White Pine was a flash in the pan. At 100 feet this chloride deposit of almost unexampled richness pinched out. The booming towns collapsed: the adventurers went away.

It was the Comstock itself that was destined to provide the antidote to the decay of White Pine and of its own older mines. Thanks mainly to the Crown Point mine, the yield of the district increased from $8,000,000 in 1870 to $11,000,000 in 1871 and $13,500,000 in 1872, and the market value of Comstock shares rose more than correspondingly. But these results were eclipsed by the Consolidated Virginia and the associated California, a group of mines acquired some years previously by two Californian miners of Irish origin, James G. Fair and John W. Mackay, in partnership with two retailers of liquor in San Francisco. Mackay's discernment was of great value in building up the strength of the group: Fair excelled in energy and mining technique. The richness and extent of the ore body which they began to work late in 1873 were such that by the end of 1878 the Consolidated Virginia had produced over $60,000,000; and the California in 1875–78 produced over $43,000,000. The total yield of the Comstock in 1876 was at its maximum of $38,000,000, though the speculation in San Francisco had fallen from its giddy peak in 1875 after the failure of the Bank of California. Sharon, however, had already been dethroned by the twin bonanza kings, Mackay and Fair.

The population of Virginia City was now at its maximum of about 25,000. In spite of the booming stocks it was a more sober city than in the days of the Washoe rush. It was still in appearance a great straggling village, but it had a well-organised municipal government, an efficient police force, numerous churches and schools. Saloons and gambling houses were much less obtrusive than of yore. It was swept by fire in October 1875, and the Consolidated Virginia's hoisting works and the California's mill were destroyed: but they were rebuilt, with improvements, in fifty days. It was a strenuous life. The miners seem to have lived well, and their unions were strong. The majority of the foremen, engineers, firemen, carpenters, machinists seem to have been Americans, of the miners proper English or Irish. The work was well organised. But as the mines went deeper one great enemy to good working conditions appeared —the heat. The rock often reached 130° to 150° F., and even the air supplied in pipes to the miners 90°. Sutro's tunnel, completed at last in 1878, had the same problem as the mines.

By 1878 the two great mines had begun to decline. It was thought best to work out the 'big bonanza' quickly lest the heat and moisture should decay the timber supports or the mine catch fire. Share values, depending as they do on prospects rather than results, fell from $262,000,000 at the beginning of 1875 to $7,000,000 at the end of 1880. But by that time 7,000,000 tons of Comstock ore had yielded $306,000,000.[1] Of this perhaps $130,000,000 was in gold, though the silver produced not only a larger sum but also a greater effect on men's minds. It was estimated that $62,000,000 had been invested and $116,000,000 paid out in dividends. Much of the investment no doubt was in rapidly depreciating works,

[1] By 1934 the total had risen to $400,000,000: C. G. Tilton, *William Chapman Ralston* (Boston, 1935), p. 289.

for although the Comstock mines sank deeper and continued to produce, the population of Virginia City declined, there being no alternative resources on the spot. Nevada was a silver rush State even more than California was a gold rush State, and after the decline of the Comstock, became something of a political anomaly. But the effects of its silver were felt far outside its borders. Its great production may have helped to frighten European countries into demonetising silver: its speculative extravagances may have done more harm than good to legitimate mining. But its bullion was of great value in the financing of the American Civil War and of the post-war expansion. As for its speculation, that followed inevitably from the technique developed in the Californian gold rush. The feeling that all should have a fair chance of wealth, the reckless optimism but also the abounding energy which had characterised California in the gold rush years, concentrated by circumstances upon a single group of highly capitalised mines, necessarily produced a series of speculative booms. The orderly development which was theoretically best for the mines was practically out of the question. In spite of the fever Nevada brought much solid profit to California. Moreover if Nevada was the daughter of California, she herself was a mother of rushes. After Washoe the prospector had silver as well as gold inscribed upon his banners.

§ 3. Pike's Peak and Colorado

When gold was discovered in California the sole denizens of the main Rocky Mountain region were the Indian tribes, occasional military detachments and fur-traders, and the Mormons of Salt Lake City. It had of course been visited by Spanish explorers. American explorers and traders at intervals from the beginning of the nineteenth century found traces of gold. But the reports were vague, and until the Californian discoveries no particular importance was attached to them. Some of those who crossed the plains to California, however, had experience of mining in Georgia; and one such party, composed of Cherokees from the Indian Territory, prospected some tributaries of the South Platte on their way across, and found gold. It was not enough to detain them; but they did not forget it, and later they passed the information on. In the winter of 1857–58 a Georgian miner, William Green Russell, who had Californian experience also and had come to hear of the Cherokees' prospecting, decided to follow it up. He organised a party to join some Cherokees at a rendezvous on the Arkansas next summer and prospect what was vaguely termed the Pike's Peak country. The assembled company numbered over a hundred at first, but it began to crumble when little gold was found. Russell, however, thought he had found enough to justify another season's work, so he went back with some others for supplies, and left what remained of his party in winter quarters at the mouth of Cherry Creek on the South Platte. His party had not been the only one to prospect the region for gold that summer. In the spring an Indian had appeared with gold at Lawrence, Kansas, and a party had accordingly set out from that frontier town across the plains; and later a Kansas trader brought in a small quantity of gold which encouraged further parties to leave the Missouri River before the season closed. Some hundreds wintered near that camp on Cherry Creek.

Enough gold had certainly not been found as yet to

justify a rush. But the frontier was suffering from the financial panic of 1857. A new gold rush would be an incalculable boon to the Missouri River towns, and a new gold rush they were determined to have. They gratuitously distributed publications containing exaggerated statements of the value of the 'mines' and they attributed the more cautious accounts of Russell and others to a selfish desire to keep their riches to themselves. They employed special agents in the principal cities of the West, on every Missouri steamer and in every westbound train. Labourers out of employment, farmers weighed down by crop failures and debts, professional men anxious to get on in their own profession or any other, were eager listeners. The Missouri had its rush next spring. The river steamers and the railways were crowded with men. The roads from the Mississippi to the Missouri were covered with waggons. From Omaha and St. Joseph by the Platte, from Leavenworth by the Smoky Hill River, from Kansas City by the Santa Fé trail they set out from early spring across the plains with waggons, with hand-carts or barrows, or with packs on their backs. There is no mention of the 'companies' of 1849: perhaps the distance was deemed insufficient. Yet it was sufficient to exhaust the supplies of many.

A proportion were men who had been in California. Yet the majority seem to have had no knowledge of gold-mining and none had any but the vaguest knowledge of where they were going. There were no mines at Pike's Peak or within a hundred miles of it. At Cherry Creek there was little mining done during the winter. The chief activity was in politics and in the laying out of town sites. Rival groups sponsored towns on either side of the creek—Auraria and Denver City.

They at least provided a first objective for the rush. The only thing needed to complete the gold rush was in fact a genuine discovery of gold. In April, none such being known, the spring tide of immigration began to flow back, gathering momentum as it went. The trail was strewn for hundreds of miles with abandoned goods. The authors of *Guides* to Pike's Peak met with many maledictions and were in some danger of a worse fate, as foreshadowed in the threatening rhyme—

> Here lies the body of D. C. Oakes
> Killed for aiding the Pike's Peak hoax.

In early May the rival towns were almost deserted, some of their founders having left in search of gold, others to escape the vengeance of the disappointed.

As a matter of fact a miner of Californian experience, George Jackson, had made a rich find on 7 January on a branch of Clear Creek, but thought it wise to return to his base of supplies. In the early spring he came up again accompanied by a Chicago party with waggons, and they took out nearly $1900 in seven days. The news reached Denver early in May, but it was over-shadowed by news of a discovery, actually later in date, on another branch of Clear Creek by a Georgian miner, John H. Gregory. Gregory had set out the previous year for Fraser River, but was stopped before he reached the Rocky Mountains either by lack of means or by the lateness of the season. It may be that he also made his discovery in the winter and returned to work it in the spring: the details seem doubtful. At any rate one of his companions came down to Denver in May for provisions with enough gold to stimulate curiosity, and a second arrival a few days later caused an exodus to the mountains. 'Traders locked up their stores; bar-keepers

disappeared with their bottles of whiskey, the few mechanics that were busy building houses abandoned their
work, the county judge and sheriff, lawyers and doctors
and even the editor of *The Rocky Mountain News* joined
in the general rush.' [1] The discovery was hardly more
than thirty miles away in a direct line, but the narrow
valley, densely wooded with tall yellow pines, in which
it lay, was only accessible by a journey of from two to
four days across the mountains. Loaded waggons at one
point had to be taken up an ascent of 1600 feet in little
more than a mile. Yet by about 21 May there were
already some hundreds of miners there, working with
rockers, long-toms and sluices, and camping in tents
and huts of pine branches. A fortnight later there were
4000 or 5000.

The news of Gregory Gulch revived building and
trading in Denver, and with the issue of a statement by
Horace Greeley of the *New York Tribune*, one of the
best known Americans of the day, who happened to be
on the spot and had himself visited the gulch, those who
had refused to be turned back by the croakers regarded
their faith as justified and went up in a body. At one
time there were at least 10,000 crowded within an area
of four square miles. It was too many. There were rich
pockets, but the real wealth of the gulch was in the
quartz lodes, which inexperienced miners without resources were not capable of working. Some made a
reasonably good living—'good wages' in the current
phrase—but the great majority 'toiled from sun-up to
sun-down without securing enough to pay for the
sharpening of their picks'. By the end of June they had
grown tired of these fruitless exertions, and in the course

1 H. Villard, *The Past and Present of the Pike's Peak Gold Regions* (St.
Louis, 1860—reprinted Princetown, 1932), p. 36.

of the next month it was estimated that from fifty to a hundred waggons daily passed through Denver on their way back to the Missouri River.

Enough remained, however, to prospect the adjoining mountains pretty thoroughly. On yet another branch of Clear Creek a rich discovery was made by Green Russell, who with his party of ten took out a little over 100 pounds of gold in a little less than four months and thus had some reward for his pioneering activity. Later in the season many miners found their way into the South Park region, the high valley of the Arkansas, and some promising places were discovered. Miners swarmed from one discovery to another; but nowhere was there ground enough for all.

According to a contemporary estimate, 100,000 left the Missouri on the Pike's Peak rush; but only 25,000 actually reached the mountains and perhaps only 3000 engaged in serious mining—more than half of them as hired hands.[1] There were placers, but many of them were really decomposed outcrops of quartz; and the quartz lodes, though here and there a beginning was made this season with working them with *arrastras* and small stamp mills, would not yield much of their wealth amid the hurry, confusion and makeshift conditions of a rush. There is no reliable estimate of the gold yield of 1859, but pretty clearly it did not reach $1,000,000— no very large sum considering the size of the rush. It did indeed carry Auraria and Denver through the stage of mere camps and they became the terminus of an express line across the plains and a base of supply and recreation, with its customary parasitic accompaniments, for the miners in the mountains. Moreover the sale of surplus provisions by dissatisfied immigrants

[1] H. Villard, *op. cit.* pp. 92, 116.

kept the prices of necessaries from soaring to the usual heights.

Among the gold rush immigrants there were several hundred Frenchmen and many Mexicans, but the miners proper were for the most part Americans from the Missouri and Mississippi valleys with contingents from other states, and especially from Georgia. There is no record of direct immigration from California this season, but the miners organised themselves in districts like the Californian camps to regulate and record their claims and to provide for the hearing of disputes.[1] At any rate in Gregory Gulch, however, more regard was paid to priority and less to public opinion than in the Californian camps. It was resolved that each miner should be entitled to hold one 100-foot mountain or lode claim, one 100-foot gulch claim and one creek claim for the purpose of washing: and lode claims lacking water or machinery might be held until 1 June 1860 without being worked. Demands by newcomers that claims be cut down to 25 feet were successfully resisted by a clever manipulation of the meeting. At 'Graball' in the South Park district the claims were 150 feet long; the name—soon changed by its permanent inhabitants—suggests that miners, even while respecting vested rights, could voice their opinions.

Outside the mining districts a section at any rate of the people was much exercised with wider problems of government, but did not arrive at a solution. In the winter of 1858–59 the Kansas element predominated in the small settlements on Cherry Creek and, as they fell within the territory of Kansas organised in 1854, a request was sent to the territorial legislature for the

---

[1] Before the end of the season California was absorbed in the Washoe silver rush.

establishment of a county. But they aspired far higher, and in November elected delegates to proceed to Washington and induce Congress to organise a new territory in the mountains. This request from a few hundred persons in the light of expectations of gold which had not yet materialised naturally made little impression on Congress; but its promoters, undeterred, proceeded next spring to organise a convention to take into consideration the propriety of organising either a territory or a state. The convention met in June, adjourned until August to permit members to give some attention to the gold rush, and then resumed and drew up a constitution for a large, though as yet nearly empty, 'State of Jefferson'. The poll held in September was light, particularly in the mining districts, but it sufficed to indicate a preference for the less expensive territorial form of government in which the Federal Government appointed the officials and paid some of the bills. But Congress had still to be persuaded, and though it appears that the polls were swollen by such devices as the stuffing of ballot-boxes and the manufacture of returns from imaginary voting districts, it was deemed wise to organise a provisional government until the Federal authorities were suitably impressed. On the other hand Kansas still had its partisans, who would not support or pay taxes to the new government, so that there was a threefold division of authority between the government of Kansas, the provisional government, and the mining camps in the mountains. If these divisions did no one any particular harm it was because murders and robberies, which occurred rather in the towns than in the mines, were kept to some extent in check by vigilance committees. The main economic task of government in such a community, the improvement of roads to the mines, was undertaken voluntarily by the miners.

Perhaps 4000 or 5000 men wintered in the country, half of them in Auraria and Denver, and all awaited the season of 1860 with expectancy. The rush across the plains was repeated this second summer, and for about two months there were not less than 5000 arrivals weekly. The majority went to the Clear Creek region: there were soon about 20,000 intent on mining within twelve or fifteen miles of Gregory Gulch. But there were no new discoveries, only a suspicious willingness to sell claims at good prices. Thousands, however, particularly of those who arrived by the Arkansas, directed their steps to the South Park region. There, late in 1859, a party of prospectors from Clear Creek had found gold on the headwaters of the Arkansas in a heavily timbered ravine which they called California Gulch. In April miners began to pour in and the whole six miles of its course was taken up in 100-foot claims. The number on the ground rose to 5000 or 6000 and the gulch may have yielded $1,000,000 in its first season.

1860 was a season of progress in certain directions. A private mint was opened by a reputable banking firm in Denver. Ditches were constructed to remedy the lack of water for placer mining. The lack of progress in developing the quartz lodes was, however, disquieting: the stamp mills seemed to be less successful than the simpler *arrastras*. The miners' camps were apparently orderly: courts were organised in some, probably in most of them; in some there were actually regulations against bawdy-houses, grog shops and gambling saloons. In Denver, on the other hand, order was a good deal disturbed: a regular gang of desperadoes was in operation, and the editor of *The Rocky Mountain News* was threatened and on one occasion seized for denouncing them. The provisional government was faced with increasing apathy. Such vigour as there was seemed to reside in People's Courts, which could act drastically but could not fill the place of an effective, generally recognised legal authority. Fortunately Congress acted before the next mining season, and in February 1861 the territory of Colorado came into being.

A territorial government did not in itself mean that primitive conditions of living and rough-and-ready methods of government were at an end. A lively description is on record of the arrival of the member for California Gulch at the second session of the territorial legislature. He and his fellow member had walked down, 140 miles, sleeping in a blanket by the side of the trail, missing the way for a day, and arriving nearly starved. 'He walked up and laid down his blanket at the door of the House of Representatives. He had been mining and possessed no other clothes than those he wore at his sluice-box in the gulch. His dress was a blue flannel shirt, trousers patched with buckskin, an old boot on one foot and a brogan on the other, an old slouch hat that he had slept in, the brim partly gone. His face was blackened by the smoke of the campfire and furrowed by perspiration, his eyes hollow with fatigue and hunger, feet blistered by walking, hair tangled and beard yellow with dust. The next day we elected this same George Crocker speaker of the house.' Nor was the choice inappropriate. 'The members of the house batched in their little assembly room, took turns in cooking at the fireplace . . . carried water in pails from the creek, and slept on the floor.' The upper house met in a tavern kitchen and adjourned while cooking was in progress.[1] Such government was clearly a genuine expression of the democracy of the mining frontier.

By this time, however, Colorado had passed a further stage in the history of the frontier. The gold rush was over. The census in the summer of 1861 revealed that after two years of mass immigration across the plains the population was only 25,000. Though for lucky claim-holders 1861 and 1862 were years of profitable and systematic exploitation of the placers, the Idaho and Montana rushes began to draw off miners who had no such luck and by 1863 the decline of the placers was unmistakable. The future of the Colorado gold industry lay in its quartz. The Gregory Gulch district in particular was now ready to concentrate on its quartz lodes. The floating population had departed after turning the valley inside out and pock-marking the hills: in place of the scattered tents there were three towns: Central City, Black Hawk and Nevadaville. But as the mines went deeper, the ores, by reason of their pyritic character, became more and more refractory to the ordinary amalgamation process, and water accumulated in them. There was clearly need for careful experiment and for capital. Now the individuals and partnerships who had hitherto, as in California, conducted operations had not made enough out of their mines to be able to finance improved processes out of their own resources. Capital had therefore to be enlisted from the Eastern States, and after the season of 1863 many Colorado gold mines passed into the hands of capitalists of New York and Boston. Nearly all the new companies proceeded to invest in powerful machinery. But it was

[1] Judge Wilbur F. Stone, a member of the legislature, quoted by Irving Howbert, *Memories of a Life Time in the Pike's Peak Region* (New York and London, 1925), pp. 72-3.

not so much power as science that the mines required, and the promotion of the companies had often been marked by misinformation on the one side and stupidity on the other. The whole of the negotiations had moreover been conducted in the hectic atmosphere of wartime inflation. This was checked by a panic in April 1864: but with the rising freights and supply and labour costs, the war-time delays in foundries and machine shops and the partial isolation of Colorado by an Indian war, many of the companies found that their resources were exhausted by the erection of their machinery and that they could hardly cope with the deterioration of the mines, let alone develop them.

It was not until about 1867 that Colorado really began to recover from this speculative fever. It had by that time become a better balanced community. The drought of 1863 which closed the Missouri River above Kansas City to navigation, and the Indian wars of 1864 and 1865 which caused much interruption and loss to freighting across the plains, drove the territory to turn more attention to its agricultural resources. Many miners must have turned to farming. In 1867 Colorado had surplus farm produce to send beyond its borders, for instance to the newer territory of Montana. Moreover mining itself was becoming a better balanced industry. It was realised that the 'process mania' had been carried too far; that for the poorer grades of ore stamp mills, simplified, improved and made more economical in their working, were after all the best; that the expensive processes of concentration and reduction of rich but refractory ores were best left to a specialised large-scale plant which would buy them after crushing. In 1868, after some years of careful study of modern processes, such a plant was opened at Black Hawk by

the Boston and Colorado Smelting Co. with an industrial chemist in charge. It was also beginning to be
realised that Colorado was a silver as well as a gold
region. Some of the lodes discovered in gold rush days
had really been silver lodes, but little was known about
silver in the West until the development of the Comstock lode. In 1864, however, a silver lode was discovered at the head of South Clear Creek, and next year
some hundreds of people took part in the silver rush to
'Georgetown'; serious attention then began to be given
to opening up and exploiting the silver resources of
Colorado.

Though the cost of supplies had diminished with the
end of the war and the development of agriculture,
the development of capitalistic mining was naturally
hindered by the absence of railway communication. In
1870–71 Denver was connected with no fewer than
three railways, which not only confirmed the city in its
position as the base of supply of the mining regions
but gave a remarkable impetus to the development of
Colorado. In 1870 its population was about 40,000:
six years later it had risen to 135,000. Admission to the
union as a State, granted at last in 1876 after many
disappointments, was the natural sequel to such
developments and may perhaps therefore be regarded
as won by the railways rather than by the mines, which
seemed capable of carrying the community a certain
distance but not the whole way towards maturity. Not
until the 'seventies indeed did Denver cease to be
a small turbulent frontier town where inefficient administration of the ordinary law had to be supplemented
by occasional interventions of a Vigilance Committee.

Far from emerging into a more settled period, however, Colorado was about to be plunged into the

greatest mining rush in its history. In the early 'seventies various silver towns were founded in the rugged and inaccessible San Juan country. About 1874 two miners who were proposing to build a ditch to carry water to California Gulch found an outcrop of silver lead ore rich enough to stimulate further search; in 1876 the secret got out and next year hundreds of miners came in; in 1878–79 the numbers attained the dimensions of a rush and a new city of 'Leadville' had arisen with perhaps 30,000 people, prospectors, miners, capitalists, business and professional men— nearly all of these backing other people's mining enterprises as well—and the usual parasites taking advantage of the usual lavish expenditure and reckless living. Leadville passed through the normal growing-pains of a mining community. The value of the claims encouraged jumping and litigation: we hear of at least one case of an armed guard-house covering the head of a shaft and barricaded with sacks of ore. The prevalence of disorder and ruffianism led to two hangings by a Vigilance Committee. But on the whole Leadville emerged from this phase quickly. The extraction of silver was itself dependent upon relative nearness to modern means of transport, and by August 1880 the pack-mule trains and stage-coaches of the rush years were superseded by a railway. A regular city government came into operation in 1879 and a fire department, water system, gasworks, schools, churches soon endowed the city with the apparatus of an advanced civilisation. Other silver rushes followed—to Silver Cliff in the Wet Mountains south of the Arkansas in 1878, to Aspen and the Gunnison country between Leadville and the San Juan in 1879–80. In 1880 Colorado produced $16,500,000 worth of silver, five times its production of gold.

It took the place of Nevada as the leading silver State.

The 'eighties, in which Colorado doubled its population, were a decade of great prosperity based on these rich silver lead mines, expanding agriculture and railway construction, and advancing real estate values in Denver, in which the silver kings invested much of their money. They came in fact to control, or to compete for control of the politics of the city and of the State. It was not a state of affairs conducive to social health: a gambling set dominated by 'Soapy' Smith, who was afterwards to achieve a new notoriety in connection with the Klondike rush, enjoyed free scope in Denver by agreement with the police. Nor was it economically healthier than any other speculative fever: the silver kings and the community generally were at first blind to the dangers of the increased world production and consequent decline in price of silver, and when these became unmistakable sought in vain to avert the consequences by Federal Government purchases under the Sherman Act of 1890. In 1893 the sharp fall in silver prices shook the whole of the United States and Denver was the storm centre. Banks, business houses, mines collapsed on every side.

Fortune, however, was again kind to Colorado: by a strange turn of her wheel she had revealed a new source of wealth within sight of old Pike's Peak. In that neighbourhood one of the persistent prospectors to be found in every mining region had been working off and on for years; and in 1891, having sunk a shaft forty-eight feet deep by his own unaided efforts, he encountered some good ore. The specimens excited the interest of a house-builder and carpenter of Colorado Springs, W. S. Stratton, who had a smattering of mineralogy: Stratton himself hit upon the outcrop which, as it contained none of the familiar associates of gold, had been ignored: and in 1892 the new gold district of 'Cripple Creek' was in being, and produced some 30,000 ounces in spite of a serious miners' strike. It was chiefly a telluride ore and problems of extraction hardly began to be solved until 1895, when up-to-date chlorination and cyanide mills were in operation. But rich it certainly was: most of the mines were able to finance their own development, and so for years were largely carried on by comparatively small local companies. It was also a common practice to lease parts of claims to working miners. On the other hand, after the panic of 1893 some of the best brains of the silver industry were diverted to Cripple Creek gold. By the end of the century gold once again had precedence of silver in Colorado, and Cripple Creek, whose production was of the order of a million ounces a year, was the richest goldfield in the United States.

§ 4. BOISÉ, IDAHO

The Indian wars which had made the interior of Washington Territory unsafe for prospectors came to an end in 1859. A movement of prospectors inland was then certain, the more so since the Fraser River was unable, as we have seen, to retain a large proportion of the miners who had flocked there in 1858. Washington was moreover better suited than it had been before the wars to be the base of a mining rush; for the military operations had stimulated the development of navigation on the Columbia River, the great highway to the interior.

There were various reports suggesting that the

country east of the Snake River, the greatest tributary of the Columbia, was gold-bearing. E. D. Pierce, a trader with the Indians, decided to follow up these reports. In the summer of 1860 Pierce found gold near the south fork of the Clearwater River, which drains the western slopes of the Bitter Root Mountains, and returned with a few ounces panned out by his party to his base at Walla Walla. His prospecting party had had to dodge the Indians, and the military tried to prevent trespass on their reservations, but it was impossible to prevent a rush next spring and the authorities wisely preferred to appease the Indians by a treaty promising that their reservations would be protected by the United States.

A few miners actually spent the winter of 1860–61 in the new mining district, and it was they who made its mining laws, allowing gulch or creek claims 150 feet long and hill claims 100 feet square and permitting one of each kind to be held. The expected rush, stimulated by a consignment of gold-dust from these men, duly took place by steamer and stage to Walla Walla, thence by pack-trail on horseback or on foot. But the head of navigation was moved about midsummer to the confluence of the Clearwater and the Snake, where 'Lewiston' very soon acquired considerable business and population: the Nez Percé Indians, on whose reservation it stood, accepted compensation, and the military then permitted a permanent town site to be laid off. At the mines themselves there were reported in August to be 2500 practical miners at work and 4000 or 5000 making a living in other ways. It was not so much a case of rich deposits in particular localities as of an extensive district with gold pretty evenly diffused through it and yielding perhaps $10 a day where it was found. Before the end of the first season flumes, sluices and bedrock drains were in operation—which means, incidentally, that even in the first season many were working on others' claims rather than on their own. There were two rival towns, Oro Fino and Pierce City. They were not really far from civilisation: a waggon road was opened that summer to Lewiston and many, especially of those from Oregon and Washington—who seem to have been in the majority—moved down to the lower country for the winter.

But there were some who preferred to go farther into the country, not out of it. Before the end of the season of 1861 some 2000 people had gone to Elk City, beautifully situated on a grassy plain amid pine-covered mountains about 120 miles to the south-east. Later still much richer finds were made farther south in the Salmon River country. The average return, got with rockers only, was apparently five or six ounces per man per day; some returns were reckoned in pounds. The country was very inaccessible: it was a sort of undulating marshy plateau, of about 6000 feet elevation, covered with small black pine and tamarack trees and rimmed with mountains: near the rim was the deep canyon of the Salmon River. But 1000 men had come in before the season closed: most of them saw the winter through, and indeed there was a steady exodus of men on snowshoes with heavy packs on their backs, bound for Salmon River, from Oro Fino. By the end of January no food could be bought except flour, and that was $2 a pound. The winter was so severe that it was not until 1 May that pack-trains could come within reach of the district, and then the last ten or twelve miles had to be packed on men's backs. Rheumatism, scurvy and other diseases had been rife.

In spite of the Clearwater mines, of new discoveries among the wooded slopes and rolling plains of Eastern Oregon, and of the rich yields of Cariboo, 'Salmon River' was the great rallying-cry of the miners for the season of 1862. By 1 June there were over 4000 at Florence, the principal camp. The rush, which had begun before the snow had melted, may have brought 20,000 or even 30,000 into the country at the height of the season. Florence could not absorb anything like that number. Its placers, though rich, were shallow and quickly exhausted, and many miners were disappointed. But prospectors were ranging far afield. South of the Salmon River canyon in high and inaccessible country a shiftless gambler named Warren discovered placers which gave a steady return to some hundreds of men. A more important discovery was made by a prospecting party from one of the East Oregon camps in a deep saucer-like area of well-timbered country some twenty-five miles in diameter, known to history as the Boisé basin. Their leader was killed in a clash with the Indians, but they reached Walla Walla early in September with some 300 ounces of gold-dust and with it purchased supplies. They then returned with a more numerous armed party to the scene of their discoveries. Such a secret could not be kept, and before the end of 1862 there were 2000 or 3000 on the ground waiting for the spring. They located claims, made rockers and sluice-boxes and built cabins so that there were four mushroom towns in the Boisé basin before the rush set in.

In came the miners in their thousands from California and Oregon when the spring of 1863 began. They came up the Columbia as far as Umatilla or Wallula. There many would 'buy a lunch, roll it up in their blankets, shoulder them and hit the road in a few minutes after they landed from the steamer, trusting to replenish their stock of grub at some packer's camp, or at some of the temporary stations established on the road'. Others would club together and purchase a pack-animal. Yet others would travel up in 'saddle trains'. 'The owner of the train would furnish each passenger with a horse and a saddle so that he could ride, would also pack a small amount of baggage for each person and furnish sufficient amount of substantial provisions for the trip, with the necessary cooking utensils. The passengers did the cooking in camp while the train-master looked after the animals.' The saddle-train fare for this trip, which might take six or seven days, was $50 at first, though reduced later by competition.[1] Such roads and bridges as there were had been made by private enterprise and tolls were paid for using them. Another early Idaho settler describes a case. 'We eventually came to a bridge, so called, which had been made by felling a tree across the stream and pinning a pole on each side near the top, which had been flattened by chopping off the bark. This structure was presided over by a very capable-appearing genius, armed with two six-shooters and an effective-looking cheese-knife. He informed us that the toll for crossing his bridge was $1 each for pack-animals and the same for footmen. Without argument we contributed $9 to his exchequer and proceeded on our way.'[2] Intending immigrants from the east seldom got as far as Boisé, for, as we shall see, there was a rush in 1863 on the other side of the

---

[1] John Hailey, *History of Idaho* (Boisé, 1910), pp. 61-2. Hailey was himself engaged in this business.

[2] W. J. McConnell and H. R. Driggs, *Frontier Law* (New York and London, 1924), p. 60. No date is given for this incident.

Bitter Root Mountains. But during the summer large waggon trains of immigrants came in from Missouri and Arkansas, refugees from the guerrilla warfare raging there. In August there were perhaps 25,000 or 30,000 people in the Boisé region.

In the Boisé basin, the rush which had been going on for three successive summers at last came to a stand. The climate was milder, so that there was less temptation to go down to the Pacific Coast for the winter. Nearby, in the valleys of the Boisé and Payette rivers, there was fertile land. Communications could be more easily improved than in the Salmon River country, and the placers, though they may not have yielded so much in their first season, lasted better.[1] There were promising quartz discoveries also in 1863, though the best were some 120 miles off in the Owyhee Mountains, a dreary volcanic region which, in spite of its rich lodes, did not retain many of the thousands who went up to investigate. These mines were an asset not to be despised, though comparisons with Washoe, which led Portland, Oregon, to set up a stock exchange in emulation of San Francisco, soon became a little ridiculous. So much of the life of the Clearwater and Salmon River districts had ebbed out in the direction of Boisé that the remaining miners were fain to allow Chinese to come in and work, subject to a special tax, abandoned claims. Only Warren's was good enough still to be reserved for white miners.

Californian technique sufficed for these mines—sluicing, and at a later stage hydraulic mining, for the placers, *arrastras* and in 1864 stamp mills, brought in

---

[1] The gold produced in 1863 and 1864 may have amounted to $5,000,000-$7,000,000—*i.e.* 300,000 or 400,000 ounces in each year. Bancroft appears to estimate the production of Salmon River in its first season at $12,000,000, but this seems too high a figure.

one instance by ox-team across the prairies, for the quartz. Californian technique was also used for the regulation of mining—though the tendency was for larger claims to be allowed and for discoverers to reward themselves with increasing liberality. The social life of the mining towns ran along Californian lines—money flowed freely and hotels and restaurants, gambling and dancing saloons flourished—though some of the lines had deepened into grooves. The German hurdy-gurdy girls, dancing for a living at fifty cents a dance, had become an institution. So had the miners' Sunday, when they flocked into town from the outlying camps to sell their gold-dust, repair their tools, buy their supplies and amuse themselves: it was treated not as a day of religious observance, in spite of a territorial law on that subject, but rather as a market day. But unquestionably life was more lurid than in the Californian camps. It may be that the sounder elements tended to go out with their gold as soon as possible, or at any rate at the end of the season: it was in winter that conditions were worst. It may simply be that social cohesion was unequal to the double strain of the gold rush and the bitter political antagonisms of the Civil War period. Clearly many of those who came from California were of southern or south-western origin and we have seen that there was some direct immigration from the southern frontier.

It was not that formal political organisation was lacking. The legislature of Washington Territory organised counties and passed an act establishing district courts. In March 1863, after petitions from the mining districts, the portion of Washington lying east of 117° W. and of the Snake River was erected by Congress into a new territory of Idaho; and, though not until some months later, a Governor was appointed by President Lincoln. But Lewiston was chosen as the seat of government, and though it was the most accessible point for communications with the federal capital, it did not even lie on a road to the Boisé basin, the real centre of the new territory. Moreover the new territory was ill served by its officers. Its first governor preferred to accept election as delegate to Congress. His deputy, the territorial secretary, though he held one useful session of the legislature, retired to his home in Oregon a few months later. Not until some months afterwards did a new governor arrive, and he was ill-chosen. The federally appointed officials and judges were moreover Republicans. From 1864 the Democrats carried the elections, and that meant that order fell between the two stools of Republican judges and marshals and Democratic sheriffs.

Disorder was in fact better organised than order. Its organisation was developed at Lewiston in its first winter, when money and food were so scarce that the disorderly elements were almost driven to violence for a living. But its most famous chief, Henry Plummer, a man of quiet and gentlemanly bearing, levied toll more particularly along the roads. His methods, as described by McConnell, were both ingenious and thorough. 'During the stay made by travellers in Lewiston . . . they were carefully sized up by Plummer's emissaries, especially those who were on the return journey from the mines, with the object of ascertaining if possible whether they carried any considerable amount of gold-dust; accurate descriptions were also taken of their saddle and pack animals, including colour and brands; bills of sale were then made out in conformity with the descriptions conveying title to the animals at some prior

date to the keeper of one of the road-houses either above
or below. . . . The bill of sale was then despatched by
courier to the man in whose name it was drawn so as to
reach him before the arrival of the men with the stock.'
The travellers were then forced to give up their animals,
or shot if they resisted.[1] Only the express riders, who
were chosen for their intrepidity and skill in the use of
weapons, enjoyed comparative immunity. Yet when an
attempt was made to meet this organisation by a vigilance committee at Lewiston, it was frustrated by an
eloquent speech from Plummer on the horrors of anarchy. Eventually, in the autumn of 1862, vigilance
committees were formed at Lewiston and Florence and
numerous gamblers and suspected 'road agents' were
banished; but most of them probably went to reinforce
their fellows in the Boisé basin. Plummer crossed the
Bitter Root range to Montana without disclosure of his
criminal associations.

In the Boisé basin southern and south-western influences were clearly predominant. There were respectable Democrats, but their party primaries and
nominating conventions seem to have been largely
controlled by saloons, gambling-houses and suchlike
interests. It was difficult to create among the still unsettled population of the mining towns, deeply divided
as it was politically, a sound public opinion such as
that to which the Californian vigilance committees had
effectually appealed. Except perhaps for freemasonry
there was no bond of union among ordinary respectable
citizens. Efforts at organisation met with an opposition
probably compounded of sheer rascality, antagonism to
the Union Government, and honest preference for the
ordinary processes of law. When W. J. McConnell, in

[1] W. J. McConnell, *Early History of Idaho* (Caldwell, 1913), p. 71.

recovering a stolen horse, found himself mulcted by the courts of costs almost equal to the value of the animal, it is not to be wondered at that he rallied his fellow settlers of the Payette valley, in August 1864, to more summary action against horse-thieves: after a further theft the gang responsible were pursued and shot. A syndicate dealing in bogus gold-dust was also driven out of the territory. But disorder in the mining towns was not yet put down. An attempt was even made to arrest the leaders of this vigilance committee. The attorney of Boisé admitted that about sixty deaths by violence had occurred in the district prior to 1865 without a single conviction for murder. Juries were openly intimidated. Idaho City, the chief of the Boisé basin towns, was set on fire in the spring of 1865 by a mob which had previously been with difficulty prevented from looting stores during a flour shortage. In July an ex-sheriff, who, though a gambler by profession, would have no truck with robbery and murder, was shot; and his friends organised a new vigilance committee which at first threatened to attack the gaol in Idaho City in which the murderer was confined. However, to avoid armed conflict with the forces of the law—composed according to McConnell of 'practically all the thugs and tinhorn gamblers in the city' [1]—he was allowed to go for trial, and sure enough he was acquitted.[2] It cannot be said that the struggle for order in Idaho was ever definitely won.

Meanwhile the regular authorities were bickering among themselves and embezzling public money. A U.S. marshal, two treasurers of Boisé county, a

[1] McConnell, *op. cit.* pp. 275-7.
[2] He deemed it wise to leave the territory, however, and was not long afterwards shot.

secretary and acting governor of the territory were guilty of misuse of public funds, and the governor wasted them and maladministered his office with a folly that was almost criminal. The lack of unity of interest and feeling between the older and the newer mining districts found expression in obstinate resistance to the removal of the capital from Lewiston to the new commercial centre of Boisé City, only ended when the United States marshal on orders from Washington removed the archives to Boisé in the autumn of 1865. When Governor Ballard arrived in the following summer there was more resolute and honest administration; but the legislature was only induced to take the oath of allegiance to the United States when the territorial secretary withheld members' pay and called in troops to suppress their revengeful smashing of furniture.

In spite of these political conflicts, 1865 and 1866 were years of prosperity for mining, and hence for all business, in the Boisé basin. Freights had been halved, at any rate in summer, by the waggon roads completed in 1864. The monopoly of the Columbia River navigation was broken by the opening of overland communication with California, though this was interrupted in 1865 by an Indian war; and the country was provisioned from Utah as well as from Oregon. Placer mining was carried on on a more extensive scale than before, and some estimates would place the yield at 600,000 and 750,000 ounces in those two years, though 500,000 ounces might be a safer estimate. But whereas in 1865 there was still a considerable immigration, in 1866 the population decreased: many placer claims had been worked out or abandoned to the Chinese, and the emphasis was definitely passing to quartz and particularly to the gold and silver of the Owyhee region, where capital had now been invested by the Eastern States and machinery introduced from California. There was indeed a new rush in 1866 to placers on the upper Salmon River; but of the 5000 estimated to have gone to 'Salmon City', only 1500 remained.

After 1866 Idaho was a more orderly community; but the period of the gold rush was over. The decline of the placers was marked. Many traders also left, disheartened by the decline in population and in Idaho City by a second serious fire, in 1867. There was indeed a development of stock-raising and agriculture, but though a boon to the local market—the price of oats in the Boisé basin was 3 cents a pound in 1867 as against 30-40 cents in 1863—it was limited by the impossibility of export. The hydraulic and quartz miners did fairly well, and various new quartz discoveries were made, but development was retarded by the expense of bringing in machinery. In the early 'seventies a number of the remaining placer miners were drawn off to the developing silver mines in Utah, and in the middle of the decade the depression was deepened by the failure of the Bank of California, which had invested money in the Owyhee mines, and the absconding of certain mining company officials. Then in 1877–78 Indian wars raged over a large part of the territory, making it unsafe for small freight trains or parties of miners.

At the very end of the decade the tide turned. The subjugation of the Bannack Indians of South-eastern Idaho permitted the rich silver lead mines of the Wood River region to be opened up, and there was a minor rush to that district. Then in 1883 placer gold was discovered in the Cœur d'Alene country in the northern part of the 'panhandle', naturally belonging perhaps to

Washington rather than to Idaho. Thousands of miners and others from all the Rocky Mountain region and from even farther afield surged in, and noisy, bustling mining towns appeared in a country hitherto covered with dense forest. Indeed the rush began whilst it was still deep in snow. Mining customs, however, had changed since the 'sixties: United States mining law favoured large claims and capitalistic exploitation.[1] In any case the real wealth of the Cœur d'Alene district lay not in its gold placers but in the rich silver lead deposits a few miles to the south-westward, discovered in 1885. With its lead mines and a railway Idaho forged ahead rapidly and in 1890 was admitted to the Union as a State. The gold rushes of the first decade, which had yielded perhaps 4,500,000 ounces altogether, had hardly been directly responsible for this later and more profitable development. Their function had rather been to open up a remote region of forest and mountain, off the main lines of communication from east to west, and, after a more than usually hard struggle for orderly conditions, to enable a small, vigorous community to strike root.

§ 5. The Montana Rushes

The eastern slopes of the Rocky Mountains by the middle of the nineteenth century were a shade less remote from civilisation than the western. There was a fur-trading post at Fort Benton, at the head of navigation on the Missouri: a little trading might be done not only with the Indians but with emigrant trains to Oregon or California to the southward: and there were even a few stock-raisers and farmers here and there. There were some pretty well-authenticated discoveries of gold in the

---

[1] On this mining law see below, p. 195.

region where the Missouri takes its rise in the later
'fifties, made by mountain traders and individual prospectors. But the real question is not which discovery
was made first but which discovery inaugurated the
rush. About 1 August 1862 a party from Colorado,
which had set out for Salmon River but could not get
its waggons over the Bitter Root Mountains, found gold
on the banks of a creek in the Beaverhead valley. The
gold occurred in shallow, easily worked gravel. Waggon
trains from Minnesota also appeared on the scene, and
about 400 men collected there for the winter, supplies
being replenished by freighting from Salt Lake City.
The camp was duly organised with a judge and sheriff
and 100-foot placer claims and was named Bannack
City. It became the resort of many desperate characters:
but of that more anon.

As soon as spring opened, prospecting parties set out
in all directions. One of these, turned back from the
Yellowstone country by Indians, found gold on 26 May,
sixty-five miles east of Bannack and 3000 feet lower, in
a gulch filled with a dense growth of alders.[1] One of the
party returned to Bannack for supplies and enough
leaked out to ensure his being followed. Granville
Stuart, riding to Bannack from his ranch, encountered
this stampede on the way—some on foot carrying packs
or leading pack-animals, some on horseback. 'The packs
had been hurriedly placed and some had come loose and
the frightened animals, running about with blankets
flying and pots and pans rattling, had frightened others
and the hillside was strewn with camp outfits and grub.
My wife and I assisted some to round up their animals
and collect and readjust the packs; soon they were all on

---

[1] The actual discovery was made by Fairweather, a New Brunswicker, and
Edgar, a Scotsman.

their way again hurrying and scurrying lest they get left behind.'[1] There was in fact room for all of them: no fewer than six mining districts were organised on the twelve miles of Alder Gulch. The creek-bed and the bars on both sides were uniformly rich, the average yield being perhaps one and a quarter ounces a day, though the bed-rock was deeper than at Bannack and some hundreds of dollars might be required before the claim began to yield. At first any sort of shelter was made from bush or dug out, or blankets were spread under trees; but soon logs were cut on the neighbouring mountains and there arose on the banks of the creek a second Virginia City.

The Bannack discoveries had in themselves been sufficient to start a rush. Owing to the competing claims of the Boisé basin, this came chiefly from the east. Four steamers left St. Louis in the spring of 1863 for the upper Missouri: failing to reach Fort Benton, where there were waggons waiting, they landed their passengers and freight from 200 to 800 miles downstream, leaving them to find a way through the wilderness and the Indian tribes as best they could. An organised company of some hundreds of emigrants was escorted across the prairies from Minnesota as in the preceding summer. Others came north from Colorado. In what proportions these were mixed it is impossible to say, but there was another and a dangerous ingredient in the mixture in the persons of Henry Plummer and other desperadoes from across the Bitter Root Mountains. There are said to have been 12,000 people at Bannack and Virginia City in the summer: though the former was the original destination, it proved to be for most only a halting-

---

[1] Contemporary diary cited in Granville Stuart, *Forty Years on the Frontier* (ed. P. C. Phillips) (Cleveland, 1925), i, 247.

place on the way to Alder Gulch, where there must have been 7000 or 8000 at least at the height of the season. Prices of food might strike newcomers as high, but they were not high by gold rush standards: flour seems to have been 25 cents, sugar 60 cents, bacon 40 cents, fresh beef 15-25 cents a pound.

After its successful season this mining community struggled to arrive at some sort of order. Even before the discovery of Bannack a county of Washington Territory had been organised east of the Bitter Root Mountains. Shortly afterwards, its elected sheriff shot one horse-thief and hanged another at the request of two men who had pursued them from Elk City across the Bitter Root Mountains. But the problem of order could not be dealt with by mere county machinery. Even the inclusion of these mining districts in the new territory of Idaho, which, as organised in March 1863, extended right to the main chain of the Rockies, did little or nothing to advance matters. The mining camps filled the gap to some extent, but their machinery could sometimes be manipulated. 'These miners' meetings were most often held in the open air, and if the weather was cold, or some incident of the saloons attracted them, they absented themselves until one of the parties to the suit rallied them by signifying that a question of supreme importance was about to be decided, when they returned and voted for their favourites. These tribunals were sometimes swayed by the politics of their clients or their counsel, and sometimes influenced by the liquid refreshments furnished by one side, or occasionally by a sordid motive; but whatever consideration determined the result, it was manifested by a *viva voce* of all present . . . and was final.'[1] More-

[1] W. F. Sanders's notes on early Montana tribunals in Bancroft, *History of*

over if the criminals were strongly organised, as they were in the early days of Bannack and Virginia City, they pressed for trial by a jury and counted on intimidating it. In March 1863 Plummer and three of his associates were tried at Bannack for certain shootings, but Plummer was acquitted and the other three merely banished after a jury trial, and their sentence was later remitted.[1] Plummer actually got himself chosen as sheriff both of Bannack and of Virginia City and made a show of performing the duties. His leadership of the road agents was not of course known, but it was a plain fact that Bannack in particular was terrorised by the criminal element and the community was controlled by its enemies.

When it became a question of sending out the rich yield of 1863 the danger increased. All the roads were under the surveillance of this well-organised gang with its captain, lieutenants, secretary, road agents and suppliers of information. The road agents were armed with a pair of revolvers, a double-barrelled shot-gun of large bore with the barrels sawn short, and a knife or dagger. 'Thus armed,' wrote a contemporary, 'and mounted on fleet, well-trained horses, and being disguised with blankets and masks, the robbers awaited their prey in ambush. When near enough they sprang out on a keen run, with levelled shot-guns, and usually gave the word, "Halt! Throw up your hands, you sons of b[itches]!" If this latter command were not instantly obeyed, there was the last of the offender; but in case he complied, as

---

Washington, Idaho and Montana (San Francisco, 1890), pp. 656-7. The courts attended to some civil (*e.g.* financial) as well as criminal cases, and the judges performed marriage services.

[1] N. P. Langford, who was foreman of the jury, describes this trial in *Vigilante Days and Ways* (Boston, 1890—reprinted Chicago, 1912), pp. 137-47.

was usual, one or two sat on their horses, covering the party with their guns, which were loaded with buck-shot, and one dismounting, disarmed the victims, and made them throw their purses on the grass. This being done, and a search for concealed property being effected, away rode the robbers, reported the capture and divided the spoils.'[1] The ranchmen along the roads knew who the road agents were but were afraid of their vengeance.

The terror reached its height in the closing months of 1863. Then the body of a teamster was found and brought to Alder Gulch: the marks of a lariat were on his wrists and neck: it was clear that he had been dragged through the brush while still alive, after being shot. A small group of self-constituted agents of justice decided to track down the murderer. By employing the road agents' own methods they made a ranchman give him up and took him back. The miners of Nevada on Alder Gulch tried him by mass meeting with an advisory jury, which in due course found him guilty. The prosecutor, W. F. Sanders, then mounted the judge's waggon and moved 'that George Ives be forthwith hung by the neck until he is dead': it was carried. The pleas of Ives and his counsel for delay were met by a cry, 'Ask him how long a time he gave the Dutchman!' Ives had many friends, but hopes of rescue—or of the appearance of Plummer in his capacity as sheriff—were frustrated by the resolute attitude of the guard, and within an hour of his sentence he was led to the scaffold. Once this bold counter-attack had been begun, the wisest and safest course was to follow it up; and within a week or two a vigilance committee organisation, backed by miners, mechanics, merchants and professional men alike, ex-

[1] T. J. Dimsdale, *The Vigilantes of Montana* (Virginia City [1866]—reprinted Helena, n.d.), p. 21. I have relied on Dimsdale for what follows.

tended to all the mining camps: it was the road agents who were now on the defensive and afraid of betrayal. With a nice recognition of their official status, two were strung up with labels pinned to their backs: 'Red! Road Agent and messenger!'; 'Brown! Corresponding Secretary!' Eventually Plummer and his two scoundrelly deputy sheriffs were arrested at Bannack on the night of 10 January 1864, and all three were hanged. Plummer had in vain asked for a jury trial, and 'falling on his knees with tears and sighs, declared to God that he was too wicked to die'. Later Virginia City was surrounded with pickets and searched, and though one man escaped through a drain, he was overtaken and hanged like the rest. By early February virtually the whole of the road-agent gang, whose names had been revealed by one of them before execution, had been removed; and the Vigilantes, confident that it could no longer be perverted, determined to establish a People's Court where all offenders could be tried by judge and jury. By the time that regular courts of justice arrived on the scene the foundations of public order had been laid.

In the spring of 1864 commissions for justices of the peace and probate judges arrived from Lewiston, but their powers were limited and the popular courts continued to function alongside them. On 26 May the territory of Montana was organised east of the Bitter Root Mountains by Act of Congress; and Sidney Edgerton, who, as unofficial delegate from the miners, was chiefly responsible for the Act, was appointed governor. The choice of officials was wiser than for Idaho, and though illegal action by the first legislature delayed the completion of the organisation, this delay seems to have done no great harm. The judges, who arrived towards the end of the year, were also men of ability and integrity.

They found themselves hampered at first in deciding what laws to apply—for there was only one copy, and that a much-corrected draft, of Idaho legislation to be had—and the statutes of Montana, when made, proved seriously defective; but on the whole the courts functioned successfully, though the vigilance committee organisation remained in the background and intervened in a few flagrant cases. The trouble had been less deep-seated than in Idaho: feeling about the Civil War does not seem to have run quite so high: possibly the very boldness and completeness of the organisation of disorder had provoked a correspondingly bold and complete counter-organisation, but certainly the remedial action had been more successful.

There is another interesting case of vigorous unofficial action pointing a contrast between Montana and Idaho. In the winter of 1864–65 there was in Virginia City as in Idaho City a serious shortage of provisions. Flour rose to $150 a hundredweight and only beef was in plentiful supply. In Idaho City this situation had produced riotous looting. At Virginia City 500 armed men marched up the gulch, carrying as a banner an empty sack nailed to a staff, and conducted an orderly search of the town, keeping an account of all flour seized and promising to pay for it at $27 a hundredweight, which had been the price before the big rise: they then distributed the flour in 12-pound lots to all showing need, and duly paid for it before dispersing.[1]

1864 had been a very good season for the Montana mines. There were 10,000 people on or in the vicinity of Alder Gulch. It is true there were not claims for all, but prospectors who ranged farther afield were well rewarded by discoveries at Silver Bow in the mountains

---

[1] Granville Stuart, *op. cit.* ii, 28-30.

some sixty miles to the north-west and on 'Last Chance' Gulch on the Prickly Pear about a hundred miles to the north. The latter discovery was made by a Georgian in a party of men from Colorado. Some hundreds of miners came up and in October founded the town of Helena. Next season these districts were further developed and new gulches were discovered. In particular, Confederate Gulch, thirty-five miles east of Helena and on the other side of the Missouri, attracted thousands. Moreover the Whitlatch mine at Helena itself proved to be the richest quartz lode yet opened up in Montana.

The gold production of the territory probably reached a maximum of over a million ounces in 1866.[1] Thirty-one steamers came up the Missouri, and 2500 men and 3000 teams of oxen and mules were employed during the short summer season of navigation conveying the goods from the head of navigation to the mining centres. Others came up from the North Platte by the new 'Bozeman trail'. The Pacific Coast attempted to compete for the Montana trade by sending pack-trains over the old Mullan road from Walla Walla, made in the later 'fifties but since allowed to decay. Yet there was a certain slackening of momentum and a tendency to over-crowd the fields and to be misled by unfounded rumours. Bannack had now become 'a dreary succession of strag-gling, empty log houses'. Alder Gulch, which had perhaps yielded nearly two million ounces since its dis-covery, was showing signs of exhaustion. Confederate Gulch was at its height: in August it sent to Helena two waggons guarded by fifteen men and each carrying half a ton of gold, taken out of one of its bars by two men and their assistants in a single four-months' season. But even

---

[1] The total production perhaps reached seven or eight million ounces in the first decade.

Helena, though it was displacing Virginia City as the leading town of Montana, thanks to its combination of good mines with a central position for trade both with the Missouri and with the gulches, was feeling a reaction in the autumn 'owing to the unparalleled influx of people, merchandise and supplies, and the lack of new discoveries of placer mines'.[1] The Montana gold rush had in fact passed its peak.

The decline of the mines was gradual. Helena, with its 7500 people, struck a visitor in August 1867 as having 'all the vim, recklessness, extravagance and jolly progress of a new camp'. The newer gulches to the westward gave good returns. Thanks to the construction of a long ditch, Silver Bow, which had been cramped by a shortage of water, had its most prosperous season. In such cases hundreds of miners would flock in from other camps and the gamblers and hurdy-gurdy girls would follow them: but the influx into Montana had ceased. Quartz was attracting more attention. The ores were richer, more accessible and less refractory than in Colorado; but a quartz mill required from thirty to fifty waggons to bring it from the Missouri, and wages and necessaries of life were high. Freight costs were indeed brought down by competition and later by the approach of the Pacific railroad. But the decline gathered momentum in the early 'seventies in spite of a fairly good placer field opened up in the north-west. In the middle of the decade the Indian troubles, even previously not a negligible factor in hindering the development of Montana, came to a head here as elsewhere; and the Sioux War was fought.

[1] Captain J. L. Fisk to Governor Marshall of Minnesota (29 September 1866): *Collections of the State Historical Society of North Dakota*, ii (1908), 461.

Then the tide turned again, though as in Colorado it was turned by silver and not by gold. Congress had passed a law compelling all owners of quartz mines to perform a certain amount of labour on them within a given time or forfeit the claims. In 1875 W. L. Farlin came to Butte, near Silver Bow, where he had himself staked a claim in the autumn of 1864, and re-located thirteen claims. He erected a mill, and when his funds gave out it was completed by W. A. Clark, a typical mining *entrepreneur* of the new generation, who had mined in Colorado, kept stores in various towns of Montana and Idaho, been a mail contractor, then a banker, and later studied a year at the Columbia School of Mines. Two years later Clark persuaded Hill and Pearce of Black Hawk, Colorado, to erect a smelter at Butte. Within a few years 'a substantial city ... occupied the place of the former shabby array of miners' cabins'. It was immensely helped by the coming of the railways, which reached the Montana towns in the early 'eighties. A brief though brilliant period of cattle ranges was not really so important for Montana as these mineral developments. Silver predominated at first, at Butte particularly but also at Philipsburg and other places; but copper was known to exist, and with the decline in the price of silver and the improvement of transportation Butte and Anaconda came to be among the greatest copper-mining centres in the world—already in the late 'eighties producing about $20,000,000 worth of copper and silver a year. Set on the right road by the *vigilante* leaders of the gold rush, Montana had earned its prosperity.

CHAPTER VI

THE GOLD RUSHES IN AMERICAN HISTORY

IF a dividing line is to be found between the period of the gold rushes in and beyond the Rocky Mountain region and the period of more settled and diversified mineral development that followed it, the middle 'sixties seem the best time to choose. New gold rushes occurred later. The Black Hills, a sort of outwork of the Rocky Mountain system in South Dakota, in the years following 1875 ran through the whole gamut of mining frontier experiences: pioneer prospectors forced their way in, defying Indians and United States soldiers: a lively, tawdry mining town arose on Deadwood Gulch, with a population of 7000 at the height of the rush: the community gradually found its way towards orderly conditions: and as the placers declined the rich Homestake mine, which passed in 1877 into the hands of George Hearst and another Californian capitalist, provided the basis for a more permanent mining industry. The Cœur d'Alene rush in the early 'eighties, the Cripple Creek rush in Colorado in the early 'nineties have already been mentioned. The discovery of a rich quartz outcrop at Tonopah in 1900 led to intensive prospecting of the deserts of south-western Nevada and in the next few years they were dotted with mining camps. The richest of them, Goldfield, discovered twenty-four miles south of Tonopah in 1903, increased its population to 20,000 and its production to perhaps 600,000 ounces in 1910. In short, though the mining was mostly capitalistic, there was in Nevada for a decade something of the colour and excitement of the old mining days. But all these rushes were in the nature of an aftermath of the great crop of gold discoveries which had peopled the mountainous region from about the thirty-second to the forty-ninth parallel with American citizens. Agricultural and pastoral settlement had no doubt begun before the rushes, in the Willamette valley of Oregon, in the great Californian valleys, and round the Great Salt Lake; but until the coming of the miners they were mere isolated outposts of American civilisation.

Individual mining camps might be evanescent, though many endured for years, but the miners moved on in order to found others. The existence of the camps attracted agriculturists, and in California the gold won from the soil by the miners built up a community which within ten years became capable of serving as a base for the supply of goods and of waiting for payment for those goods—in a word, of supplying capital—to new mining communities in the mountains. Directly or indirectly the mining camps also became magnets to the railways, assuring them of a profitable traffic at the end of their journeys across the undeveloped wilderness. The railways in their turn paved the way for the development of the less valuable minerals: even silver, except on the Comstock lode, had been little worked before their approach.

In the first instance the type of American civilisation introduced into this vast region was peculiar. Politically and socially it was less advanced than the civilisation of the older established Eastern States. It did not compare altogether unfavourably, however, with life in the great southern frontier region of Texas; and in the nature of things life on a mining frontier could not progress with the steady rhythm of an agricultural or industrial community. The type was essentially American, however: we find marked differences in British Columbia, where political and social institutions were the outcome of a different tradition. The political habits and institutions of the United States—local self-government and the attainment of self-governing statehood by way of territorial government under centrally appointed officials —seemed well adapted to the people and to the conditions. But in fact the territorial form of organisation had been established to fit the conditions on the more slowly-moving agricultural frontier of the 'Old North West'. On the mining frontier its machinery was not set in motion as rapidly as the conditions demanded. American politics did not bring to the front the colonial governor type; or if it did, the American patronage system did not favour his appointment to territorial office. The territorial machinery was moreover weak on the side of police. It did not command that general respect which is the foundation of authority in a democracy, and it had no means of enforcing what authority it had except for the United States marshals, who did not easily dovetail into the local organisation based on the elected sheriff. Hence officially constituted authority had to be supplemented in the early days of the rushes by the spontaneous organisation and action of the sounder part of the community. Was this, as nineteenth-century writers frequently maintained, a supreme manifestation of democracy, or was it, as twentieth-century critics might hold, an embryonic form of fascism? The answer is no doubt that order is the foundation of all government, however different the buildings that may be erected on that foundation.

Socially the mining advance tended to develop specialised types out of the already evolved type of the American frontiersman. Adaptability had always been one of his essential characteristics, and even with the increasing specialisation passage from one class to another remained easy, and was sometimes necessitated by circumstances, but some differentiation of functions there certainly was. It was in California that the differentiation began: the later rushes saw it in operation from the beginning. The great agent of the advance from California into the mountains was the prospector —at first hardly distinguishable from the skilled placer miner, but as time went on trained by experience to locate gold-bearing quartz and even silver ores as well as alluvial gold. His experience was based on practice and observation, not upon scientific geological study— though of course observation and experiment, which is carefully controlled practice, are the foundations of science. Perhaps general impressions sufficed in the earliest days of California, but later 'likely-looking country' was reduced to the specific terms of quartz outcroppings, guided by which the prospector would seek the gulch or ravine into which flowed the washings from the hills. The prospector would 'pack' his own 'outfit'—his food, mining tools, blanket, and probably revolver or rifle—with the aid of a pack-animal if he could afford one, but if his operations were successful and a mining rush set in, the 'packer' with his 'trains' would soon appear. Perhaps the Mexican, with an experience of pack-trails and pack-trains dating far back into his Spanish past, was the first to introduce this industry or institution into the American Rockies; but the native American proved an apt pupil. Later the road-maker would appear, armed with a franchise from the legislature, and prepare the way for the teamster with his waggons and the stage-coach line. It is hardly necessary to insist on the importance of the trader, store-keeper and saloon-keeper in mining camps, and no doubt, though there is curiously little information on the point in the heyday of the rushes, they often 'grub-staked', in other words financed, the outfitting of the prospector. Nor must those excrescences of the mining camp—the 'tin-horn gambler', the 'road agent', the 'hurdy-gurdy girl', not to mention the oldest of all the professions—be forgotten; for the freedom and excite-ment of mining camp life and the boredom of the winters in the mountains inevitably produced a cancerous social growth which even the surgery of the vigilance com-mittees could not wholly cut out. The mining camps moreover found it hard to draw a line between freedom and licence, and certainly did not draw it in the same place as the older communities of the Eastern States. The churches and schools, and indeed the family—the great agencies of moral education—hardly appeared until the rush was over. Perhaps the mining rushes con-tributed more than their share as mere movements of population would suggest to breaking the crust of Puritan custom in American life.

Advanced or not, however, the civilisation of the American mining frontier certainly showed a power of development: the individuals who built it up, though they were reckless and improvident, though their allegiance to the eternal values of truth, beauty and goodness was at best very much qualified, were men of exceptional practical intelligence, hardiness, energy, initiative and resource. They were indeed fortunate in the wealth of the region they opened up. Thanks to this, and to the qualities of the men themselves, its civilisation in its earlier stages, standing though it did in a quasi-colonial relation to the Eastern States, was quite remarkably self-sufficient. Once the initial impetus had been given by the Californian gold rush of 1849 even its capital was largely supplied by its own abundant production, though its capitalists, naturally, were not its pioneer miners. The first crop of them no doubt consisted of those who, favoured by fortune or by their own abilities, were specially successful in providing the mining community with what it needed. Then a second crop was grown in the peculiar soil of the Comstock lode. The processes of mining on which this frontier civilisation rested were also developed to a considerable extent by its own skill. It adapted to the conditions the ancient processes of washing and irrigation: it certainly improved, if it did not invent, the sluice: it originated the hydraulic nozzle. It improved the methods of working gold-bearing quartz and silver ores, which had probably been little developed since the sixteenth century: for instance it substituted iron for wood in the stamps of quartz mills or batteries. By 1870, when the United States Commissioner of Mining Statistics gave a list of these improvements, California had become an exporter of mining machinery. True, it could learn from the Cornishman in the ordinary miner's technique, from the British Isles and the continent of Europe in the treatment of ores; and, whatever may be said of its mining engineers, the scientific geologist, whom it found more and more necessary, was a type of expert that it had to borrow from the wider civilisation of which it formed a part. Still the fact remains that none of the earlier gold rushes had anything like the same record of technical achievement.

After the Civil War the railways brought the

colonial period of the Rocky Mountains and the Pacific Coast communities to an end: not merely economically but institutionally they came into closer relationship with the national community. The regulation of mining on the frontier had so far, to all intents and purposes, been left to the individual mining camp. By the middle 'sixties there must have been well over a thousand of these in California and the Rocky Mountain territories.[1] But this system, we have seen, was ill-adapted to the capitalistic mining required in particular by the conditions of the Comstock lode. 'These mining customs to which the law pays such sweeping respect', wrote the Commissioner of Mining Statistics, 'are edicts passed at 24 hours' notice by mass meetings of from five to five hundred men. . . . The records of titles are kept by an officer . . . not known to the law nor answerable for malfeasance in office, except that if he were known to tamper with the books in his charge his life might be taken by the party wronged. The records are kept in a few districts in fire-proof offices and in suitable form, but more frequently in small blank books, pocket-books or scraps of paper, stowed away under the counter or behind the flour-barrel or the stove of a store or bar-room. . . . The miners' or possessory title, in spite of its frequently vaunted validity, is not one upon which money may be safely lent.'[2] Moreover organisation was so loose and the boundaries were so vague that it was often impossible to determine what code applied to a given location.

[1] Ross Browne's estimate was 500 in California, 200 in Nevada, 100 each in Oregon, Idaho and Arizona; and this excludes Montana, Colorado and New Mexico, which were outside the scope of his report.

[2] R. W. Raymond, *Report on the Mineral Resources of the States and Territories west of the Rocky Mountains* (18 January 1869): Executive Document, 40th Congress, 3rd session, no. 54.

Already certain state and territorial legislatures had begun to regulate the size and tenure of mining claims. Now that capital from the Eastern States and even from abroad was being invested in the mines, there was a strong case for ending the confusion by national regulation. Moreover mine-owners were alarmed by proposals to sell mineral lands at auction as a contribution to the expenses of the Civil War—a further revelation of the weakness of their existing title. In 1866 Congress passed a measure, drafted by Senator Stewart of Nevada and a senator from California, which provided for the grant of a United States title on reasonable terms to possessors by miners' custom and set an upper limit for the future to the size of lode claims—200 feet for any individual except for the discoverer, 3000 feet for any association. From the point of view of national land policy this was a step forward, a beginning of special treatment of mineral lands. But the individual miner could not make his voice heard in Congress as he could in the mining camp. The principle of national regulation was extended by Acts of 1870 and 1872. The latter limited lode claims to 1500 feet along and 300 feet on either side of the vein and gave possession vertically downwards, though it could not revoke altogether the permission to follow dips, spurs and angles which had caused so much litigation. But its restriction of placer claims to twenty acres set the limit higher than had been contemplated by the regulations of the mining districts. Though small claims were still permitted, Congress was clearly thinking in terms of the development of the claims by capital. The individualism of the gold rushes had reached its term.

The mining regions of the Rocky Mountains and

the Pacific Coast themselves played a significant part in the evolution of American civilisation—like Western civilisation generally—in this period from individualism, which among them perhaps reached its fullest development, to a new social integration under capitalist leadership. The equality of opportunity typical of the frontier was never better exemplified than in the early mining rushes, severe though the strain was to which it put those who took part. But more even than normally it led to inequality of fortune. It was truer perhaps to say of these men that they were seeking their fortune than that they were seeking gold: for when they found gold their custom was not to keep it but to seek their fortune further. Those who could resist this social habit, this *wanderlust*, were probably the more successful in a material sense; but the inequalities were not merely due to differences in stability of character or in adaptability. The goddess Fortune herself played a part, though not so great a part as was supposed by the more devoted of her worshippers. The most devoted were the prospectors, and their material rewards, more especially perhaps as time went on and they became more and more the slaves of their goddess, were small. But in any case as mining developed it became more and more dependent—first through ditches, then through increasingly elaborate mining machinery—on capital, and more and more demanded exploitation in large units. After the first two or three seasons this was no doubt true of every field. The mining regulations adapted to the earlier phase had to be modified, and though we read of little actual opposition, there was an inevitable time-lag and the delay was probably seriously wasteful. In the new mining industry to which he had pointed the way the miner, once the freest of Americans, was relegated to a subsidiary place. The Comstocks, the Gregorys and the Fairweathers gave way to the Hearsts and the Guggenheims.

AUTHORITIES FOR CHAPTERS V AND VI

BRITISH COLUMBIA.—The standard history is *British Columbia*, by E. O. S. Scholefield and F. W. Howay (Vancouver, 1914). H. H. Bancroft's *History of British Columbia* (vol. xxxii of his *Collected Works*) and W. N. Sage's scholarly biography, *Sir James Douglas and British Columbia* (Toronto, 1930), are also valuable. Many of Douglas's despatches were printed in British Parliamentary Papers between 1859 and 1864; and other official papers bearing on the history of the goldfields have been printed in F. W. Howay's *Early History of the Fraser River Mines*, R. L. Reid, *The Assay Office and the Proposed Mint at New Westminster* and Mark S. Wade, *The Overlanders of '62* (Memoirs VI, VII and IX of the Provincial Archives, Victoria, 1926–30). Of contemporary accounts there are none of outstanding historical importance but several of interest, such as Kinahan Cornwallis, *The New El Dorado* (London, 1858); Lieut. R. C. Mayne, *Four Years in British Columbia and Vancouver Island* (London, 1862); D. G. F. Macdonald, *British Columbia and Vancouver Island* (London, 1862); R. C. Lundin Brown, *British Columbia: An Essay* (New Westminster, 1863); Rev. Matthew Macfie, *Vancouver Island and British Columbia* (London, 1865); Viscount Milton and Dr. W. B. Cheadle, *The North-West Passage by Land* (London, 1865); R. Byron Johnson, *Very Far West Indeed* (London, 1872). A modern work deserving mention is Victor Ross's *History of the Canadian Bank of Commerce*, vol. i (Toronto, 1920).

ROCKY MOUNTAIN STATES.—H. H. Bancroft's *History of Nevada, Colorado and Wyoming* and *History of Washington, Idaho and Montana*, written by Frances Fuller Victor, are volumes xxv and xxxi of his *Collected Works*. They are less full than the Californian volumes and are as usual defective in arrangement; but their range of sources is so wide that they remain indispensable. On the Comstock lode the two other indispensable books are C. H. Shinn, *The Story of the Mine as illustrated by the*

Great Comstock Lode of Nevada (New York, 1896), and Eliot Lord, *Comstock Mining and Miners* (Monographs of the U.S. Geological Survey, vol. iv, Washington, 1883): Lord's book is especially good, not without literary touches, accurate and scholarly. The best modern account, so far as it goes, is Effie Mona Mack's scholarly work, *Nevada: a History of the State from the Earliest Times through the Great Civil War* (Glendale, 1936). On the Stock Exchange side there is useful information in J. S. Hittell, *History of the City of San Francisco* (San Francisco, 1878), and G. T. Marye, *From '49 to '83 in California and Nevada* (San Francisco, 1923). W. H. Brewer in the work previously cited, J. Ross Browne in magazine articles and in *Adventures in the Apache Country* (New York, 1869) and Albert S. Evans, *White Pine* (San Francisco, 1869), give interesting contemporary glimpses of the silver rushes. White Pine is also studied in an article by R. R. Elliott in the *Pacific North-West Quarterly*, vol. xxx. H. Villard, *The Past and Present of the Pike's Peak Gold Regions* (St. Louis, 1860—reprinted, ed. L. R. Hafen, Princeton, 1932) is an unusually good, well-balanced and lively contemporary account of that rush. O. J. Hollister, *The Mines of Colorado* (Springfield, Mass., 1867) is an informative work, though its interest is in mining rather than in social and political development. T. M. Marshall (ed.), *Early Records of Gilpin County, 1859–61* (Boulder, 1920) is useful on mining camp organisation. Jerome C. Smiley, *History of Denver* (Denver, 1903) is a very valuable work, not academic but soundly based on first-hand authorities. On Leadville, F. Fossett, *Colorado* (2nd edition, New York, 1880) is interesting; on Cripple Creek, the fullest account available here is T. A. Rickard's in *Transactions of the Institute of Mining and Metallurgy*, vol. viii. Irving Howbert, *Memories of a Life Time in the Pike's Peak Region* (New York and London, 1925) is an interesting book of reminiscences; L. R. Hafen, *Colorado: the Story of a Western Commonwealth* (Denver, 1933), a scholarly short history. W. J. McConnell, *Early History of Idaho* (Caldwell, 1913) is really a book of reminiscences, particularly valuable on the problem of order. John Hailey, *History of Idaho* (Boisé, 1910), a book of the same kind, slurs over this particular problem but gives much useful information on other matters. W. A. Goulder, *Reminiscences* (Boisé, 1909) seems to be the only book dealing with the Clearwater or Oro Fino mines, the earliest in Idaho. N. P. Langford, *Vigilante Days and Ways* (Boston, 1890 —reprinted Chicago, 1912) and T. J. Dimsdale, *The Vigilantes of Montana* (Virginia City, 1866—several times reprinted) are indispensable first-hand accounts of their subject. Granville Stuart, *Forty Years on the Frontier* (2 vols. Cleveland, 1925) makes use of a contemporary journal and is invaluable on the early days of Montana: one wishes there were more of it. On the Black Hills the indispensable book is Annie D. Tallent, *The Black Hills* (St. Louis, 1899): there is also a very useful article by Harold E. Briggs in the *North Dakota Historical Quarterly*, vol. v. On the Nevada gold camps C. B. Glasscock, *Gold in them Hills* (Indianapolis, 1934) holds the field to itself. In general there are a number of articles—some of reminiscence, some of a scholarly character—in the publications of the various State Historical Societies: but the sum-total of additional information they provide is not perhaps as great as might be expected. On general issues there is only one scholarly treatment, though fortunately it is a very good book—W. J. Trimble, *The Mining Advance into the Inland Empire* (Madison, Wis., 1914). It deals primarily with Idaho, Montana and British Columbia—not with Nevada or Colorado. On its own field, T. A. Rickard, *History of American Mining* (New York, 1932) is the work of the greatest living authority. The mining legislation is discussed in Rickard's *Man and Metals* (New York, 1932); in the official *Reports on Mineral Resources of the States and Territories west of the Rocky Mountains* (Washington, 1869–77); in Mack, *op. cit.*; and, from a different point of view, in B. H. Hibbard, *History of the Public Land Policies* (New York, 1924).

CHAPTER VII

BALLARAT AND BENDIGO

THE discovery of gold in Australia, as in California, antedated the great rush by some years. A surveyor noted the presence of gold in 1823; the Polish geologist Strzelecki found auriferous rock in 1839 and a Sydney geological enthusiast, the Rev. W. B. Clarke, a few years later; a shepherd, McGregor by name, is said to have accumulated £200 worth, and there may have been others who knew of its existence. No one, however, knew how to work gold in that thinly scattered pastoral community, and the Government, informed by Strzelecki and Clarke, had an interest in keeping the discovery quiet, for there was a large convict and ex-convict element in New South Wales and in a gold rush they might become uncontrollable. After the great Californian discoveries, however, the secret could not long be kept from those who joined in the Californian rush. Two of the many Australian miners put their heads together in one of the Californian camps: a modicum of geological knowledge on the part of the one and a vague recollection by the other, Edward Hammond Hargraves, of the country between Wellington and Bathurst, in which McGregor had made his find, combined to produce the belief that that country was probably gold-bearing. Hargraves determined to return to his wife and children in New South Wales and put this conclusion to the test. 'There's no gold in the country you're going to,' an

American acquaintance shouted as he left, 'and if there is, that darned queen of yours won't let you dig it.' 'To which', we are told, 'Mr. Hargraves, first taking off his hat and assuming a theatrical attitude replied . . . , "There's as much gold in the country I'm going to as there is in California, and Her Most Gracious Majesty the Queen, God bless her, will appoint me one of her Gold Commissioners." ' [1] Hargraves was justified in his boast. He went up-country in February 1851, and taking as his guide the young son of the landlady of a roadside inn, on the 12th he panned out some grains of gold in a creek thirty miles from the straggling country town of Bathurst. He then went with his guide and another youth to the Macquarie eighty miles away and again was satisfied with what he found. One of the youths remarked that on the Turon there was very similar country and Hargraves despatched them to examine it whilst himself prospecting another district. He then showed them how to make a rocker and re-turned to Sydney, confident that he had discovered a wide area of auriferous country. In the middle of March he put himself in communication with the Colonial Secretary, Deas Thomson, who was at first sceptical— there was very little of the gold, and it might have come from California—but at an interview on 2 April was convinced. 'If this is a gold country, Mr. Hargraves,' said Deas Thomson, 'it will stop the Home Govern-ment from sending us any more convicts, and prevent emigration to California; but it comes on us like a clap

[1] S. Davison, *The Discovery and Geognosy of Gold Deposits in Australia* (London, 1860), p. 52. Davison was Hargraves's companion in California. E. W. Rudder, another of the party, confirmed Davison's account in a pamphlet in 1861. Hargraves's own account in *Australia and its Goldfields* (London, 1855) says nothing about his companion's contribution to the discussion.

of thunder, and we are scarcely prepared to credit it.'[1]
He offered Hargraves a reward, to be dependent on the
value of the discovery, provided he disclosed the locality.
Hargraves hesitated for over three weeks and then accepted the terms. He went up with the Government
Geologist, who confirmed his report: indeed his young
companions had found a few ounces meanwhile. He
made no secret now of his discovery and by 19 May
there were 400 people of all classes on Summer Hill
Creek, making an ounce or two daily. Bathurst had been
drained of its labourers, though its smiths were busy
making pickaxes, and the squatters were deserted by
their shepherds.

The gold of California had been found on land
belonging to the United States, but the temporary
military representatives of its authority could not and
did not attempt to assert its claim. The gold of New
South Wales had been found on land belonging to the
Crown, represented by a well-established Colonial
Government. It proposed to reconcile the rights of the
Crown with the claims of the miners by a system of
licences at thirty shillings a month, to be administered
by the ordinary agents of government in the rural
districts, the Commissioners of Crown Lands. The
special commissioner despatched to the scene of the
discovery, a sympathetic and yet efficient administrator,
at first allowed miners a week's credit, but he was instructed by Government to permit no one to dig until
payment was actually made in money or gold. This was
to be taken at £3 : 4s. an ounce, and provision was made

---

[1] Hargraves, *op. cit.* p. 119. The circumstances of the discovery were
investigated in 1853 by a Select Committee of the Legislative Council on the
Goldfields Management Bill: the relevant evidence is printed in an appendix
by Davison, *op. cit.*

for an armed escort to bring the receipts to Sydney. Before long, indeed, the Government was attempting, through investigations by the Geological Surveyor, Clarke and Hargraves, to give some direction to the search for gold.[1] In actual fact the discoveries were too unexpected in extent and locality to be kept under scientific and administrative control, but the positive policy of the New South Wales Government, so sharply in contrast with Californian *laissez-faire*, did result in a certain administrative shaping of goldfields society.

Sydney soon began to feel the effects of the discoveries. Colonel Mundy, driving to the races ten miles outside Sydney on 28 and 30 May, noted the contrast between the ordinary race-going crowd and the concurrent stream of 'drays and carts, heavily laden, proceeding westward with tents, rockers, flour, tea, sugar, mining tools, etc.—each accompanied by from four to eight men, half of whom bore fire-arms. Some looked eager and impatient—some half ashamed of their errand—others sad and thoughtful—all resolved . . . utterly indifferent to and apart from the merry scene of the racecourse. . . . Most of their equipments were quite new—good stout horses, harness fresh out of the saddler's hands, gay-coloured woollen shirts, and comforters, and Californian *sombreros* of every size and shape.'[2] There was a marked labour shortage and a rise in prices. In June arrivals from Melbourne, Adelaide and Hobart began. But by that time a reaction had set in. Wet, cold weather flooded the diggings on Summer Hill creek and drove away many of the diggers,

[1] Hargraves was a failure in this capacity, as also in Western Australia in later years.
[2] G. C. Murray, *Our Antipodes* (London, 1852), iii, 316-17. In general the diggers used 'cabbage-tree hats', made by shepherds from the leaves or rind of the cabbage palm.

who were for the most part camping in or under their drays or living in *gunyahs*, huts rudely constructed of the branches and bark of the eucalyptus. The rewards were not often sufficient to overcome these draw-backs, and many of the newcomers from neighbouring colonies returned or took agricultural or pastoral employment.

The check, however, was merely temporary. The rains had favoured digging on the Turon, where at first there had been a scarcity of water, and towards the end of June there was a movement in that direction. Early in July there were perhaps 1000 working on seven or eight miles of that river, not many miles above its confluence with the Macquarie. Then, a few days before the middle of the month, an aboriginal shepherd found at Meroo Creek three blocks of quartz containing in all over 100 pounds of gold. When brought into Bathurst it was seized as Crown property, the aboriginal having had no licence to dig, but it was soon returned to his master, who rewarded the finder with 1500 sheep, two saddle-horses, a plough-team and a quantity of rations. It turned out to be a freak find, but it naturally stimulated a renewal of the rush, and results on the Turon supplied a further justification. One party of three, with five hired men, took out 40 pounds in a month. There was now more careful preparation and a better sense of proportion in the community than in May; but by the end of July the numbers on the gold-fields had risen to about 3000—arrivals from other colonies accounting for perhaps half—and excitement was still at quite a high pitch.

Mundy describes the scene at the Turon late in July. 'As we topped a ridge, the last of a series I thought interminable, my companion suddenly said, "Stop and

listen". I pulled up my horse and heard as I imagined
the rushing of some mighty cataract. "It is the cradles",
said he; and so it was—the grating of the gravel or
rubble on the metal sifters of five hundred rockers. . . .
There was no pause nor the slightest variation in the
cadence as it floated up to us on the still air.'[1] Along the
broad sloping valley were the straggling tents and huts
of the diggers, and a winding line of smoke curled up
the sides of the hills. Within the tent might be 'a piece
of bark nailed on to four posts driven into the ground
for a table, and the same sort of thing on stretchers
to sleep and sit upon; perhaps a pickle-case for the
president's seat; an old sardine-box converted into a
salt-cellar; a herring tin for a sugar-basin; and knives
that had been used for fossicking . . . outside, were
inside used for carving'.[2] The river-banks had of course
all been dug up by this time: the gold might be ten
feet down. But 'a tolerable road runs for several miles
along the course, winding among the beautiful swamp-
oaks that fringe it, and crossing frequently from one
bank to the other in spots which impinge upon the
creek. In most places this track is passable for drays . . .
or rather it would have been passable, but that some of
the more unscrupulous diggers have burrowed across it
in all directions.'[3] The centre of the diggings was the
canvas town of Sofala, where there were storekeepers,
butchers, carpenters, blacksmiths, surgeons—even by
September a circus. No licences had as yet been granted
for the sale of liquor; so the town lacked the characteristic Californian saloons.

The diggers had followed the Californian model in

[1] Mundy, *op. cit.* iii, 369.
[2] C. Rudston Read, *What I Heard, Saw and Did at the Australian Gold
Fields* (London, 1853), p. 18.   [3] Mundy, *op. cit.* iii, 370.

their costume, in their methods of working and appliances, in their partnerships: these were small, for the sluice was not yet in question, though the normal three or four men required for working a rocker were of course sometimes exceeded. But the system of claims was determined not by themselves but for them, at first at his discretion by the Commissioner. He marked out each person's ground as he gave the licence: he normally gave a frontage of from fifteen to twenty-four feet along the creek to a party of from three to six, and never more than forty feet, however large the party. Early in October the matter was determined by regulation, the size varying according to the type of claim but remaining small. The general estimate of the yield at this stage was 10s. to £1 per man per day: this was reasonably satisfactory, as living on the usual bush fare of mutton or beef, tea with sugar, and 'damper' baked in ashes cost only 12s. to 14s. a week. But a number of diggers—according to one estimate 40 per cent.—could not make a living on their claims; and unsuccessful miners tended to be employed at wages—30s. or perhaps £2 a week and food, or £3 for Cornish miners—by successful claim-holders. Indeed gentlemen came up and agreed to find tools and provisions, and if necessary purchase a claim, for a party of working miners in return for a share, perhaps a half, of the net proceeds: many claims might in that way be financed by a single man.

The community was thus not quite equalitarian but it was thoroughly democratic in spirit. There were 'merchants, cabmen, magistrates and convicts, amateur gentlemen rocking the cradle merely to say they have done so, fashionable hairdressers and tailors, cooks, coachmen, lawyers' clerks and their masters, colliers, cobblers, quarrymen, doctors of physic and of music, aldermen, an A.D.C. on leave, scavengers, sailors, short-hand-writers, a real live lord on his travels—all levelled by community of pursuit and of costume'.[1] But it was a harmonious community and submissive to authority, which was merely represented by the Commissioner and about ten police for every thousand diggers. A crowd that collected to rescue a prisoner was deterred by a bold police officer and a single mounted trooper.[2] The armed escort for the licence revenues had developed into an armed escort for all gold entrusted to the Government; but the arms never needed to be used. In two directions only were there signs of possible trouble. The licence fee caused some grumbling and evasion. At Ophir on Summer Hill Creek, where there were still a few hundred miners, we are told, the croak of a raven was the signal for one of an unlicensed party to shoulder the rocker and hide somewhere among the rocks or gulleys while the others would scatter among the idle spectators or licensed workmen. An impudent Irishman when asked for his licence, coolly replied, 'My hands are so dirty, perhaps your honour will be so kind as to put your own hand into my breeches pocket, and you'll find it benathe a roll of bank notes'.[3] At this stage the Commissioner himself, attended by a policeman, collected the licence fee: later, when miners were required to call at his offices, there were complaints of the loss of time. More justified was the complaint that the licence was levied on labour, not on produce, and little satisfaction was given by the official attitude that those who could not earn enough to pay it would probably do better at

[1] Mundy, *op. cit.* iii, 346-7.
[2] Henrietta Huxley, 'The Gold Diggings at Bathurst' (*Nineteenth Century*, xlv, 1899), quoting her contemporary letters.
[3] Rudston Read, *op. cit.* pp. 20-21.

their ordinary callings. Illicit diggers were often detected and their rockers smashed. Illicit liquor dealers —'sly grog-sellers'—were more difficult to catch. Still it was a remarkably steady-going community, all things considered. There was a good deal of fellow-feeling and sociability, and hardly any crime. Sunday work was forbidden, but Rudston Read reckoned that eight-tenths of the people would not have worked had they been allowed: many religious services were held, and they were well attended.

By October there were about 4000 miners on the Turon. It was probably too many for the field, though one effect was the discovery of large and rich deposits on the higher flats at some distance from the river and on the neighbouring hills. The discoveries had of course stimulated the search for gold over all the settled districts of the colony, and in some cases local offers of reward had given a further stimulus. The chief new discovery was southwards on the creeks of the Araluen River in picturesque country surrounded by steep mountain ranges, near the township of Braidwood. This field from September attracted and maintained about 1000 miners. But by this time there had been far more important discoveries in Victoria. What had happened in New South Wales was a mere prologue to the Australian gold rushes. A colony of 200,000 people could provide a living on its goldfields for a few thousand diggers without undergoing any serious strain. For some years they produced 100,000 ounces, more or less. But the gold discoveries were a mere episode in the life of the colony. Their real importance lay elsewhere, in their priority and in the prestige of New South Wales as the mother colony. By these means they exerted a powerful influence on the administrative and even on the social institutions of the goldfields in the daughter colony of Victoria.

The Victorian population of 97,000 was supported in 1851 primarily by its pastoral industry. About 1000 holders of squatting licences were scattered over the fertile lands of the colony, employing perhaps 20,000 dependents and owning some 6,000,000 sheep. Two rising towns—Melbourne with 23,000 and Geelong with 8000 inhabitants—acted as distributing centres for the great sheep runs. The colony was just in the throes of separation from New South Wales, having been granted this boon and a measure of representative government by Imperial Act of 1850. The first effect of Hargraves's discovery was a drain of population to New South Wales: but Melbourne citizens sought to check it by the offer early in June of a reward for the discovery of a profitable goldfield within 200 miles of the city. Even without the offer of reward no doubt shepherds would have kept their eyes open for gold and parties have been organised to prospect the creeks and gullies, for as in New South Wales there had been minor discoveries in earlier years. Various discoveries, sufficient to attract a few hundred miners and to give a more definite direction to further searches, culminated on 25 or 26 August when a prospecting party of six, led by a man named Connor, washed out thirty ounces in a day on the banks of a stream at Ballaarat, some fifty miles north-westward of Geelong. It was a region of grassy slopes, ferny creeks and low, undulating forest-covered hills, but hundreds of miners soon appeared upon the scene and began to destroy its beauty and rifle it of its treasure. The earlier finds had caused some excitement in Geelong and Melbourne and led Governor Latrobe to institute the New South Wales licence system and to detail an officer to take charge. Floods and tempestuous weather delayed the arrival of news of Ballarat, but when Latrobe received it early in September he at once sent up an officer with such police as could be collected to maintain order and carry out the regulations. 'A slight show of opposition, instigated by a few, gave way at once', he reported, 'to a general desire, expressed by the majority, to secure licences and obtain the countenance and protection of the authorities.'[1] Claims were limited in size to eight feet square for an individual and eight feet by sixteen for a party. A weekly gold escort was instituted at the end of the month.[2] Early in October Latrobe went up to see Ballarat for himself; but he had already taken the critical decisions.

By this time Melbourne and Geelong were almost emptied of many classes of their male population. Public and private works were at a standstill. The road to the diggings was a practically continuous line of vehicles and pedestrians: the latter usually had a dray or cart for their supplies but sometimes 'humped their swags'. At night the parties camped by large fires and the banks of creeks and waterholes were crowded with tents and *miamias* of branches. The soft surface of the road soon degenerated into a quagmire in which horses were lost; and sometimes thirty or forty men would pull a dray up a steep greasy hill with ropes or unload it and carry its load up on their backs. Nevertheless by late

---

[1] Latrobe to Grey (10 October 1851): *Parl. Papers*, 1852, xxxiv [Cmd. 1508], p. 43.

[2] A private gold escort ran for a few months in 1852, but did not long survive. With the Government escorts and the speedy entrance of the banks into the gold-buying market, there was no call for the American express system. Nor was there a mint in Victoria until 1872: New South Wales got in first and one was established there in 1853–54, but most of the Victorian gold was exported to England.

October it was possible to travel up from Geelong by coach. 'Golden Point', the scene of the discovery, was now cleared of wood and dug into innumerable holes down to a depth of twenty feet, for the bluish-grey 'pipe-clay' beneath the surface gravel had been found to be full of pockets of gold. The earth had to be carried in bags or wheeled in barrows to the creek-side for wash-ing, and the barrows were wheeled along the narrow strips of ground separating the claims at reckless speed. The hill above the diggings, the next gully, and the flat beside the stream were covered with all kinds of tents and shelters of bark or boughs piled against the trunks of gum-trees. The number on the ground by the end of the month was probably 6000 or 7000. A few were making fortunes. Occasionally good nuggets could be found by mere picking with a knife. But there was at any rate a minority who made little or nothing at all.

Nature, however, had only begun to display her golden bounty at Ballarat. In July a hut-keeper had come upon gold on a sheep-run some sixty-five miles north-west of Melbourne within a few miles of Mt. Alexander. He and his fellow-servants kept it quiet for some weeks, but early in September it became known, some say through roving prospectors, some through dis-closure by one of the men to a newspaper. It was then found that other creeks in the Mt. Alexander region were rich in gold; and about a month later another dis-covery was made, perhaps by another station hand, on Bendigo Creek, over a granite ridge nearly thirty miles farther north. Mt. Alexander was at first richer even than Ballarat, and the gold was nearer the surface: by the middle of December there were 20,000 on the new and only 300 on the older field. Two tons of gold (about 65,000 ounces) were arriving by the weekly escort, and it is clear that a high proportion of the diggers were doing really well.

The experience of making its fortune gave Melbourne a severe preliminary shock. Its business was almost paralysed by the exodus to Mt. Alexander; its shipping lay idle in the bay; its governmental machinery was suffering simultaneously from congestion of business and departure of staff. Civil servants' pay was increased 50 per cent. early in October, but when prices were 30 to 100 or more per cent. above the level of the previous year and the alternative to steady service seemed to be sudden wealth, the strain on their loyalty was often too great. Labourers' wages were up by 200 per cent. or more and there was 'a rapidly decreasing number of persons willing to enter upon any engagements whatever'. Compensations for the business community at least began to appear at Christmas-time, for to the natural tendency to celebrate success there was added a dearth of water on the goldfields. There was a reflex not of disappointed but of successful diggers for an orgy of extravagance and dissipation.

Governor Latrobe, an intelligent, amiable and conscientious rather than a strong administrator, coped with these problems as best he could. The newly elected Legislative Council, resenting his claim that the gold revenue like the land revenue was at the disposal of the Crown, refused to relieve him of any of his responsibility. He made one serious mistake, in attempting to double the licence fee. The miners at Mt. Alexander held a great meeting and refused to pay. At a heavy cost to the prestige of Government, Latrobe abandoned the proposal. He felt the licence system to be unsuitable to a problem so much larger in scale than that of New South Wales and without an adequate trained service to

administer it: but though the alternatives of a royalty
and assay office or an export duty on gold were discussed by the Legislative Council and by the public the
matter never passed beyond the stage of expressions of
opinion. Latrobe's mistake was all the more unfortunate
because the actual force at his command, in spite of help
from New South Wales and from Van Diemen's Land,
was ludicrously small. His financial problem was very
serious, for apart from large increases of salary he had
to create a new department to administer the goldfields
licences and revenue, escort, police and magistracy, with
a chief commissioner in Melbourne, and commissioners
and assistants, numbering twenty-seven early in 1852,
on the various diggings.

Meanwhile in December the second stage, the intercolonial stage, of the gold rush had begun. For some
months there was an influx of from 5000 to 7000
monthly from neighbouring colonies into Melbourne.
A certain number came from New South Wales, but
those disposed to dig gold had already had their chance
on their own goldfields and the rise in wages was a
further inducement to stay. A few came from Western
Australia or New Zealand, the majority from South
Australia and Van Diemen's Land. The initial effects in
South Australia were alarming. The streets of Adelaide
were deserted, houses were abandoned, property became unsaleable; the banks were drained of accumulated deposits to provide outfits for intending diggers
and were obliged accordingly to contract their circulation of notes. Some enterprising traders shut up their
shops, packed up their goods and took ship to Melbourne, where they sold them off and used the proceeds
to import fresh stocks to Adelaide from England. But
everyone was not in a position to leave. The Governor

and his officials, the Chamber of Commerce, and the managers of the banks conferred upon the crisis, and from their deliberations proceeded a measure, passed into law at a special session of the Legislative Council, authorising the establishment of an Assay Office and the issue of notes by the banks against its stamped ingots, which were to be received at £3 : 11s. an ounce. The South Australian authorities were counting upon the willingness of their own colonists at least to send their gold-dust to Adelaide, the more so as the price offered was several shillings higher than the ruling price in Melbourne or Sydney. The passage of the Act on 28 January 1852 was followed by the despatch of the Commissioner of Police to organise an overland escort from Mt. Alexander. He found at least 4000 South Australian diggers there and they welcomed his enterprise. Meanwhile the Bullion Act had restored confidence and stimulated both the import of gold in the way of trade and the export of produce. Hundreds of thousands of ounces of gold were attracted to South Australia by the Act and the escort; and her lands, which were available in small areas and had a wonderfully expanding market near at hand, were a richer gold mine than the few gullies within her borders where gold was found. After the initial crisis the effect of the temporary exodus was not a loss but an enrichment of her population. Van Diemen's Land, which was still on a basis of convict labour, was differently situated. It lost more than 10,000 of its population of 70,000 to Victoria in the first six months of 1852. The arrival of new cargoes of convicts and the expanding market in Victoria for timber and grain were a partial offset to these difficulties, and some of the diggers returned after a season's toil. But the immigrants, being largely ex-convicts, were much less welcome in Victoria, which was soon seeking to erect barriers, at any rate to the extent of requiring arrivals from Van Diemen's Land to prove their absolute freedom.[1]

The strain imposed by this intercolonial rush upon accommodation in Melbourne was considerable. Rudston Read, arriving about the end of February 1852, found it impossible on his first night to get permission anywhere to sleep on the floor or even sit in a chair and was given a shake-down by an old shipmate in the forepeak of a vessel lying alongside the wharf: the second night he slept in the open by a fire, the third in a stranger's tent, the fourth in a lodging with eight others in the same room. But there seemed to be no overcrowding at Mt. Alexander, to which most of the newcomers betook themselves. With its rich, shallow ground it was an ideal field for the novice. But skill was of course an asset: inexperienced miners were apt not to recognise auriferous ground or to throw away the richest stuff in their anxiety to get down to bedrock. Shortage of water restricted the use of the long-tom, which had been introduced on the Turon; but skilled miners were before long supplementing the rocker by a puddling tub, made out of half a barrel, to break down and dissolve the stiff Victorian clay.[2] As the summer wore on, this lack of water became really serious not only for mining but for health. Forest Creek, the richest

---

[1] The home authorities strongly objected to this measure, but in the end, in 1855, they left it to its operation.

[2] 'The tub is half filled with the "washing-stuff"; water is baled in from the creek, and the whole worked about with the spade, the miner cutting up and turning over the clay till it gradually is dissolved in the water; and as the water becomes charged with earth it is poured from the tub, and a fresh supply added.' Eventually nothing would remain but clean gravel, sand and gold: Wathen, *The Golden Colony*, p. 71.

of the Mt. Alexander creeks, became a misnomer. 'The road, which winds along the creek through the diggings', wrote a *Melbourne Argus* correspondent, 'is, from the constant traffic, ten times more dusty than even dusty Melbourne, and the heavy gusts of wind, which pour through the gullies with great violence, whirl it up in clouds, and scatter it far and near upon everything around. The newly-erected tent does not, therefore, long retain its brilliant whiteness. . . . In the same way, such trees as have escaped the axe are dusted to an unnatural brownness. . . . Even off the road, the earth is so trodden and worn by the thousands of feet that are constantly passing and repassing, that not the faintest sign of verdure remains upon the ground . . . while, on the southern side of the creek, the hills are so pierced, and the subsoil so tossed and tumbled about upon their face, that they look like nothing but gravel or chalk-pits and stone-quarries. When to this is also added the constant feeding of the innumerable horses which throng the diggings, eating off the grass on the few hills that have not been ransacked, and even cropping the shoots of the few shrubs that grow amongst the rocks, baring them of every particle of verdure, and the rude, rough look of the jagged rocks which protrude from the bare surface—anything but a refreshing picture meets the eye.'[1] Water supplies had been used for mining with reckless improvidence, and now that they were polluted or exhausted, dysentery was rampant. The drought had one compensating effect; it scattered the miners in search of other fields. Bendigo, where the gold-bearing creeks were as numerous as at Mt. Alexander or more so, became from about April 1852 the most frequented

[1] *Melbourne Argus*, March 1852: quoted by F. Lancelott, *Australia as it is* (London, 1852), pp. 133-5.

of all. There too gold was often found on or within a few feet of the surface, though there were also very productive small hills, where shafts had to be sunk through very hard cement-like material to reach the auriferous pipe-clay. There were more nuggets at Bendigo, though it had the disadvantage of being more remote and therefore more expensive. At the end of February there had been 30,000 people, according to the official estimate, at Mt. Alexander: at the end of June there were perhaps 40,000 at Bendigo. The escorts from these two fields brought down 220,000 ounces in July, and of course all gold was not brought down by escort. Diggers who were not making an ounce a day were discontented with their takings.

The population of the goldfields was a mixture of all classes of society. It was on the whole orderly, as Latrobe stoutly maintained in a despatch of 2 March 1852 to the Secretary of State. 'With regard', he wrote, 'to the statements of the universal unchecked prevalence of crime and disorder at the workings, detailed with such effrontery and recklessness in the profligate public prints of this colony itself, or greedily retailed and commented upon for evident purposes in the New South Wales press, all I can say is, that they are not true. . . . Viewing the position and character of no inconsiderable number of the persons frequenting the workings, a far greater amount of crime might prevail without the Government of the colony . . . being in any degree justly blameable. In such a crowd, one half utter strangers to the other and to the colony, met together in a wild tract of broken forested country, full of secluded hollows, honeycombed with hundreds or thousands of ready-made graves, under such strong inducements to cupidity, disorder, and crime, the imagination is free and unrestrained to picture the extent to which crime may . . . prevail in secret without the possibility of discovery. . . . Many a murder may take place, of the existence of which no evidence will ever transpire or record exist; but I can assure your Lordship that whatever crimes may really be perpetrated, no indifference to it on the part of the authorities could have existed, and that no such general disorder and rejection of law and constituted authority as these statements would represent has ever been observable.'[1] This statement carries conviction. But Latrobe himself admitted that there were difficulties in enforcing two of the most important goldfields regulations—the licence fee and the prohibition of the sale of liquor. It might well be that drink was the besetting weakness of the Australian working man. But law-breaking was an equally bad habit to form, and the attempt to check it by a provision that half the fine in cases of 'sly-grog-selling' should go to the informer or party prosecuting led to undue concentration on this particular law and did not stop corruption. Sly-grog-sellers' tents might be pulled down and burnt and the kegs of liquor confiscated. But the profits were high and it was freely asserted that many sly-grog-shops, often the most disreputable, were winked at. Respectable shopkeepers would give liquor with goods as a 'present', not forgetting to add a little to the price of the goods. Rudston Read, who was in the goldfields service, declares that many policemen left the diggings after a few months with £1000 or more in their pockets. On the licence question he is equally outspoken. The practice of evasion, begun in the New South Wales fields, spread to Victoria: the signal was

---

[1] Latrobe to Grey (2 March 1852): *Parl. Papers*, 1852–53, lxiv [Cmd. 1607], p. 170.

now the cry of 'Joe' and not the croak of a raven. But in Read's opinion the unpopularity of the police was their own fault. Many of them were accustomed to dealing with convicts, and 'it was not in their nature to perform their duty quietly without bouncing, bullying and swearing at every one'.[1] If respectable men remonstrated, they were liable to be handcuffed and charged with obstructing the police in the execution of their duty. There were hold-ups on the roads: diggers were made drunk and then robbed of their gold: yet Latrobe himself suggests that the police were apt to neglect the detection and pursuit of the perpetrators for more remunerative duties. He hardly concealed his uneasiness from his superiors at home, but said in effect that he must work with such materials as he had. There was indeed no active resistance, and perhaps the overbearing attitude of the police had its effect with the most dangerous element on the goldfields, the ex-convicts from Van Diemen's Land. As for the goldfields service itself, its best members deserved and enjoyed respect; but some were inexperienced young men whose authority went to their heads. Circumstances and deliberate policy had given the Government a far more active rôle on the Victorian than on the Californian goldfields: it performed services which were there performed by the express, and services like that of police which there rested upon public opinion alone: but it was a long time before its administration could claim to be more worthy of public support than the rough-and-ready improvisations of California.

As winter set in, the Government was faced with another problem insoluble for the time being. The

[1] Rudston Read, *op. cit.* pp. 146-8. Cf. also *Lord Robert Cecil's Goldfields Diary* (ed. E. Scott) (Melbourne, 1935), pp. 27-8.

unbearable dust of March was converted into an almost impassable sea of mud. Pack-horses were used where carts and drays could not get through, but they too often stuck fast. Transport charges rose from £10 or £20 to £80, £100 or £120 per ton to Bendigo. But what could the Government do? 'Men would never leave off gold digging for any sort of good wages to go breaking stones on a road: those even that were obtained . . . required as many overseers almost as roadmakers to keep them at work, and then perhaps if they were spoken to, would coolly tell him to go to the devil, and take themselves off into the bargain.'[1]

In spite of these disabilities, however, the escorts in July reached, as we have seen, the highest figure yet: new discoveries were still being made, and if the tide of immigration had slackened somewhat in the winter it was soon to flow again with unprecedented force. It is true that the production to date of a million ounces of gold, and probably a good deal more, gives no very princely reward when distributed among 30,000 or 40,000 miners, particularly when a miner at Bendigo might receive only fifty to fifty-two shillings an ounce for his gold. It is also true that many successful diggers squandered their gains—the old bushmen perhaps especially. But many took them back to their colonial homes and invested them for example in land. Many a storekeeper or baker or drayman or blacksmith must have acquired a competence, and many a Melbourne merchant must have laid the foundation of a fortune. Nor had the pastoral industry, the stand-by of the early years of the colony, collapsed. Shepherds went off to the diggings and left the sheep to the tender mercies of the dingoes. The cost of carriage of wool and station supplies rose

[1] Rudston Read, *op. cit.* p. 163.

enormously. But the diggers had created in the wilderness an almost unlimited market for meat, and further opportunities of gain in selling horses or pasturing them in paddocks near the diggings. The first few years of the gold rush were in fact one of the most flourishing periods of the squatting industry. Thus the first year of the goldfields had broadened the economic basis of the Australian communities, and notably though not solely of Victoria, even though, as we shall see, the mercantile community also had wasted much of the gold in speculative orders of goods from England. The existing social order had been disturbed. 'There are no gentlemen in the colonies now', writes one emigrant. 'There are only rich men and poor men; and as the latter may be rich in a week, every one is "hail fellow, well met" with everyone else.'[1] Former shopkeepers, errand-boys, shepherds and hut-keepers might be drinking champagne at a guinea or a guinea and a half a bottle. But social revolutions are not made by champagne. A social effervescence there had indeed been, and as the adult male population of the Australian colonies at this time cannot have much exceeded 100,000, it is safe to say that more than half of it had taken part in this general shake-up. The natural progress of the colonies towards democracy had been accelerated. But a governmental machine which was certainly not democratic in its methods of control had stood the strain: in spite of the bushrangers and the sly-grog-sellers there had been no general breakdown of order.

A third phase of the gold rush was now beginning. In the last four months of 1852 goldseekers, attracted especially by the extraordinary richness of Mt. Alex-

[1] G. B. Earp (ed.), *What We did in Australia* (London, 1853), pp. 141-2.

ander, flowed in from the British Isles and Europe.[1]
There was a cosmopolitan element, certainly, but it was
never as strong as in California. The presence of aborigines with their blankets and Chinese with their
pigtails and loose trousers, the contrast between 'the
successful digger in his blue serge shirt and with green
veil still hanging round his wideawake' and the new
arrival in his English clothes might give an exotic air
to the Melbourne streets, but the solid bulk of the immigration was from England, Scotland and Ireland, with
the two latter countries together exceeding the former.
Still it was the most vigorous and diversified body of
immigrants that Australia had yet received: the real
doubt was as to its eligibility for the goldfields. Some
had come from the mining villages of Derbyshire or
Cornwall or Somerset, but these must have formed a
small proportion of the whole. 'It is evident', wrote
Latrobe, 'that amongst the newcomers not one in ten is
prepared to encounter the crush and labour of the Gold
Fields, and that the great majority are probably totally
unfitted and unsuited by previous habits, occupation or
temperament to surmount the difficulties which must
beset them in becoming colonists at the present time.
The strong and active labourer, the clever mechanic,
the thoroughly competent clerk, and the energetic of all
classes, may gradually work their way at the Gold Fields
or elsewhere; but what is to become of the multitude of
decent men of small means and large families, decayed
or unfortunate tradesmen, half educated clerks, young
men of no decided calling or character, professing their
willingness to do anything, with the power of doing

---

[1] The total arrivals were about 15,000 a month. About 20,000 adult males
arrived from the United Kingdom, and about 20,000 from the Australian
colonies, but against the latter must be set perhaps 15,000 departures.

nothing well, to say nothing of the horde of weak or irregular characters, whose expatriation has been advocated and assisted by relatives for the sake of their connexions quite as much as that of the individuals, or of the undisguisedly worthless and dissolute, numbers of whom are evidently included in this immigration?' [1] There was no element in the Victorian gold rush of 1852–53, as there was in the Californian rush of 1849– 1850, accustomed already to the makeshifts and hardships of frontier life. Few if any of them can have been prepared to find that the boatmen who took them from their anchorage in Port Phillip to the low sandy shore, the draymen who carted their effects from there to Melbourne, might charge more than the cost of their passage from London; and that a week or ten days in Melbourne preparing to go to the goldfields might deprive them of the means of going there. Hundreds had to relinquish their golden schemes from the very outset. It occurred to some that it would pay them to dispose of all they could spare of their outfit, for what it would fetch, rather than undergo the costs of cartage and storage, and for some time a sort of beach market flourished at which sharp shopkeepers renewed their stocks. Melbourne itself was choked with the new arrivals until the pressure was eased by a fungoid growth of tents and grass *miamias* known as Canvas Town. 'Many workmen were induced to make their homes there; and, stretching calico on light spar frames, with a calico door framed on hinges, a turf fireplace and chimney at the end, they were enabled to live comfortably enough in mild weather. Men with small means—builders in the first stage of development—erected such places, and let

[1] Latrobe to Pakington (28 October 1852): *Parl. Papers*, 1852–53, lxiv [Cmd. 1607], p. 261.

them by the week. Small shops were opened; hand-printed cards, announcing that tailoring or cobbling was done within, began to appear, pasted to the sides of doorways, with perhaps a pair of newly-mended boots, or a small sheet of square cloth patterns. Before long, jobbing carpenters and coopers found they need not cross the river, or go to the adjoining townships in search of work, when the want of benches and stools and water-barrels increased with the growing inclination of their neighbours to settle permanently. Habitations that in the beginning of the week had stood alone, would before the close have become hemmed in all round by a crowd of new erections. The buzz of life grew louder, and the hillside began to be trodden bare by the increasing multitude of feet. Tents where, on a stall before the door, a modest trade in harmless effervescing drinks had been established, began, as the neighbourhood became more populous, to outgrow their early humility and aspire to stronger liquor.'[1] The site being on a Government reserve, Government made a rent charge of five shillings per tent weekly, but otherwise left the place alone until robberies and assaults began to call for interference by the police. To meet the case of the actually destitute and derelict, homes of temporary refuge were erected by the Government, by the Wesleyan community, and by a newly formed Immigrants' Aid Society; and two large ships in the Bay—for ships, deserted by their crews, found it difficult to get away[2]—were also hired for this purpose. Trade of course flourished, goods being sold at three or four times their prime cost, though there may have been

---

[1] J. Armour, *The Diggings, the Bush and Melbourne* (Glasgow, 1864), p. 45.
[2] The ship's company sometimes went up to the goldfields as an organised party: Westgarth, *Victoria, late Australia Felix* (Edinburgh, 1853), p. 157.

something in the complaint of a French immigrant that the requirement of a licence for street trading made it less lively and colourful than in San Francisco and played into the hands of established traders.

Those who could afford to go on to the diggings would if possible assemble a party and buy a strong light cart and 'a staunch horse, such as no depth of mud, no swamp, and no steep hill will daunt'. The cart would then be packed with the heavy tools and stores at the bottom, the gold washing-tubs and tent above, and the blankets and clothes at the top. The frying-pan was stuck on one side, the camp-kettles hung jingling underneath. A white tarpaulin was spread over the load and any women in the party seated upon it.[1] Many were of course too poor for such an outfit, and there would be a trail of unfortunate 'new chums' and of experienced men from other colonies, their 'swags' festooned with tools and with pistols in their belts, all the way to Mt. Alexander or Bendigo. Goods were mostly conveyed by bullock-teams, eight yoke strong. There were of course bush inns on the way. One had grown in nine months from a borrowed tent with a little tea and sugar to a large weatherboard house with accommodation for a hundred guests and 'a capital cold dinner of meat, bread, cheese, coffee, tea, etc. at 3s. apiece'. But this was exceptionally good. The same traveller at Kyneton farther up paid thirty shillings for a night's stabling for a horse. Travelling was neither cheap nor good nor even safe, for one part of the road—the 'Black Forest'—was infested with bushrangers. Bendigo was the favourite destination. It was now a city of 40,000 people, living in tents and log huts roofed with bark or canvas or bullock-hides, with chimneys of curious contrivance.

[1] G. H. Wathen, *The Golden Colony* (London, 1855), pp. 53-4.

Each gully had its quota of tradesmen; but there was a street of shops seven miles long, with large flags hoisted 'of every shape, colour and nation, from the lion and unicorn of England to the Russian eagle'. There were lodging-houses, tents with stringy bark couches ranged down each side, supplying their lodgers with mutton damper and tea three times a day at five shillings a meal and five shillings for the bed. In the daytime the place resounded with 'the rattle of the cradle as it swayed to and fro, the sounds of the pick and shovel, the busy hum of so many thousands', and every evening with an irregular fusillade, for practically all were armed and indulged in this nightly firing 'partly with a view to intimidate the ill-disposed, and partly because of damp'.[1] But the extension of Bendigo had ceased. Miners were sinking deeper, clearing out and re-working old holes left by hasty or inexperienced miners, hunting between the holes for unworked spots, re-washing old tailings, though as yet there was no machinery and claims were apparently only eight feet square. Escorts were at their height in the latter part of 1852, bringing down about 300,000 ounces monthly, chiefly from Bendigo and Mt. Alexander; but there was a restless, floating element in the population. The population and production of Ballarat were increasing again. Thousands were drawn off in October to the Ovens River, not far from the boundary of New South Wales, many of whose miners came there overland. Next month 3000 at least joined in the rush to Korong, across the Loddon fifty miles west of Bendigo, but this turned out a 'duffer' and nearly all returned. But with the summer water

[1] Mrs. Charles Clacy, *A Lady's Visit to the Gold Diggings of Australia in 1852–53* (London, 1853); Armour, *op. cit.*; W. Howitt, *Land, Labour and Gold* (London, 1855).

shortage Bendigo was even less able to hold its population.

The Ovens diggings, like so many others in Victoria, had first been found by a shepherd, who is said to have made £1400 in a few weeks. By New Year, 1853, there were nearly 20,000 there. Howitt, who went up in December, enables us to picture the scene, the broad wooded valleys already dotted with thousands of tents and huts of boughs, bestrewn with felled trees and garbage, pitted with holes, dug up in the centre into a waste of pale clay. The distinctive feature of the Ovens creeks, however, was that much of the gold came from the creek-beds themselves. The claims were worked by parties of from ten to fourteen men, for the water poured in so fast as to require constant baling, day and night, with buckets or pumps. The sides of the ten- or twenty-foot holes continually tumbled in, and had to be encased with slabs or sheets of stringy bark. 'In these dismal and troublesome holes you see groups of men working under the broiling sun, streaming with perspiration, and yet up to the middle in water.'[1] The actual centre of interest was constantly shifting as old claims were worked out and new discoveries made; and prospecting parties, keenly watched, were going out into the bush. These might be followed, or a wisp of smoke or a discoloured stream might betray their presence. Howitt describes how a bullock dray well loaded with tools and provisions was followed by a cart and by two Americans with their swags on their backs who declared that they would 'dog the dray to the world's end if necessary'. The dray party declared that they had three months' provisions and would not move a step farther while the others remained. On the third morning

---

[1] W. Howitt, *op. cit.* i, 168 ff.

before daybreak they gave their pursuers the slip by sending two of their party off on pack-horses and riding other horses to and fro in the scrub to conceal the tracks. No doubt the small size of regulation claims made it profitable to monopolise new diggings as long as possible. Nevertheless the two Americans eventually tracked down this party; and Howitt's own well-equipped party was similarly tracked down by two lightly-laden diggers. Prospectors, good bushmen no doubt, were often sent out by parties who continued working at their old claims. But in spite of new discoveries and consequent dispersal of the diggers, the Ovens was a remote and therefore expensive field and its population began to fall quite early in 1853 and more rapidly when the approach of winter raised doubts as to supplies.

At the end of January, when the labour market seemed likely to become overstocked, new excitement was caused by the discovery, by four working men, of a nugget of 132 lb. 8 oz. sixty-six feet down in Canadian Gully at Ballarat. This proved to be merely one of a series of rich claims known as 'The Jewellers' Shops'. The history of one of them, related by Kelly, illustrates both the richness of the claims and the slapdash methods of working. It first belonged to a blacksmith and seven other men. 'When they reached the gutter on the bottom, being ignorant of the proper mode of carrying on the workings, they washed out all the stuff they could reach without opening a regular drive, and after dividing £1600 per man . . . they offered it for sale. Several parties of inspection went down without making a bid, being frightened at the appearance of the shaft, as well as at the wetness and rottenness of the ground below. At length one party plucked up courage, purchasing all right and title to the claim and utensils for £77. They

entered into possession at noon, ten in number, and at
quitting time the same day divided £200 per man.
Charmed with their luck, they continued working in
spells night and day until the following Monday, when
they declared another dividend of £800 per man,
[whereupon] they sold out to go on the spree for a week,
then to regain possession. The succeeding party . . .
were regular-bred miners who . . . spent the first four
days of their term in opening two regular drives, one at
the point where the gutter entered the shaft, the other
where it made its exit. . . . Before the remaining three
days had elapsed, [they] took out . . . £1200 per man
to a party of twelve. . . . The other party then returned,
and after digging out £900 per man in a week, princi-
pally by day work, they sold out [for £100] to a well-
known storekeeper . . . who put in a gang of men to
work it in shares. After a fortnight's irregular work
they divided £500 per man, when one of them, an old
hand, undermined the props on a Saturday night, and
before Monday morning the whole workings fell in.
This fellow then marked out a claim on the surface of
the ruin, and went down as straight as an arrow on the
old gutter, having engaged a hired party.' The old
rascal cleared £1920 from his first puddling-tub and
£6880 in all, so that an area twenty-four feet square had
yielded over £55,000.[1] But to sink deep or buy a claim
required a modicum of capital, and even now Bendigo
and Mt. Alexander remained more attractive to the
individualist digger. Lack of water at Bendigo attracted
attention to McIvor creek, a remote forested district
about thirty miles east of it, actually discovered twelve
months before: there were 16,000 there in June, but it
was rich only in patches and plagued with bushrangers,

[1] W. Kelly, *Life in Victoria* (London, 1859), i, 225-7.

and two months later more than half the diggers had gone away.

The second season of the Victorian diggings was probably the most productive.[1] Supplies still were dear in winter and fluctuated considerably in price. The distribution of labour was becoming better balanced as colonial participants in the rushes returned to their old occupations and new immigrants, perhaps after a few months of digging, turned to something else. On the older diggings miners' wives and families were introducing greater comfort and stability: schools were opened, though, like the churches, in tents only. Though the dominant characteristic of the digger was manly independence, there was a certain turbulence in the digging community. Gangs went about, finding out good claims and trying to bully or bounce men out of their ground. The Van Diemen's Landers remained the most serious problem, though the Irish, as usual, were in most of the fights. Latrobe was justified in his belief that the immigration would help him in his police difficulties. With officers of good standing and education, a corps of cadets, a smart, well-housed, well-paid rank and file and an efficient detective force, the police in the course of 1853 cleared the midnight prowlers and assassins out of Melbourne, made the older mining districts pretty secure, and drove the bushrangers off the main roads into the bush. There they were a pest to remote diggings like the McIvor. Many, however, were executed or condemned to the chain-gang. But goldfields administration was not merely a matter of police. The

---

[1] The estimates of yield are given by years. Westgarth, President of the Melbourne Chamber of Commerce, and Khull, a bullion broker, make the yield of 1852 the maximum at four and a half or four and a quarter million ounces, the yield for 1853 three millions.

new immigrants were even less likely than the colonists
to submit to being dragooned; and the advent of more
settled conditions made it easier to concert resistance.
A sly-grog raid at Castlemaine, the chief centre of the
Mt. Alexander diggings, in which an innocent man's
tent was burned through perjured information, was
made the subject of a public meeting. This matter was
settled by the payment of compensation. The general
issue of the licence fee was not so easily settled. Returns
were tending to diminish and the monthly payment of
thirty shillings became more galling, whilst the mooting
of a reduction in New South Wales encouraged the
grumblers. The common grievance gave the heterogeneous digger communities a sense of unity and there
were now among them men trained, for example by the
Chartist movement in England, in the art of agitation.
The prevailing sentiment among the diggers, though
probably little influenced by theory, was inevitably
democratic, and that the goldfields administration certainly was not. A Government which collected an
unpopular fee through the agency of armed police inevitably appeared to be governing by force rather than
by consent. Even though a fee on a particular occupation
might differ from a general tax, it raised the question
whether those who paid it had not a moral claim to
representation. Now, partly because of the difficulty of
enfranchising a migratory population, partly because the
constitution was at the moment being considered by a
committee of the Legislative Council and in due course
to go for reconsideration before the home authorities,
but partly from opposition on principle, the miners had
been given no political rights. In the winter of 1853
there was a serious political agitation at Bendigo, in
which the Mt. Alexander and McIvor miners also took

some part. Miners' meetings, petitions and deputations demanded that the licence fee be lowered to ten shillings; that its collection — which, so they claimed, caused serious interruption in their work—be less frequent and less officious; that the penalties be made less severe; that better facilities be given for the purchase of land, which was locked up in large holdings in the nominally temporary occupation of the squatters; and that the goldfields be given political representation. Latrobe wisely suggested the abolition of the licence fee in return for an export duty, but this idea still did not find favour. When the Bendigo miners in September organised a movement against the payment of more than ten shillings monthly, the Legislative Council did however reduce the fee, offering further reductions for licences taken out for longer periods. It thus testified to the influence of goldfields public opinion, but it left the problem of goldfields administration still unsolved.

Meanwhile the general commerce and finance of the colony, in the second season of the rush, had been conducted in an atmosphere of unlimited optimism. 'The publicans and shopkeepers', says Turner, a historian who speaks with special authority on these matters, 'elate with their enormous profits, and confident of an ever-increasing army of customers, sent forth their orders for replenishment without limitation. Many of the owners of well-established shops, scorning the intervention of the warehousemen, through whose medium they had previously dealt, sent their orders direct to England, where, on the reputation of the colony's growing wealth and progress, they found themselves commanding unlimited credit. The banks soon acquired the control of the gold shipments and by negotiating drafts against them, at 10 per cent. discount, realised that exchange was the most profitable and important part of their business. Their coffers were gorged with money, for during the year 1852 the deposits rose from £820,000 to £4,330,000, and the notes in circulation from £180,000 to £1,320,000. For the millions thus poured into them they had no profitable use, no local discounts, and very scanty demand for accommodation. Naturally they refused to allow any interest on deposits which involved responsibility without any compensating advantages. But it was necessary to earn profits somehow, and by force of circumstances they gradually merged into their business the functions of the indent merchant, and established credits for hundreds of thousands of pounds for their customers whose prospects looked so promising. The wholesale warehousemen in their turn plied their English agents with orders, based on a bare market and great expectations.' [1] Moreover there were venturers in England, who, like their fellows in the Atlantic States at the time of the Californian rush, managed to secure credit and ship out anything they could not sell otherwise. When the winter of 1853 made the roads to the goldfields practically impassable again, the first effects of congestion showed themselves. To quote Turner again, 'auctioneers' licences were taken out by the score, and all day long the clanging of bells and the cries of the bellmen echoed through the streets urging the citizens to take advantage of the "awful sacrifices" which the importers were compelled to make. . . . Piles of merchandise remained unclaimed on the wharves. Consignees, who had often been drawn upon without permission, refused the responsibility of accepting drafts against unsaleable goods. Such as were dutiable were sold almost daily by the customs authorities,

[1] H. G. Turner, *History of the Colony of Victoria* (London, 1904), i, 376.

often for only the amount of their claim. Others were sacrificed by the wharfingers and lightermen for their charges, and vast quantities remained to be gradually pilfered or destroyed by exposure to the weather.'[1] Yet it was nine months before the news of this glut could bring a check to the influx of goods. In urban land values similarly all sense of proportion had been lost, and though no doubt there would have been speculation in any case, the Government contributed to it by failure to adjust the supply of town lands to the demand. These were the growing pains of a community which was in 1853 making real progress in coping with its new population. Kelly, returning to Melbourne in September after four months' absence, noted the new buildings of brick and mortar and bluestone, the gradual advance of macadamised roads into the suburbs, kerbs and gutters and some flagstone pavements in the most frequented thoroughfares. The city still had to pay the price, however, of the wasteful extravagance which had gone alongside of this solid investment.

The third season of the gold rush saw a continuance of immigration—15,000 adult males from the United Kingdom, 5000 from foreign ports—though no doubt many came to live upon the digger rather than by digging. It saw also the opening-up of new goldfields, especially to the westward of Castlemaine and Bendigo. The Korong rush had been the first invasion of this district, and some were still working on that field. Towards the end of July 1853 a rich patch was accidentally discovered at Moliagul, about thirty miles west of Bendigo, and a rush set in, not particularly large or lasting. By November there was a new rush in progress to promising workings on the Avoca River. In February

[1] H. G. Turner, *History of the Colony of Victoria*, i, pp. 377-8.

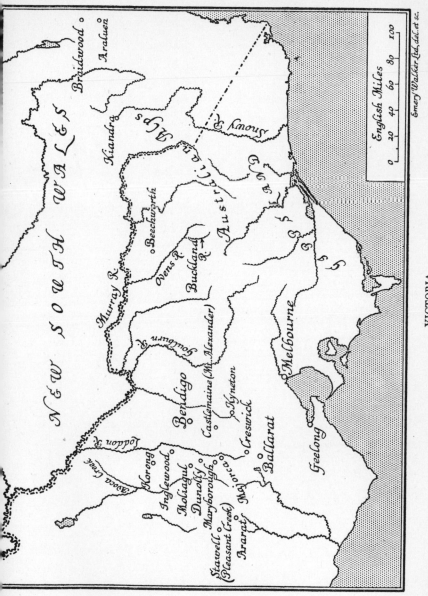

VICTORIA

1854 the Governor notes a rush of 20,000 miners to
Tarrangower, ten miles west of Castlemaine. Auriferous
earth had at first to be carted eight miles to the River
Loddon for washing, but sanguine diggers piled up
thousands of tons of washdirt and waited for rain. When
the rain came the results were disappointing, but
thousands still lingered. Then in May a further discovery was made some miles to the westward, and,
though here also the dirt had to be carted three or four
miles to water, there was a rush of perhaps 30,000 to
'Maryborough' in July. The Ovens region also had its
new rush of 5000 or 6000, in January 1854, to the Buckland among the forests and mountains sixty miles southward. On all these new rushes, however, there was overcrowding. 'The rush and struggle', wrote Howitt, 'is
awful, and the only chance is to fly off at the first sound.
. . . The mischief is that you hear so many wonderful
stories that prove false, that you will not listen to a first
rumour, and by the time that something authentic
reaches you, it is too late. There are thousands of men
at the diggings ready to start at a moment's notice, and
having neither baggage nor good luck to detain them.
At the first whisper, therefore, of a new field, they
shoulder their picks and shovels, and their swags, and
stalk away with all the speed they can put forth. If
there be any good ground, they at once secure it, and
by the time those who have carts and provisions to
bring up arrive, there is no ground left.'[1] In this state
of affairs, wasteful though it was of effort, there was
a certain rough justice; but it was symptomatic of the
fact that a continued expansion of the goldfields could
no longer be taken for granted.

On the older fields, however, mining was now becom-

[1] Howitt, *op. cit.* ii, 139-41.

ing more systematic and elaborate. The survey difficulties were overcome and land was at last sold in the goldfields centres, which were thereby helped to evolve from camps of boughs and canvas into towns of brick and stone. In their mining methods the main fields developed characteristics of their own. On the Ovens alone water was plentiful all the year round, and California miners adapted their toms, their sluices, their ditches or 'races' bringing the water to the spot. At Bendigo and Mt. Alexander the puddling tub was elaborated into a sort of horse-power mill. 'The puddler . . . first secures a considerable supply of water on one side of the site he has selected, and a fall for it to pass away into a sludge channel on the other. He then digs a sort of ditch, in a circular form, about two feet deep, and three or four feet wide, and lines the sides and floor with closely fitting wood. Into this chamber he fits a couple of teethed separators, like harrows . . . and these he attaches to a shaft working on a pivot in the centre. He next builds a path all round for his horse, and having made a conduit for the water which he pumps from the dam into the mill from time to time, on the one side, and a sluice on the other, by which he can regulate at his pleasure the discharge of the liquid mud, the mill is complete. The washdirt is then carted, and when several loads have been deposited in the mill, and a sufficiency of water pumped in, the horse is sent on his melancholy walk round and round, and the separators, crossing again and again the heaps of dirt, soon tear them up and liquefy the mud, wash the stones, and let the gold drop to the bottom of the mill. Thus the process goes on, perhaps for a week, when the water is let off, the large refuse shovelled up and carted away, and the gold lifted from the bottom, or washed out from the dirt by the long tom, the cradle, and the pan.'[1] Ballarat, on the other hand, was the field of deep sinking—a lottery in which there were richer prizes than anywhere else, but many blanks. In the favoured gullies parties would spend six months putting a shaft down from 130 to 160 feet. 'The whole surface', writes Howitt, 'is thrown into heaps of clay from six to ten feet high. . . . Between these muddy mountains thrown up by the diggers the water accumulates in deep pools, which they avail themselves of to wash out their gold . . . and the heaps of clay are trodden by hundreds of men constantly crossing them in all directions into a slippery, adhesive limbo of bird-lime and filth.'[2] Competition still kept the claims small, twenty-four feet square, for a party of at least eight, being the maximum. But the 'gutters' of the ancient water-courses which formed these 'deep leads' were very changeable in direction. It was therefore customary not to sink in real earnest until some neighbouring claim had hit the gutter and thus reduced the risk that six months' toil would be all in vain. This 'shepherding' of the claims actually being worked was in itself char-acteristic of the more prudent methods of the miners of 1854.

This year the Melbourne boom burst in good earnest. Gasworks, waterworks, a railway to the port were being built; but land speculation had overreached itself, and in particular Melbourne was full to repletion of goods which, from their character as well as from their quantity, were quite unsaleable. They could not be unloaded upon goldfields storekeepers, who were find-

---

[1] J. C. Paterson, *The Gold Fields of Victoria in 1862* (Melbourne, 1862), p. 316. Howitt's much briefer description in 1854 seems to indicate that there was no substantial change in the puddling machine. Kelly says it was first introduced at Forest Creek, but he is not a very accurate writer.

[2] Howitt, *op. cit.* ii, 274.

ing it hard to cope with the keen competition and with the drift of customers and debtors off to every new rush. The era of fancy prices was over. Banks were obliged to refuse accommodation and there were many failures. Moreover the Colonial Government, which had embarked on heavy expenditure on roads and police, was caught off its guard, and the imprest system under which the departments had been working made it almost impossible to ascertain the full extent of its commitments. Sir Charles Hotham arrived as Governor in June 1854 to find Victoria in a critical condition. Hotham, a naval officer of high reputation, had no doubt been sent in the belief that Victoria needed a strong administrator. He soon showed a determination to grapple with his financial difficulties by clarification and economy. But the end of the great rush had political repercussions also.

Not unnaturally, as their returns declined, the miners' disinclination to pay even the reduced licence fee increased. Hotham, on a visit to the goldfields in September, told a deputation that the miners must pay for liberty and order; but his warm reception was chiefly due to the belief that there would be speedy reforms. Had he not said—and it was by no means a truism among mid-nineteenth century governors—that he proposed to act on the principle that all power proceeded from the people? But the miners were impatient to have this principle applied to the administration of the goldfields. The first clash came on the liquor question. Partly no doubt from a desire to tap a new source of revenue, liquor licences had now been introduced on the goldfields. In October a Scottish miner, popular among his fellows, was killed at Ballarat in a scuffle with the proprietor and barmen of one of the public-houses, to which he had apparently demanded admission after closing-time. The innkeeper and his wife, whose voices were thought to have been recognised, and two barmen were brought before the police magistrate and two Gold Commissioners, who determined by a majority that the evidence was insufficient to warrant their committal. The innkeeper was an ex-convict who had often used brute strength to eject undesired customers from his premises, and so had many enemies: moreover grog-sellers who had not obtained licences were probably enemies of all who had: and it was soon whispered that the licence had been corruptly obtained and its holder corruptly acquitted. A meeting of miners determined upon an act of 'popular justice' and, brushing aside the timid restraints of the police and magistrates, burnt down the hotel. Its owner took refuge with the authorities. Hotham at once sent up 450 soldiers and police, but at the same time appointed a board of enquiry to investigate the charges of corruption. One of the barmen having turned informer, the innkeeper and his associates were convicted of manslaughter: the police magistrate was dismissed: but three persons charged with complicity in the burning of the hotel were sentenced to short terms of imprisonment.[1] Hotham was, in short, seeking to combine firmness with justice, but the affair was a further revelation of the diggers' lack of confidence in the goldfields administration. The jury which tried the hotel-burners had some justification for their rider that 'they would never have had their

---

[1] G. W. Rusden, *History of Australia* (London, 1883), ii, 671-2; H. G. Turner, *op. cit.* and *Our Own Little Rebellion* (Melbourne, 1913); J. D'Ewes, *China, Australia and the Pacific Islands* (London, 1857). D'Ewes was the police magistrate in question. He of course denies the charge of corruption, and his account of the affair should be balanced against the usual accounts hostile to him.

painful duty to perform if those Government officials at Ballarat had done theirs properly'.

The miners, regarding this affair as a triumph, soon went on to raise more general issues. The very fact that many of them were more or less permanently settled in the goldfields towns encouraged the habit of meeting to discuss grievances and formulate a programme. A Ballarat Reform League was formed on 11 November and aimed at the abolition of all licence fees, the disbanding of the Gold Commissioners, and political reform on Chartist lines. Hotham believed that the political demands came from mere agitators, and foreign agitators at that, but he was quite ready to see the diggers receive the franchise, as was proposed by a Bill actually before the home authorities, and he was just about to appoint a commission to review the administration of the goldfields. A deputation from Ballarat was firmly but temperately handled on 27 November. But the miners' exasperation against the licence system was being inflamed by the press and by a few theoretical revolutionaries. The Governor thought it wise to send more troops to Ballarat. The extremist leaders for their part induced the meeting which received the deputation's report to pass a resolution in favour of burning the licences and protecting those who might be arrested for having none. Emissaries were moreover sent to other goldfields. A further licence hunt next day (30 November) was taken, rightly or wrongly, as the sign of a determination to force the issue: there was a clash with the crowd and eight diggers were taken to the Government camp. The physical force men—among whom Irishmen and Germans were prominent—seemed for the time being to be in control on the side of the miners. An Irishman, Peter Lalor, a man of more admirable character than some of the others, was chosen commander-in-chief of 'the diggers under arms'. There was something of the ritual of revolution, the swearing of oaths, the hoisting of a flag with the silver stars of the Southern Cross upon a blue ground.[1] Arms, ammunition and horses were requisitioned: drilling was begun, and at Eureka, a mile and a half away along the Melbourne road, a rough stockade was formed of logs and slabs of mining and building timber. The military skill and sense of realities on the part of the extremist leaders was, however, small. The stockade was stormed easily enough by a force of 182 soldiers and 94 police before dawn on 3 December. A few of the troops and about thirty miners lost their lives: the Goldfields Commission believed some of the latter to have been the victims of unnecessary brutality on the part of the police. On hearing how matters were going, the Governor had proclaimed martial law in Ballarat and the Commander of the Forces came up in person. But there was no further trouble at Ballarat: though an appeal for special constables failed, a public meeting on the 6th regretted the resort to force and admitted the necessity of asserting the supremacy of law and order. Thirteen prisoners were committed after magisterial enquiries, but the situation was tactfully handled by the Commander of the Forces and on the 9th martial law was revoked.

The democrats of Melbourne sought to take advantage of the crisis. A sort of revolutionary constitution was printed and secretly circulated; but though strong enough to carry resolutions ascribing the events at Ballarat to military coercion, the leaders had no widespread revolutionary sentiment to work upon and their con-

[1] The existence of this flag seems good evidence that there was a group with revolutionary designs.

stitution was never actually submitted to a public meeting. In spite of wild talk in the press, the real sense of the community was in favour of conciliation and peaceful reform. Discussions as to the exact number of miners present in the Eureka stockade are beside the point, for it is quite clear that the great majority of the population of Ballarat, though embittered by neglect of their grievances and unsympathetic administration, were opposed to revolutionary violence. Similarly the Melbourne public, though inclined to visit upon the Government the blame for the Ballarat outbreak, was not thinking, like those who devised the constitution and the flag, in terms of constitutional conventions and provisional directories, even when coupled with a general amnesty for officers of the superseded government of the Queen. A general amnesty for the Eureka prisoners and fugitives (the wounded Lalor was one of these) was more to the point, and for this the newly appointed Goldfields Commission, supported by widely signed petitions and by the newspapers, strongly pressed. Sir Charles Hotham did not think it consistent with his duty to grant the request. But public opinion found a way of making itself felt. The thirteen Eureka prisoners were defended by leading members of the Bar when they were put on trial for treason, and though in some cases no evidence was offered for the defence, they were one and all acquitted.

The real if limited aims of the digger community were attained when the Goldfields Commission appointed by Hotham proposed and the Governor accepted an entirely new system of goldfields administration. It was relieved of its most invidious task by the abolition of licences. As a source of revenue they were replaced in April 1855 by an export duty on gold of two shillings and sixpence an ounce. As a title they were replaced by miner's rights, issued annually for a fee of one pound. 'It is not intended', said the Commission, 'that any active search be instituted by the authorities as to whether a miner has or has not taken out this qualification.' But without it he would have no legally enforceable right to his claim or to his gold. At the same time the Gold Commissioners were to be given the old English mining title of wardens, and their autocracy was to be limited by local courts, elected for six months by miners' meetings, which were to make rules and regulations and, with assessors if necessary, to adjudicate mining disputes. The miner's right was to qualify for the franchise, and the principal goldfields, Bendigo, Ballarat, Castlemaine, Avoca and the Ovens, were in the next session given representatives, who took their seats in the Legislative Council in November 1855.

The gold rush had been primarily responsible for converting Victoria within five years into a community of 400,000 souls—more than 250,000 of them males. In 1856 the colony became self-governing under its new constitution. But the gold-diggers as such were not destined to become politically dominant. The gold-diggings were a democratic school in which many Victorians—no doubt at this stage a substantial majority of the male adults—had graduated, but it was not there but in the capital and its press that the motive power of the democracy of Victoria was to be found. Only about an eighth of the registered miners troubled to cast their votes at the first elections. The real significance of the changes of 1855 was rather that they swept away an objectionable system and gave the diggers a voice in the affairs that primarily concerned them. With that they were content.

The gold-diggers' position in the community was in fact changing. The economic basis of Victoria was broadening: the number of persons engaged in farming increased from 7600 in 1854 to over 26,800 in 1857. Mining was becoming a skilled industry. The Act of 1855 encouraged the formation of companies on the cost-book system common in English mining districts; but these spread slowly. For the moment the growth of mining was more affected by the rates of wages and state of employment in the towns, and especially in Melbourne. Many made their way back to the goldfields after the collapse of the Melbourne boom. Gold production increased in 1856. The numbers on the fields reached their peak—147,000—in 1858. But the effect was rather to keep wages high than to lead to a much-increased gold output.

One characteristic of the new phase of Victorian gold-mining—the first phase of its decline—was the appearance of thousands of Chinese after 1854. By 1858 they numbered 33,000. The Goldfields Commission thought they should be discouraged, and on its recommendation a poll-tax of ten pounds was imposed in 1855, and coupled with a limitation on the number of passengers on any one ship. But the tax was evaded by landing in South Australia. Chinese on the road to the diggings became in the later 'fifties a familiar but nevertheless curious sight with their loosely-hanging blue jumpers and trousers, 'slippers turned up at the toes, umbrella-like hats of basket-work, and long bamboos on their shoulders, from each of which were suspended their goods and chattels, consisting of tent, blanket, rice-bags, tin dishes, and in some instances a gold-washing cradle'. As in California they were for the most part under indenture to merchants and speculators of their own nation. Their great centre was at Guildford, south of Castlemaine on the Mt. Alexander field. In large companies they re-worked this old field by 'paddocking', stripping the superincumbent soil over a large surface, removing the washdirt, and then restoring the ground to something like its first condition. 'Rapidly the camp grew, in regular lines of streets, narrow and primitive, but highly populous and busy. . . . So large became the trade . . . that Chinese omnibuses . . . became numerous on the Castlemaine road, and special Chinese coaches plied from it to Sandhurst, Castlemaine, and Ballarat.' It had its cobblers' and tailors' shops, its restaurants and tea-houses, 'scholars to write your letters and interpreters to read them', its joss-houses, a theatre and a circus. This camp was apparently at its zenith in 1859. After riots at the Buckland a residence tax, of six pounds per annum at first, was imposed on the Chinese in 1857, and South Australia was induced to restrict their immigration. By these means the increase in their numbers was checked.[1]

Meanwhile new discoveries and rushes continued. There were 20,000 at Creswick near Ballarat at the end of 1854, an early discovered field having been found to give rich yields at a depth of forty to seventy feet. Next April there was a rush to Fiery Creek, some twenty miles west by north of Ballarat. Dunolly, between Moliagul and Maryborough, was the scene of a rush in June 1856; Ararat, in thickly wooded country fifty or sixty miles west-north-west of Ballarat, in the summer of 1857; Pleasant Creek, northward of Ararat, a little

---

[1] These measures were revoked in 1862–65, the numbers of Chinese having begun to decline. The account of the Chinese at Guildford is based on J. C. Paterson, *The Goldfields of Victoria in 1862* (Melbourne, 1862), pp. 132-5. On anti-Chinese legislation see Myra Willard, *History of the White Australia Policy* (Melbourne, 1923).

later; Back Creek, in the Maryborough district, early in
1859; Inglewood, north-east of Moliagul and on the
edge of the mallee scrub country, in October. These
and other minor rushes led to considerable movements
of population from the older fields, though the estimates
of 50,000 to 60,000 sometimes given for Fiery Creek,
Dunolly and Ararat seem exaggerated, and despite rich
individual finds none of the fields were as productive as
Ballarat and Bendigo had been. The rushes were, however, less helter-skelter than in earlier years: miners
would often go to some firm of carriers and arrange for
their families and goods to be conveyed to the spot in
waggons. Often the new field was within one day's
tramp of the old. But it is interesting to find glimpses of
'popular justice' of the American type operating before
the arrival of regular authority. At Fiery Creek, we are
told, 'roughs and thieves were not allowed much immunity, even before the police kept order'.[1] At Pleasant
Creek there was organised thieving and rescue of
captured thieves, but on the other hand a man caught in
the act of stealing a tent had his head shaved and was
expelled from the diggings.[2] At Ararat there was a less
reasonable popular action, following the bad example
set at the Buckland: the Chinese were expelled and their
tents burned, though it was actually a party of them, on
its way from South Australia, that had made the discovery.[3] It is curious also that the first explicit mention
of dancing saloons is at the Woolshed diggings in the
Ovens district and at Pleasant Creek.[4] One is tempted to

[1] W. E. Adcock, *The Gold Rushes of the Fifties* (Melbourne, 1912), p. 168.
[2] H. Brown, *Victoria as I found it* (London, 1862), p. 358.
[3] J. E. Jenkins, 'Early Ararat' (*Victorian Historical Magazine*, viii, 140).
[4] At the Woolshed, barmaids and housemaids at the hotels were bound by contract to dance at night: E. Carton Booth, *Another England*, p. 100.

suggest that it was in the later 'fifties that the Victorian miner began to find himself and to develop his own way of living. It was at this time, too, that he first began to launch out beyond Victoria. In 1858, as we shall see, an exaggerated report drew ten or fifteen thousand miners to Port Curtis, Queensland. In 1860–61 thousands crossed the New South Wales border, first for Kiandra near the Snowy River, 4600 feet up in the Australian Alps, later for Lambing Flat or Burrangong and the Lachlan, farther north. At Lambing Flat, incidentally, popular feeling against the Chinese, of whom about 2000 had arrived from Victoria after the new discriminatory measures and many more from China, again took violent form; and when the ringleaders in the disturbance were arrested by the police, they were rescued and the court-house was burnt down. Another exodus in 1861 took the direction of New Zealand. There was clearly a growing feeling that the tale of Victorian discoveries was almost told.

Gold production maintained itself well, reaching three million ounces in 1856 and not falling below two million ounces until 1861. This was mainly due not to new rushes but to more intensive working of the older fields, by puddling machines and quartz-crushing mills at Bendigo, longer races at the Ovens, yet deeper sinking at Ballarat. More intensive working, however, meant more capitalistic methods, and one characteristic of the Victorian goldfields at this period is a stubborn rearguard action of the individual miner against the advance of capital. In this the system of local legislation inaugurated in 1855 proved a handy weapon. This Victorian approximation to the mining camp system enabled independent miners, who were still in a majority, to limit the size of claims and prescribe the number of men to be employed. The local court at Bendigo, according to Kelly, at first allowed only ten yards along a quartz reef: Brown, who succeeded in getting 120 yards, complains of its obstructive attitude. More than once local courts are charged with corruption. In 1857 they were replaced by mining boards with legislative functions only: judges were appointed to determine, with assessors if necessary and subject to appeal, all cases of dispute.

In the struggle between the individual miner and the capitalist Ballarat was the most interesting terrain. The depth of the sinking made fairly elaborate machinery and large-scale working essential. Yet, when the first steam-engine was put up to work a shaft, a body of men set out to smash it and were only deterred by the fact that the owner threatened to shoot the first man who approached. At the same time the irregularity of the leads and the small claimholders' lack of capital led to the 'shepherding' already described—a patent evasion of the obligation to work a claim. The Ballarat local court sought a corrective to shepherding in a system of 'frontage claims', bounded by the circumference of concentric circles with the first strike at the centre. Whatever course the gutter might take, each party would then have its allotted length of thirty-four (later fifty-eight) feet upon it. When a new lead was discovered, the discoverers or the general body of registered miners on the lead were given the option of applying to the warden for it to be worked as a frontage lead, and in that case it was managed by a committee. It was an ingenious remedy, but almost worse than the disease. It failed to allow for the multiplicity of leads, for the fact that 'block claims' might still be taken up, for residences and business sites. Before it was abolished in 1866 the frontage system gave rise to a bewildering network of overlapping claims and a luxuriant crop of litigation. The practice of co-operation was a more sensible line of development. It became common for parties to spread their risks by taking shares in one another's enterprises, or to economise labour by sinking a joint shaft. There were at Ballarat in the later 'fifties a number of successful co-operative companies—some working deep alluvial, some quartz—financed by the savings of the members, or by storekeepers who were given an interest, or by 'furnishers' who supplied machinery, locally made, on similar terms. Once matters had got so far it was unlikely that companies would remain purely co-operative; and Ballarat's mining exchange soon became famous. In 1859 Melbourne began to take an extensive interest in Ballarat mines, though as usual many lost money in the first flutter. On the whole, however, Ballarat emerged from its difficulties so successfully as to enjoy in the late 'fifties and early 'sixties the reputation of being the most enterprising and successful goldfield in the colony.

In 1861 the population of Victoria had risen to 540,000. 240,000 of these lived on the goldfields and 110,000 were reckoned as miners, though many clearly spent only part of the year in gold-digging. The return per miner was only about a fourth of what it had been in 1852, though of course costs had fallen very considerably. Carriage, which in the early years had averaged perhaps £60 and in the winters had cost £120, and to the Ovens £160 per ton, had now fallen to £2 : 10s.–£7 per ton. There were more miners in the Maryborough, Ovens and Ararat districts than in the wealthier and more stable mining centres of Bendigo, Castlemaine and Ballarat. But it was with these

more advanced districts, reached by the railway in
1862,[1] that the future of mining really lay, and the
'sixties began to make the point clear. Surfacing and
shallow sinking were still very widespread in 1861, and
old ground was re-worked again and again, with a
certain tendency for Chinese to replace Europeans in
the later re-workings. There was still a floating population to be skimmed off by any new alluvial rush, and
of these there were quite a number in Victoria even in
the 'sixties, though on most it was a question of hundreds rather than thousands of miners. The chief new
districts opened up were the mountainous upper
reaches of the Goulburn and the mountains of Gipps-
land. New finds would from time to time be made even
in older districts: Majorca, for instance, within five
miles of Maryborough, attracted 15,000 people in
1863. On the whole, however, the more adventurous
of the independent or even of the wage-earning miners
tended to be attracted to other colonies—to New
Zealand at first, later to Queensland, and in a few cases
even to British Columbia or South Africa—whilst the
less adventurous, as their yield declined, eked it out by
a plot of land taken up under the Land Act of 1865,
whereby they might cultivate land on the goldfields
under an annual licence. 'It is quite a common thing',
wrote an ex-Inspector of Settlement in 1869, 'for these
men to work away at their little farms for a month or
two, and then some fine morning to fold up their little
six by eight tents, and a pair of blankets, and with
pick and shovel on shoulder, start off for some gully
ten or twenty miles away, of which they have, by some
means that diggers only understand, heard good news.

[1] Hitherto they had depended for passenger transport on the stage-coaches
of a famous American firm, Cobb & Co.

There they will dig for a few weeks, returning home, if possible, every Saturday night.'[1] Or again, they might be absorbed as wage-workers by the public companies, now increasing in number, or by the railways or public works or other occupations.

Capitalistic mining enterprise made progress in Victoria in the 'sixties, but its fortunes were chequered. The keen interest of Ballarat in its own and later in other mines culminated in 1864 in a speculative boom, which was followed by marked dullness. There were other difficulties arising less from universal human nature than from particular Victorian circumstances. The local boards' regulations were discordant, unstable, often uncertain in meaning and sometimes of doubtful legality. There was no provision for the important matter of co-operative drainage: the lack of it had greatly hampered the development of quartz-mining at Bendigo. Suspicion of companies survived. Every individual member must produce his miner's right before a company could institute legal proceedings, and some members might well have left the district. The precautions necessary to avoid forfeiture of claims were adapted to competitive individual mining rather than to large-scale, long-term working. In 1862 a commission was appointed to consider these matters, and the result was the comprehensive Mining Statute of 1865, which provided for cheaper and longer leases, for the issue of a 'consolidated miner's right' to the manager or trustee of a company working registered claims, for the division of an interest in registered claims into transferable shares. In these matters and in the more elaborate judicial machinery it set up, the Act recognised the increasingly capitalistic character of

[1] E. Carton Booth, *Another England* (London, 1869), p. 221.

Victorian mining. But the local legislation system and the power of local boards to determine in particular the 'quantity of land whether in one or in many claims, to be held under a miner's right' still remained; and the miner's right was reduced in cost to five shillings per annum and might be extended in term to fifteen years.[1] The individual miner could still make his opinions felt; and it is significant that an increasing proportion of the companies worked their mines by a modification of the Cornish practice of 'tributing' which left him room to indulge his penchant for independence. Ground would be let for a term of five years, or sometimes more or less, to a party of working miners for a percentage, varying from ten to thirty, on the gross quantity of gold extracted from the claim. The proprietors imposed stringent conditions of working, but in effect they were sleeping partners only; and, according to Trollope, one-third of the 1200 mining companies of Bendigo in 1872 were tribute companies.

The spread of tributing, which is reported as early as 1862 at Tarrangower, seems to have been one factor in the marked revival of quartz-mining at Bendigo at the end of the 'sixties, though there had been pertinacious efforts to improve the crushing machinery and the gold-saving processes and a number of reefs now rewarded richly the tedious work of development. There was an influx of thousands of people. But though there were miners in the rush it was not a rush of the old type. Thousands blocked the path and roadway opposite the Exchange: and it was the Exchange and

---

[1] If a miner's right expired, a claim might be 'jumped'. In the 'sixties and 'seventies jumpers were active in Victoria, looking with an eagle eye for flaws in title: see especially W. B. Withers, *History of Ballarat* (2nd edition, Ballarat, 1887).

not the reefs that formed the real centre of interest. So many companies were launched that in 1872, when Bendigo's gold yield reached 360,000 ounces, much the highest since the 'fifties, the boom had already passed its peak and calls were having to be made on shareholders. In 1873 and subsequent years the trend of the yield was downwards and many of the mines had to stop work.

In spite of the Bendigo quartz boom and occasional spurts elsewhere, the general downward trend of Victorian mining could no longer be concealed. Indirectly this no doubt contributed to the bitter political struggle of the 'sixties over protection, in which the working men in the towns were ranged on one side and the mercantile and squatting interests on the other. The miner was to some extent identified now with the town wage-earning class to which the protective policy made a particular appeal: many wage-earners must have been former miners. It was sought to ensure the support of the mining districts by including in the protectionist programme the abolition of the export duty on gold. The issue of mining rights on private property, which was not settled until 1897, also divided the mining interest from the squatter-landowners. But there seems to be no evidence that the mining districts provided much of the driving force behind the new anti-squatting, protectionist policy. Nor can more than a minority of displaced miners have been absorbed in new industries created by protection.

It seems unnecessary to follow further the fortunes of Victorian gold-mining, which had now become a predominantly capitalistic industry, with about half of its product coming from Bendigo and Ballarat and the rest from widely scattered localities. In the 'seventies, when the rich Ballarat deep leads were virtually exhausted, some compensation was found in new alluvial discoveries at Creswick; but in general quartz-mining was in the ascendant. Gold, however, was losing its former predominance among the industries of the colony.

The great gold rush had given an immense stimulus to Victorian development. It wrought a marked change in the conditions of labour. It opened up the interior to closer settlement and even benefited the squatters, incidentally obliging them to fence and thus improve the carrying capacity of their runs. It seems clear that the great majority of the male adult population until 1854 or 1855 spent some time on the goldfields and thus participated in the rush. But the rush had not as in California evolved an organisation of its own: its early organisation had been devised by the Government of New South Wales, its later was devised for it by a Royal Commission, after taking evidence, it is true, from the miners. This local self-government was clearly appreciated, for we find it extended to New South Wales goldfields in the late 'fifties and early 'sixties, and less successfully to Queensland in the later 'sixties. It still flourished in Victoria at the end of the century. Even so, it was not as complete as in the American mining camps: its structure was remodelled from time to time by the legislature, and it was qualified by the existence of the warden, who heard certain classes of dispute which in America would have been settled by the mining camps, and made the executive side of the mining camp unnecessary. Moreover the wardens as an institution spread farther afield than the local boards, and one may presume, therefore, met a more widely felt want. Had the digging communities had a *tabula rasa* on which to write they would no doubt have organised themselves; but working as they did from the beginning within the framework of a larger organised community, they concerned themselves mainly with administrative reforms and with securing a measure of freedom to organise their own industry.

There are interesting contrasts between the Victorian digger and the Californian miner. By Californian standards the opening-up of the Victorian goldfields was decidedly slow. It is impossible to dogmatise as to the reasons. But probably the chief was that the Californian miners were in large measure trained frontiersmen: the Victorian in the first instance—or at least after the intercolonial stage of the rush—came untrained in colonial life, and thought in terms of a year or so's work on the diggings and then something else. In these circumstances the miner-prospector type developed more slowly. Another interesting contrast is in the attitude to capitalistic enterprise: there was no such jealousy in California or its daughter communities as was shown by the local boards in Victoria. The Californian was accustomed to a free frontier society in which each man had or seemed to have an equal chance of material prosperity. The Victorian was a recent immigrant from industrialised Great Britain or from the half-submerged nation of Ireland, accustomed to concentration of wealth in a few hands and determined if possible to avoid reproducing such conditions in the freer society of the colonies. In the gold industry the trends were against him. He did not yet perceive that the best course was not to prevent such concentrations of wealth and power, which are inevitable in one form or another in a modern industrialised community, but to use political machinery to control economic power.

In fact, the accumulation of wealth was one of the most marked effects of the gold rush upon Victoria: Melbourne became the leading financial centre of Victoria, and its enterprising men were to be found investing not only in their local industries and real estate but in the flocks and herds and mines of Queensland, in the tin and copper and gold of Tasmania, in the silver of Broken Hill, in the gold of Western Australia. The gold rush, however, produced another type besides the enterprising business or mining man of Ballarat or Bendigo or Melbourne—namely, the skilled individual miner-prospector—and he, after his work in Victoria was done, played a great part from the 'sixties to the 'nineties in opening up what we may call the Australasian mining frontier.

AUTHORITIES

Two fairly full histories, G. W. Rusden, *History of Australia* (3 vols., London, 1883), and H. G. Turner, *History of the Colony of Victoria* (2 vols., London, 1904), cover the gold rush. Rusden held important official positions during the rush, and is therefore of particular value on the political side: his anti-democratic bias gives unity and freshness to his point of view. Turner was an immigrant of 1854: his interests are more commercial and financial, but he has some good general surveys of mining. T. McCombie, *History of the Colony of Victoria* (Melbourne, 1858), is of value where he speaks from first-hand knowledge. W. E. Adcock, *The Gold Rushes of the Fifties* (Melbourne, 1912), though hardly a work of scholarship, is sometimes useful: so are W. B. Withers, *History of Ballarat* (Ballarat, 1870 and 1887), and G. Mackay, *History of Bendigo* (Melbourne, 1891). It is indispensable to refer to the British Parliamentary Papers for the first five years of the rush. Of the numerous contemporary books it is not possible to do much more than enumerate a few of the most valuable: J. E. Erskine, *Short*

Account of late Discoveries of Gold in New South Wales (London, 1851); G. C. Mundy, *Our Antipodes* (3 vols., London, 1852)—a very popular book in its day; W. Westgarth, *Victoria, late Australia Felix* (Melbourne, 1853) and *Victoria and the Australian Gold Mines in 1857* (London, 1857); C. Rudston Read, *What I Heard, Saw and Did at the Australian Goldfields* (London, 1853); W. Howitt, *Land, Labour and Gold* (2 vols. in one, London, 1855)—by a writer, well known in his day, who actually worked on more than one of the goldfields and visited them all; G. H. Wathen, *The Golden Colony* (London, 1855); R. Caldwell, *The Golden Era of Victoria* (London, 1855); E. H. Hargraves, *Australia and its Goldfields* (London, 1855)—chiefly of autobiographical interest; A. Fauchery, *Lettres d'un mineur en Australie* (Paris, 1857); W. Kelly, *Victoria in 1853 and 1858* (2 vols., London, 1859)—inaccurate in detail but useful; H. Brown, *Victoria as I found it* (London, 1862); J. A. Paterson, *The Goldfields of Victoria in 1862*—very useful on that period, the more so because there is a gap in official printed information between 1856 and 1864, and well informed on earlier history; R. B. Smyth, *Goldfields and Mineral Districts of Victoria* (Melbourne, 1869)—a storehouse of information on the 'sixties written by the permanent Under-Secretary for Mines. *Lord Robert Cecil's Goldfields Diary* (ed. E. Scott—Melbourne, 1935) is decidedly interesting, though the future Prime Minister's visit was short. Sir T. A. Coghlan, *Labour and Industry in Australia* (4 vols., London, 1918) is authoritative upon economic and statistical matters. The only modern scholarly treatment of the goldfields is the excellent chapter by Professor G. V. Portus in *The Cambridge History of the British Empire*, vol. vii, pt. i, Australia (Cambridge, 1933).

CHAPTER VIII

THE AUSTRALASIAN RUSHES FROM THE 'SIXTIES TO THE 'NINETIES

§ 1. OTAGO AND HOKITIKA

AFTER 1851 it was unlikely that the discovery of gold in any of the British colonies in the Southern Seas would depend upon the investigations of a geologist or the chance notice of a shepherd; for all over the colonies there was a sprinkling of men with Victorian or even Californian experience, and merchants and even Governments were prepared to encourage their investigations. A reward offered in 1852 by a committee at Auckland, New Zealand, was soon claimed for a find on Coromandel harbour, but, in spite of a minor rush, unsuccessfully. Not long afterwards there was a small find near Massacre Bay, but in spite of stimulation by a Gold Bonus Committee in Nelson it was not until early in 1857 that any rush occurred. Then some hundreds took up claims on deep ravines on the Aorere River. There was a rough community life, diggers gathering for an evening meal and music about a great common fire; and the township of Collingwood grew up on the bay (renamed Golden Bay) as a base of supply. But in spite of a few new discoveries it was merely a miniature rush. Its chief effect was to lead the New Zealand legislature to pass, in 1858, a Goldfields Act adapting the new Victorian law with the miner's right and the export duty to New Zealand conditions.

As legislative and administrative powers were then distributed between the General Government and the provinces, it was as well that the administrative framework was erected before the first important discovery in New Zealand was made.

A reward of £500 offered by the Provincial Council of Otago for a remunerative goldfield was more than once claimed unsuccessfully. One unimportant discovery tempted a miner with Californian as well as Australian experience, Gabriel Read, to leave his home in Hobart; and in 1861, on the bar of a stream in the Tuapeka district, Read found 'payable gold'. 'I shovelled away about two and a half feet of gravel,' he relates, 'arrived at a beautiful soft slate and saw the gold shining like the stars in Orion on a dark frosty night.' [1] On 4 June he returned from his prospecting trip and informed the Superintendent of the province that he had panned out seven ounces in ten hours' work.

Further enquiries confirmed Read's report. Early in July a rush set in which almost emptied the little town of Dunedin of its male population. In the neighbouring farming districts master and man went up together, agreeing to return at harvest time. The country on the way was fairly open and the cart-horse road was at first considered good, though it failed to stand up to the heavy winter traffic. After an initial hesitation, due to a suspicion that the reports were inventions of the shipping interests, Victorian miners joined in the rush and poured into, or rather through, Dunedin at the rate of 2000 per week. By the end of October the little Scottish community of 13,000 in Otago, relying mainly for prosperity on their 700,000 sheep, had been doubled

[1] Gabriel Read's Narrative in V. Pyke, *History of the Early Gold Discoveries in Otago* (Dunedin, 1887), p. 127.

and, it seemed, transformed. Indeed Gabriel's Gully and other gold-bearing localities near by were rather over-crowded. The Government thought it wise to issue restraining notices and employed hundreds of disappointed diggers at five shillings a day on public works. Some returned in disgust to Victoria: but the influx continued until the winter of 1862 set in.

The earlier discoveries had led the Superintendent of Otago to apply for a delegation of powers by the General Government under its Goldfields Act, and the administration of the goldfields was consequently in the hands of the Provincial Government, with the rather inconvenient exceptions of appointments to the magistracy and constitution of warden's courts. At first disputes were settled by a committee elected by the diggers, who even passed a resolution—which remained a dead letter—against the sale of spirits. But the Government soon stepped in to take control, with the benefit, however, of Victorian experience. A Gold Commissioner was on the field by the middle of August; soon afterwards a commissioner from Victoria was secured to organise the provincial police. A Government gold escort, also, was soon in working order. The Government thus implicitly accepted responsibility for meeting miners' grievances. They were insistently demanding improvement of the roads; a supply of coal, for there was nothing but scrub to burn and the gullies were cold and bleak in winter; a proclamation of townships in which storekeepers could establish themselves with a good title; and a hospital. The provincial authorities made what haste they could. Their first mining regulations were not issued until October, though there must have been a rough working arrangement on the ground. In April 1862 the miners of Gabriel's Gully and its neighbourhood were allowed to elect a mining board to frame regulations, but, perhaps because of conflicting interests, nothing came of its deliberations. In July Vincent Pyke, a Victorian miner-politician, drafted for the Provincial Government a set of regulations better suited to a mature goldfield, with its amalgamations of claims, its sluicing and puddling machines, its shepherding: these were found to answer well, and the mining board was soon superseded. The size of claim varied according to its character, but the standard (at first twenty-four feet) was still only thirty feet square. Thus the interests of the small independent miner still had first place. On the whole the Government had performed its duties with creditable energy and intelligence, and in spite of grumbles its goldfields officials and police commanded the confidence of the miners. In May and June 1862 it organised a Goldfields Department and Pyke was placed at its head. Despite some fears of the submergence of the 'old identity' of the province, it was resolved to do its duty by the newcomers. It attempted, though as yet unsuccessfully, to induce them to settle on the land. It was no doubt in its interest to encourage mining, for the first season of the goldfields produced about 400,000 ounces of gold; and many of the canny Scots of Dunedin must have laid by a goodly store. They may have been mildly shocked by Gabriel's Gully with its public-houses, restaurants and shanties of all descriptions; but its frivolities do not appear to have extended much beyond nigger minstrels, and the diggers with their wideawake hats, open shirts, crimson sashes and moleskin trousers tucked into their boots, were on the whole a steady-going set of men.[1] There had been some 'sticking-up' on the road to the diggings in

[1] C. L. Money, *Knocking about in New Zealand* (Melbourne, 1871).

October; but since then the good order of the province had not been disturbed.

There were perhaps 7000 on the goldfields in July 1862, but it was an exceptionally severe winter. 'Tent life was miserable. No fuel for warmth, only for cooking; and when the billy was boiled the sticks had to be put out and saved. . . . About the beginning of July a heavy fall of snow took place which lay until the second week of August. . . . We had excavated places for our tents—cuttings in the hillsides. This secured them from being blown away, but did not mitigate the cold. . . . Work or bed were the only alternatives. . . . Saturday evening would occasionally be passed in a public-house, cowering over the miserable shadow of warmth diffused by a stove fuelled with bad lignite, emitting a most disagreeable sulphurous stench.'[1] No wonder many of the Victorians shook the snow of New Zealand off their feet and made their way home. But some remained and were rewarded. One evening in mid-August Cobb & Co.'s coach arrived as usual from Dunedin with newspapers which soon set the diggings on fire. 'The news was read from the vantage-ground of a barrel or a dray, with the assistance of a bottle lantern, to attentive audiences.'[2] It was to the effect that two men had arrived in Dunedin with eighty-seven pounds of gold taken from the bed of the Molyneux (or Clutha) River at the foot of the Dunstan Mountains.[3]

The two men, Hartley and Reilly, had learned in California how to work river-bed claims, and had made their way up the Molyneux in February: having found

[1] Mr. John Mouat's memoranda in V. Pyke, *op. cit.* (Dunedin, 1887), pp. 61-2. [2] *Ibid.* p. 74.

[3] The Clutha and Kawarau join to form the Molyneux; but the term Clutha is quite commonly used of the whole stream.

encouraging prospects, they returned for supplies and settled down to a winter's work, quietly adding to their store whilst informing a neighbouring runholder that they were 'just making tucker'. But in fear lest they might be forestalled by another party, they finally came to Dunedin and on promise of a reward of £2000 divulged the locality of their find. Dunedin was in a fever of excitement, and clerks, shop assistants, working-men, and some in comfortable situations, set off for 'the Dunstan', whilst 5000 left the Tuapeka diggings within a week. A week's journey from the Tuapeka practically exhausted the supplies of those who had no pack-horses; and nothing but meat was to be had on the spot. Nor was there any timber to make rockers or peg out claims. However, the miners strained every nerve to overcome these difficulties. The river rose at the end of September and drove them off their claims; but they prospected the surrounding country and found many rich gullies. Dray-loads of supplies arrived, guided by the police, who took the opportunity of beating down extortionate charges. In October a new rush set in from Victoria—partly perhaps of miners who had gone home for the winter—and there were 9000 arrivals in a month. A miner named Fox who came to the Dunstan in October for supplies was rumoured to have made a further discovery in some remote and unexplored region. He was followed, but eluded his pursuers. In the end, however, a party of miners crossing the ranges perceived the smoke of camp-fires rising from the narrow gorge of the Arrow River. A number of parties had found their way in, and thirty or forty men were quietly working there. The little camp had adopted Californian methods. Fox, the strongest personality though not the actual discoverer, had been elected

'Commissioner' and had allotted each man sixty feet on the river and forbidden jumping on penalty of having to fight him. His party got 40 pounds, another 82 pounds, a third 110 pounds of gold in the few weeks before the secret was revealed. A new discovery was soon made on the Shotover, another fast-flowing tributary of the Kawarau. The Arrow gorge could only be ascended by wading: the Shotover could not be ascended at all: the miners had to go over the ranges and descend or be lowered by ropes to its beaches when and where they could. But they were well rewarded for their pains, and by January there were estimated to be 6400 on these new fields near Lake Wakatipu, more than compensating for a certain decline at the Dunstan.

By the end of 1862 there were, in addition to quite respectable hotels and stores, two dancing saloons and a theatre and numerous sly-grog shanties at the Dunstan—concentrated in three canvas towns. The miners celebrated Christmas Day by sports and at a communal feast. At the Arrow there had been some ill-feeling at first: 'a mob of Tipperary men were going about and jumping portions of the richest claims'. But by Christmas-time order had been restored by the firm bearing of the police, and assessors appointed to settle disputes pending the establishment of regular authority. Until an escort could be inaugurated gold was deposited with the local runholder, who would take it to the foot of Lake Wakatipu in his whaleboat as opportunity offered and bring back stores, which, in spite of some complaints of his monopoly, he seems to have distributed equitably to the hungry miners.[1] Unquestionably the dispersion of the miners in these new rushes outstripped the efforts of the provincial authorities, handicapped by

[1] R. Gilkison, *Early Days in Central Otago* (Dunedin, 1930); Pyke, *op. cit.*

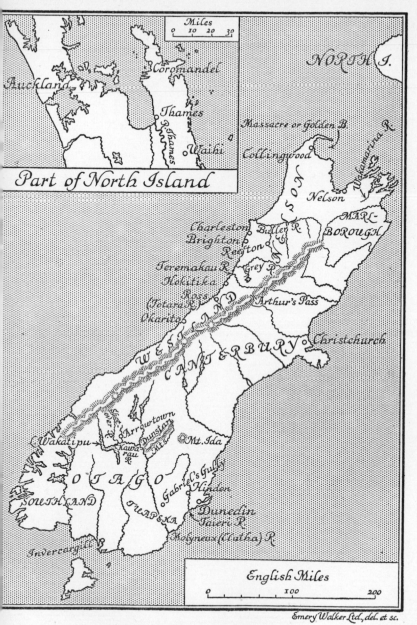

0 10 20 30

Part of North Island

Auckland

Coromandel

Thames

R. Thames

Waihi

NORTH I.

Massacre or Golden B.

Collingwood

Wakamarina R.

NELSON

Nelson

MARL-BOROUGH

Charleston

Brighton

Buller R.

Reefton

Teremakau R.

Grey R.

Hokitika

Ross

(Totara R.)

Arthur's Pass

Okarito

WESTLAND

CANTERBURY

Christchurch

Arrowtown

Dunstan Mts.

Mt. Ida

L. Wakatipu

Kawarau R.

OTAGO

Gabriel's Gully

Hinden

SOUTHLAND

TUAPEKA

Dunedin

Taieri R.

Molyneux (Clutha) R.

Invercargill

English Miles
0   100   200

Emery Walker Ltd., del. et sc.

SOUTH ISLAND OF NEW ZEALAND

the limitations of their powers and their finances, to keep abreast of the work of administration. But they were far from inactive, and the Provincial Council, which had met at the end of November, attempted to equip the province by a loan of £500,000 for public works such as roads, telegraphs and harbour improvement to cope with the problems raised by the gold rush. Moreover holders of miners' rights with six months' residence were empowered to elect three members to the Council. The miners, however, with the support of the press, were clamouring for more wardens, more police, more and better roads, and proclamation of more townships. A further complication lay in the fact that the natural outlet of the Wakatipu goldfields seemed to be through the newly created province of Southland, which organised its own gold escort from Invercargill: but when the gold arrived the bank in Invercargill thought it wise to send it by coasting steamer to Dunedin, and the ridicule arising from this incident seems to have been fatal to the escort.

The second season of the Otago goldfields had produced 550,000 ounces; but the increase in production did not correspond to the increase in population, a further 15,000 having arrived, three-quarters from Victoria, in the first six months of 1863. Pyke estimated the goldfields population at 24,000 and the total population of the province at 60,000. But the July escorts only amounted to 30,000 ounces. In this very month a winter rush took 3000—perhaps even 5000—to the foot of Mt. Ida in the Upper Taieri district, where payable prospects had been found at the end of May. Further discoveries were made later in the season in this district, the best at Hamilton's, eighteen miles south, and others to the north-westward in the Upper

Manuherikia valley. Yet another rush took place in
October to Hindon, in the gorge of the Taieri only
twenty miles or so from Dunedin. Some of these rushes
attracted 5000 miners: but this did not indicate that the
new fields were as rich as the old—rather that there
was not sufficient ground on any field to retain all who
wished to dig. Prospectors penetrated through the wild
mountains beyond Lake Wakatipu right to the West
Coast, but they did not find the country auriferous. The
gold yield this season fell to 450,000 ounces, and much
of this must have come from the older fields, where
there were sales of land, beginnings of cultivation and
other signs of a more settled way of living. Progress
Committees were formed in many of the goldfields
townships and financed improvements by voluntary subscription, though they also devoted much attention to
urging their needs and grievances upon the Provincial
Government. This new phase of goldfields life, accompanied by larger claims, amalgamations, mining leases,
and water-race undertakings indicated that there was
much gold still to be got from the Otago goldfields, but
it marked a transition from the enthusiasms of a gold
rush to the more sober outlook of a regular industry.
The territorial expansion of the goldfields was practically at an end. In 1864 more than 7000 people left
Otago in three months, a reported discovery at Wakamarina in Marlborough being a magnet for many.

A period of reaction and financial difficulty was inevitable. There was unemployment in Dunedin. Naturally when news arrived of rich gold discoveries on the
West Coast there was a further exodus, amounting to
perhaps 4000, in the early months of 1865. That year
was one of retrenchment of officers and works, naturally
producing complaints from the smaller and remoter

fields, and of declining returns. The half-million loan had to be negotiated at 75-77 in order to reduce the overdraft to the bank. But in 1866 comparative stability was reached on a level of gold production of about 150,000 ounces, coming chiefly from large-scale working of sluicing claims, held by co-operative companies, and worked by water from the races which scored the hills. Chinese began to appear on the goldfields after a visit of enquiry by some of their compatriots in Victoria to see if they could rely on proper protection: there was no trouble, and as usual they proved themselves adepts at making a living from abandoned ground. Many of the goldfields townships became municipalities, with subsidies from provincial funds. Agricultural leasing areas were extended to fifty acres and were fairly widely taken up. The provincial administration, despite the usual grumbling, seemed to retain the confidence of the miners in general even in 1867, when for a time it was paralysed by a dispute between the Provincial and General Governments. The provincial authorities for their part were careful to call representatives of the miners into consultation in the revision of the goldfields regulations.

In short, the settled gold-mining community was assimilated pretty completely by the general population of Otago. The gold rush had brought new energy and wealth, and for a generation Dunedin was unquestionably the leading commercial and financial centre of New Zealand. But the character of the province had broadened rather than fundamentally changed. Only one gold-rush immigrant, Julius Vogel, forced a way into the circle, mainly composed of Dunedin business men, which controlled the affairs of the province through provincial institutions; and Vogel rose to prominence, not through gold-mining but as editor of the first Dunedin daily newspaper. He was indeed the inspiration of a political movement for the separation of the two islands, which was active intermittently from 1862 to 1866, and was probably an outgrowth of the gold rush. Otago then felt itself to be the leading province of New Zealand, considered that its interests were not taken sufficiently into account by the General Government and Assembly, and resented the absorption of the time and money of the General Government by the Maori wars in the North Island, with which it professed to have little or no concern. But this movement had no staying power and never really came near success. A new democratic movement which arose in Otago in the later 'sixties and early 'seventies had no discernible connection with the gold rush. It was the independent 'Free Kirk' traditions of the founders rather than the gold rush that gave the province of Otago its undoubted individuality.

The community in New Zealand most powerfully influenced, indeed created, by a gold rush was that on the west coast of the South Island. Wakamarina in Marlborough, which had attracted so many miners from Otago in the autumn of 1864, proved unable to retain more than a few and was in fact only a half-way house to the West Coast. It was only in 1859–60 that these lands had been purchased (subject to the setting aside of a few native reserves) from their scattered Maori inhabitants. They were covered with thick forest and traversed by fast-flowing rivers draining the western slopes of the snow-covered Southern Alps. Politically the long stretch of coast from the Grey River nearly to the Otago sounds was part of the province of Canterbury on the other side of the mountains. Small finds were made near the mouth of the Buller in 1859–60 and these attracted a few score miners from the Nelson goldfields. But the main discoveries were a by-product of the interest of the Canterbury Provincial Government, which offered rewards and sent out parties of surveyors. There were some prospectors at work in 1863, but the finds which inaugurated the rush were made on a tributary of the Teremakau in the middle of 1864. A Nelson storekeeper interested in the Buller and the agent of the Canterbury Government at the mouth of Grey, who returned to Christchurch with specimens to report to his Government, were the chief instruments of diffusion of the news. There was no one outstanding discovery. A trickle began in the later months of 1864: this became a rushing stream early in 1865, as the first-comers wrote back to their friends that brilliant prospects revealed themselves wherever a pick or shovel was put into a terrace or a creek-bed. Thousands came, as we have seen, from Otago and from Wakamarina by sea, thousands also overland from Canterbury, though there was nothing more than a bridle-path over the pass. The geologist von Haast, setting out at the end of March with an official party, found a constant stream of waggon traffic to the end of the waggon road, and above it an endless train of gold-diggers with pack-horses or carrying heavy packs themselves, most of them obviously accustomed to such journeys but some, equally obviously, novices. It was possible to ride to the summit of the pass, but the descent was steep 'over smooth slippery blocks of rock, or through pools of slush full of roots and large and small stones, over and between which the poor horses tried to pick their way, panting and trembling, and often sinking up to their girths'. Eventually the track debouched at the mouth of the

Teremakau, but before the end of 1864 Hokitika had
arisen out of nothing into a town of canvas and calico,
saplings and brushwood, at the mouth of the river of
that name, and had become the distributing centre of
the goldfields. Hence the ocean beach from the Teremakau to Hokitika became a highway covered with
'horses and riders, pack-horses and their drivers, men
with swags, waggons drawn by horses or bullocks'. By
April at Hokitika 'the principal street, half a mile long,
consisted already of a large number of shops, hotels,
banks and dwelling-houses. . . . There were jewellers
and watchmakers, physicians and barbers, hotels and
billiard-rooms, eating and boarding-houses, and trades
and professions of all descriptions. . . . There was shouting and bell-ringing, deafening to the passers-by; criers
at every corner of the principal streets, which were filled
with people.' Miners had already begun to arrive from
Victoria, and indeed German, French, Italian, Greek
and several other tongues were to be heard in the
streets.[1] Even the majority who arrived by sea had a
journey not free from hazard, for all vessels had to cross
the river bar and the merciless surf strewed the beach
with wrecks. The losses in 1865 were estimated at
hundreds of thousands of pounds.

For the most part the diggers travelled up the rivers
and creeks rather than attempt to penetrate the thick
and trackless forest. Roads would cross and re-cross the
creek-bed every few hundred yards, and what roads
they were! 'Roots of all sizes, torn and mangled when
small into a sort of macaroni squash, and when large
remaining a dead hindrance to both horses and men,

---

[1] J. von Haast, *Geology of the Provinces of Canterbury and Westland* (Christchurch, 1879). There cannot have been many of these foreigners. Later,
Scandinavians are the most generally mentioned.

caused the mud ploughed by cattle and pack-horses to assume the appearance of a torrent; so bad was it that the whole distance was marked by the bones of dead animals. The price given for the package of stores [for a distance of twelve miles] was £3 per 100 lbs.' [1] All provisions had to be brought up: there was no fresh meat on the spot as in Otago and Victoria. Gold-buyers in these early months had to carry their gold on their backs, to cross, often to swim, dangerous rivers, to sleep out in the open with their bags of gold as a pillow. The gold was fairly well distributed over a number of creeks with euphonious Maori names—the Arahura, the Totara, the Waimea, the Kanieri being successively centres of attraction until in the winter interest shifted northwards to the Grey. Each retained a few hundred steady miners with good claims. At first, though prospecting was of course difficult, actual working was fairly easy, but winter floods made many claims unworkable and cut communications between the goldfields and the coast. Miners besieged the shipping offices at the Grey and Hokitika, trying to leave at any rate for a season, but not many vessels negotiated the bars.

Australasian miners expected Governments to help them in their difficulties, and by this time the Government of Canterbury was grappling with its novel task. The West Coast was proclaimed a goldfield on 2 March 1865. Soon afterwards the Provincial Secretary and the Collector of Customs (a General Government official) visited Hokitika, and in addition to a warden, a Commissioner was appointed as the chief representative of the Provincial Government with wide powers to subsidise improvements made by the inhabitants and carry

[1] C. L. Money, *Knocking about in New Zealand* (Melbourne, 1871), pp. 101-2.

out public works. Not unnaturally, the Government at Christchurch had a certain predilection for land communications. It sought to establish a Government gold escort; but this was an expensive failure, the gold being collected by buyers on behalf of the banks and sent away by sea. It put forth great efforts, and spent £150,000, to construct a dray road over a newly discovered pass (Arthur's Pass) into the Teremakau. It set about the construction of a telegraph line to Hokitika. The problem of order was far less troublesome. 'I've got a matter of 25 ounces of gold on me', a Californian miner told Archdeacon Harper, 'and if I was in California I'd have a couple of revolvers also; you won't see a weapon here on any man.' [1] There were occasional robberies nevertheless. But the Commissioner (though destined to spend the best years of his life as Professor of Classics at Otago University) was well suited for the post, won the confidence of the miners, and did much to develop an orderly community out of the bustle and confusion of the rush.

The discouragement of the winter soon passed and the second season of the goldfields was inaugurated by a rush to 'Ross' on the Totara and by a rich find on the beach about nine miles north of Hokitika. In the Grey district also there were new discoveries, but the richest were on the beaches of Okarito, fifty-five miles south of Hokitika. Thousands of miners were taken down by steamer, five pounds being charged for the twelve-hour journey. The gold was in a layer of black sand only a few feet down, and for three miles the beach just above high-water mark was pegged out in claims. Meanwhile races and wooden flumes were being constructed and the older fields re-worked by more elaborate methods.

[1] H. W. Harper, *Letters from New Zealand* (London, 1914), p. 104.

It is possible that the population on the Coast rose to 25,000 or 30,000 in the early months of 1866. The gold production is only available in the annual export figures, but was probably rather less than half a million ounces in the season.[1] Before it was over, the telegraph and dray road to Christchurch were open and a Cobb & Co.'s coach began to run in July. The miners had been granted representation in the Provincial Council, and Hokitika had been proclaimed a municipality. Provisions had cheapened considerably and there were other indications of a more settled era. There had even been a sitting of the Supreme Court, though on the other hand a gang of Australian bushrangers had been operating and there had been a few murders. Probably the most hopeful sign of improving conditions was the arrival of many diggers' wives and families from Australia.

The new rushes of the spring of 1866 were much farther north, to a plain covered with low fern and reeds some twenty miles south of the Buller. Several parties were caught on their way up north by flooded rivers and some were drowned. Further prospecting led to another discovery about fifteen miles farther south. Every steamer on the Coast was requisitioned to bring the miners up, and the two towns of Charleston and Brighton soon arose out of the wilderness. There may have been 10,000 or 12,000 on the two fields. But there were still some thousands in the Hokitika region, especially deep-sinking in the lovely forested valley of Ross and sluicing the terraces at Kanieri and elsewhere. On the other hand most of the Okarito beach claims were worked out after six or nine months, and in spite of other beach discoveries the number of miners in that region had greatly

---

[1] I use 'season' as a convenient term, but this winter was so fine that work was probably continuous.

diminished. There was on the whole a rise in gold production, and it probably totalled well over half a million ounces.

This was the maximum yield. A rush of 8000 to a new lead discovered by a coloured man, Addison, in the Buller region in May 1867 was the last for many years of real importance. Miners drifted away to Gympie in Queensland or to the Thames in Auckland. In 1868, as it happened, there were several serious fires in the goldfields towns, and next year depression was general. The decline, however, was less precipitate than in Otago. Many settled down to some seasons of steady work. High terraces topped with big trees were washed away by ground-sluicing; 'paddocking' was used at Ross; shafts were sunk in the hard conglomerate at Charleston and stamp-batteries were introduced to crush it. In secluded places small parties would be found or even individual diggers come to rest at last, 'content with the solitude of well-kept huts, a few books, hard work, their dog as companion, perhaps some poultry, and a weekly visit on Saturdays to the townships to sell their gold and see friends'.[1] Thanks to the gold rush, a community of some thousands of people had taken root on this lovely, lonely coast. It was not a political unit. The Buller diggings were under the government of Nelson and seemed content with it. The Canterbury Government, though it had done its best to govern the goldfields well, found it hard to overcome the handicap of distance. The West Coast rather grudged that coach road over the mountains which formed the link between the two communities, holding that the money would have been better spent in improving communications on the coast itself. Quite early a strong movement grew up for

[1] H. W. Harper, *op. cit.* pp. 143-4.

separation from Canterbury. In 1867 the General Assembly sought to satisfy this demand by erecting the West Coast of Canterbury into a county directly dependent on the General Government. Next year, the miners having complained that this kept them too closely under the tutelage of the General Government, the powers of the County Council were enlarged. In 1873 the county of Westland became a province, though not for long, as three years later provincial governments were swept away altogether. The West Coast in its reduced and rather impecunious condition could hardly support the machinery of provincial self-government.

Meanwhile the occasional discoveries and intermittent work on the Coromandel peninsula in Auckland province had culminated in August 1867 in a modest rush. The real difficulty all along lay in the existence of a substantial native population. In 1867 certain chiefs agreed to the opening of the Kaueranga or Shortland district in return for the money raised from miners' rights. Others remained obdurate, and miners from the South Island were with difficulty brought to see that any attempt to prospect in despite of them would be met by armed resistance. Fortunately Mackay, the man in charge of the negotiations, understood miners also, having been warden of the Nelson goldfields. The miners began by looking for alluvial gold: it was quartz they found, though many claims were rich and inexpensive to work at first. In 1868, 11,500 miners' rights were issued in the district. Later, however, the work of mining was neglected for the sale of scrip. The wonderful crushing results of a single mine, the Caledonian, raised the yield of these Thames goldfields in 1871 to 330,000 ounces; but in general the trend both of production and population was downwards, there being only 2000 miners left in 1874. The Thames acquired a reputation for speculative holding of unworked ground, despite regulations designed to check it. Its gold rush, though many steady, persevering men took part in it, lost its way in speculative blind alleys.

The Thames goldfield thus provided little compensation for the decline of the others. Queensland drew off some of the floating population, and many men found employment on public works. 'When the yield of gold diminishes till it only affords a mere livelihood, which is now the case,' wrote one of the Westland wardens, 'mining loses its attraction, the excitement consequent on rich diggings ceases, and it then falls to the level of ordinary labour, when most miners are ready to leave it for other industries which insure a safer return.'[1] On the West Coast itself, however, there were two new rushes of some importance. In 1870 quartz claims began to be taken up in rugged, heavily timbered country on the Inangahua, a tributary of the Buller. It was difficult to get machinery up, but returns were so good that 3000 people came up and founded the prosperous, if speculative, mining town of Reefton. In 1872 three men who, it is said, were digging foundations for an illicit whiskey still, found alluvial gold between Hokitika and Greymouth.[2] They obtained a grant for a water-race and a mining lease of three acres, and worked on for four years undisturbed, making £10 each per week. Then information elicited in a case in the Warden's Court inaugurated the Kumara rush, which brought the population up to 6000 by Christmas 1876. The ground required three or four months' preliminary work before

---

[1] Report of the warden at Okarito (7 April 1876): Appendix to Journals, N.Z. House of Representatives, 1876: H-3.

[2] A. J. Harrop, *The Romance of Westland* (Christchurch, 1923), pp. 75-6.

returns could be expected; but Kumara retained about half its rush population and ten years later remained the most prosperous alluvial field in New Zealand. Elsewhere on the West Coast roads and tracks, water-races and drainage-tunnels, many of them constructed with Government money, did not avail to arrest the decline. There were fewer miners—only 5000 or 6000—in Otago, and nearly half of these were Chinese. Many, miners by choice, spent part of their time in farming in a small way or betook themselves to sheep-shearing or harvesting if things went ill.

Not until the 'nineties was the long downward trend of New Zealand gold-mining arrested. Then the Waihi mine some thirty miles south-east of Thames, on a bare knoll surrounded by swampy plains, discovered in 1878 but not seriously worked until English capital was introduced in 1887, began, with the aid of the cyanide process, to yield its wealth. Sixteen years' output was valued at £4,500,000: the company employed 1400 men in the first decade of this century and there were 5000 in the town. The steady improvement in appliances for getting gold from the rivers of Otago also culminated in the later 'nineties, and there was a dredging boom, fittingly centred on the Molyneux not far from the scene of Hartley and Reilly's labours. Thus the gold production of New Zealand exceeded half a million ounces again in 1902, and it maintained an important place among New Zealand industries down to the Great War of 1914.

The gold rush era had of course ended long before. Even in the 'sixties the rushes had been less important to New Zealand as a whole than the Maori wars, however much they might dominate the outlook of individual provinces. They made some contribution

perhaps to the national community that was evolving in
New Zealand and certainly provided it with some of its
most enterprising citizens. The energetic, far-sighted,
speculative Vogel of the 'seventies, the shrewd, tenacious, rugged, broadly democratic Seddon, Premier from
1893 to 1906, had been gold-rush immigrants. The
rushes carried settlement up into the mountains of
Central Otago and into the forests of the West Coast.
But the settlement that made modern New Zealand was
in the fertile valleys of the North Island when gold
rushes and Maori wars alike were over.

§ 2. QUEENSLAND

The few thousand settlers of the Moreton Bay region,
then forming part of New South Wales, had their share
of the gold excitement of 1851 and tried to conjure up
gold by the approved method of offering a reward. But
though there were agitating rumours, no gold was found
until 1858, and then it was seventy miles up the Fitzroy
River, much farther north. The discoverer was a Cornish
miner in the employment of Captain O'Connell, Commissioner of Crown Lands at Gladstone on Port Curtis.
He reported the fact to Captain O'Connell but also
divulged it to the landlord and loungers at the hotel.
After further investigation by a party sent up to the
spot, the news was reported both by the official and by
the unofficial channel to Sydney about the end of July.
By early September a rush was setting in from Sydney
and Melbourne, every available vessel being pressed
into the service. Yet the gold consisted of a shallow
alluvial deposit at Canoona a few acres in extent,
ludicrously disproportionate to a rush of 10,000 or
15,000 persons. As there was no telegraphic communica-

tion with the south it was impossible to stop the rush at once: but a great number remained only an hour or two on the field, many went no farther than Rockhampton, the disembarkation point, and the later arrivals, met by returning diggers, often refused to land at all. In October the tide turned. Captain O'Connell, who had been appointed Gold Commissioner, handled the crowds in firm but conciliatory fashion and there was no serious trouble. But there was much distress and great numbers had to be taken back at the expense of the New South Wales and Victorian Governments. By November there were only 200 or 300 on the ground at Canoona. It was an inauspicious beginning for the goldfields of the new colony of Queensland which came into existence next year.

Canoona left its mark, however. Rockhampton, which had previously consisted of a bush inn, a store, a rough woolshed and a few bark 'humpies', now had some money to spend on building. And if only a few thousand ounces had been found at Canoona, a stimulus had been given to prospecting. In the early 'sixties there were a number of small discoveries in the hinterland of Rockhampton. The most important were those near Clermont in the beautiful Peak Downs country some 200 miles inland, made by a shepherd in 1861, and on Crocodile Creek, only fifteen miles or so from Rockhampton, in 1866. The former lasted better, but the latter, being less remote, attracted the larger rush. By Christmas there were over 3000 on the field, a third of them Chinese, who came, as we shall see, at earlier stages on the Queensland fields than elsewhere. The flat was covered with 'habitations of various kinds, ranging from commodious tents and neat slab huts, down to primitive hovels made of sheets of bark, or

galvanised iron, supported by sticks'. The field produced probably 80,000–100,000 ounces, mostly in the
first twelve months; but it soon was eclipsed by a more
important discovery.

The early 'sixties were a period of rapid immigration
and development in Queensland, whose population
reached 100,000 in 1867. But the general monetary
and commercial crisis of 1866 had serious repercussions
in the colony: bank failures and a consequent suspen-
sion of railway works caused unemployment and commercial stagnation in the towns just when farmers were
suffering from prolonged drought. In September 1867
a prospector, James Nash, reached the upper waters of
the Mary River with his 'pick, shovel, tin dish and bag
as tools, a blanket, billy and quart-pot as equipment'
and was directed by a cedar-getter to a likely-looking
gully, in which he found gold. The returns were
sufficiently promising for him to go down to the coast
for supplies and return with a horse and dray, a stock
of provisions and a mate. 'For some days they worked
away undisturbed. When the stockman from the neighbouring run would pass, they remained quiet, but he
found them out, and they allayed his suspicion by
giving a poor account. . . . But one day a stranger
passed, and, their dog barking, he stopped and looked
around. The dog was silenced, but fears of being discovered induced Nash to leave for Maryborough to
make his discovery public'—and make sure of his cash
reward and enlarged discovery claim.[1] The news was
followed by an immediate rush from the Queensland
towns and, when other gullies were discovered to be

---

[1] 'An Eight Years' Resident' [E. Thorne], *The Queen of the Colonies* (2nd
edition, London, 1876), pp. 133-8. The bag was to carry wash-dirt to water
if there was none near.

auriferous and a large nugget was found, from New South Wales, Victoria and New Zealand. Most made their way up through the bush from the sleepy little port of Maryborough, sixty miles away. The horse-track was beaten by the tramp of men on horse and foot and the roll of ponderous bullock-drays into a broad highway. Nash made his report on 16 October. Very soon the ridges and vine-scrub gullies were covered with tents, 'humpies' and grass wigwams, the latter often constructed with the aid of the aborigines of the neighbourhood. By about the end of February 1868 Nashville, or Gympie as it later came to be called, had a street half a mile long with good weather-board buildings, shops, banks, a theatre, and a Christy minstrel show. '*The* night *par excellence* was Saturday night: the whole length of the street was so full of diggers that we could hardly move at all, and what with singing, swearing, fighting, drinking, bargaining for loaves, beef and sausages for Sunday's dinner, the noise was tremendous, while every public-house was crammed with men discussing their various finds . . . while they frequently paid for their drinks with small samples of gold.'[1] Sunday was 'devoted to gossip and nobblers': some took the opportunity of washing their clay-soiled clothes, though others preferred to do this on Saturday afternoons, for the day of rest now commonly extended to a day and a half. Religious services were held, but they were not very generally attended. Order was better observed than religion, though there were very few police and a few fights: according to one account, 'an appeal to the law, except over mining disputes, was held to be unmanly.'[2]

[1] E. B. Kennedy, *Four Years in Queensland* (London, 1870), p. 214.
[2] A. J. Ivimey, *The Gympie Mining Handbook* (Brisbane, 1887), p. 15.

The population by this time had risen to perhaps 10,000. Claims were forty feet square per man. They might be jumped if left for more than twenty-four hours, not counting Sunday. Even so there was barely room for all, and 'great', we are told, 'was the ire of the Southerners against the "Banana men", as they chose to call the Queenslanders, for their luck in holding all the payable ground'.[1] Most of the wash-dirt had to be put into sacks and carted in one-horse drays or wheeled in barrows down the steep ridges to the Mary River a mile away, where each claim-holder had his allotted length of river-bank. 'First of all', wrote a visitor, 'it is shot into long hollowed trunks of trees, and well puddled by raking it about in the water. From that it goes into the cradle, and there the gold is gathered into a little heap with the finest of the sand, and is eventually washed quite clean in little tin basins at the river's edge. . . . The river is perfectly yellow from this constant washing of earth.' In other parts enterprising men brought water down from creeks in flumes and erected puddling machines, washing dirt for seven shillings and sixpence a load.[2] At this stage most of the gold was from alluvial ground at a depth of ten or twelve feet. But quite early promising quartz reefs were discovered, and though it was some months before crushing-mills could be brought up, Gympie made a fairly quick transition from an alluvial to a quartz field. In 1868, 85,000 ounces were taken down by escort and doubtless some addition should be made for unescorted gold: after 1869 Gympie settled down to a production of rather under 50,000 ounces, but

[1] 'An Eight Years' Resident', *op. cit.* p. 151.
[2] C. H. Allen, *A Visit to Queensland and her Goldfields* (London, 1870), pp. 135-6.

enjoyed a modest prosperity. The mines were in the hands of small companies, but many wage-earning miners were shareholders or even directors of another mine.

On the other hand many miners without capital were obliged to leave Gympie, and the prospecting which had begun in the early 'sixties now spread over a wider area. More than one writer of the early 'seventies speaks of gold-prospecting as a regular profession. Minor discoveries continued, the best being in the country behind Townsville, at Cape River and at Ravenswood. A generalised description will perhaps serve for all the minor rushes. 'Springing from their horses, every man, without troubling himself for the time what becomes of his steed, quickly paces off two or four men's ground, and drives in his pegs. The old stagers have cautiously cut four pegs with their toma-hawk some distance back, and have them all ready to drive into the hard ground. . . . When the four pegs are in, there is time to breathe. . . . On every side is confusion, hallooing, swearing, quarrelling, and gener-ally one or two fights will take place. It is best not to leave your claim until things are a little settled. With his pick, the old digger will at the corners of his ground indicate his boundaries by digging little trenches at right angles, and at one mark off his shaft or hole and turn out the sods so as to bring it into shape. . . . Old stagers, when mates, will generally each peg out ground enough for all in various localities, and by "shepherding" each claim, i.e. working or sitting on it daily for an hour, from 10 to 11 A.M., find out from the efforts of their neighbours which way the run of the gold is; when, as is nearly always the case, some of the ground is worthless, this will be given up and . . .

"the likeliest ground" will be retained. Here, as elsewhere, the weakest sometimes go to the wall, and a little weakly man will be overpowered by some big ruffian. As a rule, however, the diggers act with the greatest justice. . . . After the men have pegged out the ground, they have time to wait on the Commissioner, who goes to the prospector's claim, sees a prospect washed and declares the ground payable or otherwise. In the former case he marks off their ground and hears any disputes which may have arisen in marking out the other ground. . . . By and by the drays and pack-horses of the storekeeper come up, and there is now a second rush for business sites. . . . Pegging out . . . is evidence of title: but the owner is obliged to reside. If his lot is unoccupied for 24 hours it may be jumped. . . . A shrewd fellow will peg out two or three and pay miners to erect their tents on the extra ones. If the diggings succeed, in a week or two a wealthier class of storekeepers come in than those who usually "follow the rushes" and, finding all the good sites occupied, are forced to give round sums to their proprietors.' [1]

Late in 1871 two prospectors made a valuable discovery thirty miles westward of Ravenswood near a cluster of conical, square-topped hills—Charters Towers. By the end of 1872 there were about 4500 people scattered over a large barren undulating flat about three miles square. The finds were chiefly rich 'blows' or outcrops of ferruginous quartz. Some miners could not afford to work them, and others were deterred by the refractory ores found deeper down. But throughout the 'seventies Charters Towers, though it never yielded more than about 80,000 ounces a

1 'An Eight Years' Resident', *op. cit.* pp. 140-42.

year, was the steadiest producer in the colony. Like Gympie it seems to have depended mostly on its own capital in these early stages.

To the alluvial miner the next discovery seemed more attractive. It was made on the Palmer River in about 16° north latitude in August 1873, by a party fitted out and led by J. V. Mulligan, after an official exploration party had found traces of gold the previous year. Some miners came up overland, regardless of the difficulty of replenishing supplies and the danger of aboriginal attack. Thousands more came up by steamer to Cooktown, where 'a lovely little seaport gleaming with white tents and noisily busy with workmen' sprang into existence in October in the wilderness. Before long the wet season set in, and thousands had to camp at Cooktown until the rivers became passable: they were preyed upon by pickpockets and card-sharpers, ran short of food and were struck down by dysentery. Those who persevered found that the road up 'was really a track or belt of morass, some ten chains wide, in which one had to wade at times up to the knees. . . . The whole road . . . was strewn with clothes, boots, saddles, rations, in such quantities that there would have been enough to have opened a good store. Sometimes horses would be found dead in the mud still saddled and packed.' On the other side of the Normanby River, half-starving diggers, lucky or unlucky enough to have got in before the rains, were waiting to cross and replenish their supplies, having been reduced to eating their horses and their dogs.[1] Little wonder that many gave up, and that the official

---

[1] *Missing Friends, being the Adventures of a Danish Emigrant in Queensland, 1871–1880* (London, 1892), pp. 211-27. He says they ate their boots also, but I suspend belief at that point.

estimate of the population on the field in 1874 was only 3000. But it was a rich field, yielding 150,000 ounces in its first season. Next year the population increased to 9000, the yield to 250,000 ounces. In 1876 thousands of miners seem to have moved off to the Hodgkinson field, also discovered by Mulligan. Some at least of them returned disappointed—for the Hodgkinson only produced 60,000 ounces in 1876 as against the 200,000 ounces of the Palmer—but found Chinese in occupation of their claims. By the end of the year the Chinese predominated markedly in numbers, and in the first four or five months of 1877, 7000 arrived direct from China, raising the population to its maximum of 20,000. Afterwards there was a sharp decline. Quartz was found, but mining was excessively difficult with transport, timber and provisions so expensive, and in 1879 a serious influx of water, necessitating expensive pumping machinery, caused many reef claims to be abandoned. Nor could even the industry and simple living of the Chinese prevent a steady exhaustion of the alluvial ground.

The first phase of the Queensland goldfields may be said to have ended with the Palmer and Hodgkinson rushes. In the middle 'seventies production approached 400,000 ounces annually. The gold rushes were never the sole attraction of Queensland, for its pastoral wealth was being opened up and its sugar industry beginning at the same time. Administration followed Victorian models, with its miner's right system, its export duty on gold, its wardens, its police escorts, bringing the gold down in coaches or on pack-horses to the ports. At Gympie a local court of the Victorian type was instituted in 1868. Its regulations were said to be hampering to capital, but the influence of the working miner's point of view was still perceptible in the Act of 1874, which among other things put an end to the Gympie Local Court. The small alluvial claim—50 feet by 50, or 100 in wet alluvial ground—was still retained, and though provision was made for renewable twenty-one years' leases they were not to be granted within two years of the proclamation of a field.

The influx of Chinese was the most difficult problem of Queensland goldfields administration. They were chased off the Crocodile and Gympie fields; but they reappeared on the Palmer in greater numbers than ever. Cooktown was said in 1876 to be more like a Chinese than a British port. The Government determined to discriminate against them and restrict their immigration by law. The first proposal was to charge them three pounds instead of ten shillings for miners' rights and ten pounds instead of four pounds for business licences, but the Imperial Government objected to this measure. Finally in 1877 a head-tax of ten pounds was levied upon them, the number per ship was restricted, and in 1878, with other Asiatic and African aliens, they were excluded from goldfields for three years after their discovery.

Apart from this issue, the miners as a body do not seem to have interested themselves in Queensland politics. The grant of manhood suffrage after six months' residence in 1872 removed any danger of agitation on that score, and the miners do not appear to have contributed, except indirectly by opening up the interior of the districts in question, to the movements for the separation of Central and Northern Queensland from the South which were more or less continuously in existence during the later 'sixties and the 'seventies.

Though there was still a pioneering fringe of pros-

pectors and Government geological expeditions, the
rush element in Queensland gold-mining was less
important after the Palmer discoveries—and the alluvial
production steadily dwindled. In the 'eighties it was
for the first time a question of developing the mines by
outside capital and large-scale enterprise. The production of Gympie and of Charters Towers—now connected with their ports by railways—rose to over
100,000 ounces annually, though the consequence in
each case was speculation in scrip, culminating in
Gympie in 1884 and in Charters Towers in 1887, and
followed by the usual sharp reaction. But the most
remarkable results were achieved by a new mine, the
Mt. Morgan, twenty-five miles from Rockhampton.
The hill, covered with trees and dark, rough, metallic-
looking boulders, was part of a grazing selection whose
owner was later obliged to abandon it and earn his
living as a miner. In 1882 it occurred to him to show
it to Mr. F. A. Morgan, the Rockhampton hotelkeeper
who owned the mine at which he worked. Morgan, a
miner of 1851, with his brother, tested the ground and
acquired it for £640—one pound an acre. A crushing
mill was erected, and crushing began in February 1883,
at the foot of the mount. Though there were various
rumours, nothing was publicly known about the mine
until March 1884. In fact, however, the top was so
rich that it all had to be carted down the mountain,
and before long a continuous line of loaded carts was
to be seen winding slowly down and up again. In 1886
a limited liability company with a capital of £1,000,000
was formed, and in 1889 production reached over
323,000 ounces. The fame of the mine extended all
over the world, and although the ore became much
poorer at greater depths, no other mine in Queensland

could compare with it in yield or probably in progressive technical management. Though naturally a town grew up at Mt. Morgan, it was less important as a rush than the Croydon goldfield, discovered by the owner of a Carpentaria cattle station and his employees in October 1885. This was a quartz field, though for the first year anything beyond the small quantities that could be crushed or 'dollied' by pestle and mortar had to be carted 100 miles to crushing mills. However, the yields of these were so rich as to attract attention not only locally but throughout Australia, and in 1887 Croydon was transformed from a rough mining camp into a flourishing, well-stocked town of 3500 people, even though it had not produced much more than 30,000 ounces of gold.

In the 'nineties the yield of the Queensland gold-fields reached its height: towards the end of the decade the figure verged on three-quarters of a million fine ounces. Charters Towers was in the lead, helped especially by the treatment of old tailings by the cyanide process, and in 1899 the population of the field was estimated at over 26,000. Mt. Morgan, reducing expenses by an improved chlorination process, came next. But Gympie and Croydon and other fields contributed about a third of the total. The various fields had settled down more or less to company production, but not very contentedly. The companies complained of the high cost of labour, and when in 1893 many were paralysed by a banking and commercial crisis through-out Australia small co-operative parties came to the fore again, re-working abandoned ground and pros-pecting new. Still the army of prospectors had moved on from Queensland, not without leaving their mark, for clearly the opening-up of the north, and especially of the northern interior, would have proceeded far more slowly without them.

§ 3. COOLGARDIE AND KALGOORLIE

Western Australia, separated from the other Australian colonies by a thousand miles of desert, had sought for gold sporadically, by exploration and offer of reward, since 1852: Hargraves himself visited it in 1862. The prospectors, however, had their first success only after a scientific geologist on expeditions to the Kimberley district in the far north had found favourable indications in 1883 and, more definitely, in 1884. In 1885 these were followed up by a party of six miners from the eastern colonies, and the hopeful reports and specimens it brought back to the coast in August inaugurated a rush quite early in 1886. One shipload of miners came from New Zealand to the port of Wyndham. Many arrived from Queensland, some overland. By 30 June there were probably 1500 or 2000 men scattered over the auriferous area. The warden who was sent up a month or so later with a party of police reported that there was no fixed camp: men moved from place to place daily, stripping the surface in the ravines and fossicking on the bars in the creeks. There were isolated rich patches, but no continuous leads. Water was scarce: from one spot 200 or 300 men walked seven miles daily to get it. The New Zealand miners especially, accustomed to deep, defined leads, were dissatisfied with Kimberley. Unable to get gold enough to buy flour or tea, they had to leave the country or starve. Valuable equipment was sacrificed, 'waggons, carts, horses, disposed of for a mere trifle, or abandoned, and . . . eventually . . . destroyed for the timber to construct "cradles", and for the iron work'.[1] The exodus was checked by the discovery in September of a promising reef at Hall's Creek, though nothing beyond 'dollying' of the surface rock was feasible;[2] and with the coming of the rains in December more extended prospecting became possible; but by February 1887 the population had declined to about 600, packers and teamsters on the roads from Derby and Wyndham included. Faced as they were with great distances from sources of supply, struggling against fever and ague, dysentery and scurvy, it is no wonder that the miners gradually drifted away until ten years later Hall's Creek became a supply post for a few score prospectors only.

The Kimberley rush had, however, stimulated public interest, and minor discoveries followed in widely separated parts of this vast colony with its 40,000 people. At Christmas 1887 gold was found on a sheep station seventy miles east of Roebourne by a boy who picked up a stone to shy at a crow. A few months later a solitary prospector found rich alluvial gold farther inland, setting in motion a rush of some hundreds to the Pilbara field. In the same year, 1888, a more purposeful search in the country east of the agricultural centre of Northam, by a party fitted out by a Settlers' Association with Government aid, led to the discovery of a quartz reef at 'Southern Cross', and another minor rush. In 1890 there was another alluvial discovery about 200 miles from the coast in the Murchison district.

These goldfields between them had produced only a few scores of thousands of ounces in five years. The gold was often easy to get. At Cue, on the Murchison field,

---

[1] Report of Warden, Kimberley Goldfield (30 June 1887): Votes and Proceedings, Legislative Council of W. A., 1887: Appendix: A 17.

[2] On dollying, see below, p. 301.

hundreds of men walked about day after day 'specking', turning over every stone with a forked stick to see if it might not be, or conceal, a nugget. But scarcity of water made washing as a rule impossible, and miners had to extract alluvial gold by 'dry-blowing', as the Mexicans had done. Boilers brought to Southern Cross were clogged with salt. Nevertheless enough had been found to ensure further prospecting and even to attract some capital from Adelaide and Melbourne.

In June 1892 two prospectors, Bayley and Ford, who had been in the Croydon rush in Queensland, made an even more encouraging discovery about 100 miles east of Southern Cross. They secured about 200 ounces by specking and dry-blowing and then returned for supplies. They were tracked back by another party and it was this second, less experienced party, apparently, that made the richest find. They omitted, however, to peg out their claim and next morning found Bayley and Ford in occupation. In the middle of September Bayley made his way back to Southern Cross and secured their 'discovery claim'. At Southern Cross the wage-earning miners were on strike against a reduction of wages, and virtually the whole of the little community followed Bayley back to 'Coolgardie' on horseback, with teams, or on foot. After the news reached Perth and Fremantle, everyone seemed to be preparing to go to the new gold-field. The lack of water was at first a severe deterrent to the rush, and for a time the influx of miners was virtually controlled by the requirement that everyone should obtain a water permit from the warden at Southern Cross. But very soon about 700 collected on the new field—an open forest of eucalyptus dotted with white tents. 'Water . . . was carted by horse teams in waggons with large tanks on board, or by camel caravans, from a distance of 36 miles, drawn from a well near a large granite rock. The supply was daily failing, and washing was out of the question; enough to drink was all one thought of; two lines of eager men on either side of the track could daily be seen waiting for these water-carts. What a wild rush ensued when they were sighted! In a moment they were surrounded and taken by storm, men swarming on to them like an army of ants. As a rule, eager as we were for water, a sort of order prevailed, and every man got his gallon water-bag filled until the supply was exhausted.'[1] The cost as a rule was a shilling a gallon. About Christmas-time the shortage was such that scores of men daily left for Southern Cross. Of purely mining problems the only one causing immediate difficulty was the conflict of interest between quartz and alluvial miners owing to the finding of alluvial in proximity to quartz reefs.

As soon as the summer drought was over thousands rushed to Coolgardie, some with pack-horses or teams, but some pushing one-wheeled carts, four to a cart, and some carrying their swags on their backs—hard work in all conscience on that sandy, spiky plain. At Coolgardie all was bustle and confusion. Auctioneers sold flour, bags of oatmeal, pounds of tea and tins of butter, picks and shovels from their rostrums. Schools of as many as a hundred men played pitch-and-toss in the streets. With all this liveliness in the town prospectors were out scouring the surrounding country. Whilst on their way to a reported discovery, two prospectors, Hannan and Flanagan, discovered good alluvial gold about twenty-four miles north-east of Coolgardie. Joined by a third man, they collected over 100 ounces, and Hannan then returned to Coolgardie on 17 June 1893, and applied

[1] Hon. David W. Carnegie, *Spinifex and Sand* (London, 1898), pp. 7-8.

for a discovery claim. With that a rush set in, only of a few hundreds at first but destined to be the greatest in Australia since Bendigo. Early in July the representative of an Adelaide syndicate discovered a rich reef, paving the way for the 'Golden Mile' of Kalgoorlie.

Kalgoorlie, however, was not a 'poor man's field'. Prospecting continued, the difficulties of the summer drought being overcome by small portable condensers and in cases of real distress by the despatch of tanks of water on drays by the Government Water Supply Department. Carnegie describes the scene on one small rush. 'The nearest water . . . was a salt lake seven miles distant, and this at night presented a strange appearance. Condensers of every size and capacity fringed the two shores of a narrow channel; under each was a fire, and round each all night could be seen figures, stoking the burning wood or drawing water, and in the distance the sound of the axe could be heard, for at whatever time a party arrived they had forthwith to set about "cooking water." ' But the results of the prospecting appeared disappointing until in June 1894 a party returning empty-handed to Coolgardie found, twelve miles south of it, a moss-covered outcrop from which the six of them in a few weeks dollied out about 8000 ounces of gold. The secret of the 'Londonderry Golden Hole' was revealed by one of the finders, it is said, in his cups: however that may be, the reward claim was applied for on 23 June, and before long the supposed reef was pegged out for miles. The atmosphere of a gold rush was revived and intensified.

So far the West Australian goldfields had been dominated by the prospector and digger, and the ideas that had been worked out in Victoria and applied in New Zealand and in Queensland. With so many small scattered rushes it was difficult always to have a representative of law and order on the spot, but the diggers' sense of justice found expression in the institution of a 'roll up'. 'Immediately a man is caught stealing . . . a tin pannikin is beaten vigorously drumwise, and . . . all the miners in the camp hurry up to the place. The case is roughly explained to them, an impromptu court is immediately formed, a president is elected, and there and then the culprit is tried. If he is found guilty, and when he has been caught *in flagrante delicto*, there is of course no doubt about it; he is ordered to leave the camp within a given time—generally a few minutes only— and never return to it again under risk of being tarred and feathered.'[1] In such circumstances the diggers were adopting the methods of Californian 'popular justice', though with less severity. But in general the wardens and police were there to maintain order, and did so to the general satisfaction. On the other hand the escort system which had been maintained in Victoria as a safeguard against the bushranger and in Queensland perhaps against the aborigines, never really struck root in Western Australia, gold being sent down by the ordinary coach with a trooper or two as guard, as soon as coaches ran, and on the remoter fields usually brought down by the miner himself or by a trusted mate. It would have been difficult to escape with the booty unless with horses or camels, which could be tracked, or by resorting to known supplies of water.

Though the aborigine was sometimes a danger, the real enemy of the West Australian miner was not the bushranger but the bush. 'As far as the eye can reach one sees only this ocean of blue-grey leaves, undulating

---

[1] Julius M. Price, *The Land of Gold* (London, 1896), p. 103. Cf. also John Marshall, *Battling for Gold* (Melbourne, 1903), pp. 142-7.

in giant curves—no hills, no rivers; here and there a bare patch of salt pan or lake, here and there an outcrop of white quartz; no birds, no beasts, only ants and flies.' [1] In particular the lack of water in this wilderness governed the operations of the prospector and the miner. Though the best bushmen used a compass and kept a reckoning, 'a good many prospectors, depending on their black boys almost entirely, wander from one range of hills to another, dodge here and there for water, keep no count or reckoning, and only return by the help of their guide when the "tucker-bags" are empty'. The manner of trying a promising locality depended on the distance from water. 'The party may have to divide, some camping in the likely country, engaged in prospecting solely, while the others tail the horses or camels at the watering-place and pack water to their mates; it may happen that good country must be passed over from the want of water within reasonable distance.' [2]

Once the goldfield was actually in being the problem was eased. The alluvial dirt could be treated with fair efficiency by dry-blowing after large stones had been picked out and any lumps of clay or earth broken up by a heavy billet of wood. In the simpler form of the process the miner would gradually empty a dish above his head into another at his feet, the dust and lighter material being carried away by the wind, until after several repetitions the dish could be shaken from side to side and the remaining light material brushed off with the hand or blown off with the mouth. If the soil were wet and sticky a sieve might be useful. In the early days of Kalgoorlie, in spite of the absence of water for washing, the ground was so moist that fires had to be kept

---

[1] R. Radclyffe, *Wealth and Wildcats* (London, 1898), p. 44.
[2] Carnegie, *op. cit.* pp. 75, 126-7.

going all night, piled on heaps of alluvial soil dug out during the day, and ashes and dirt were dry-blown together in the morning. A more elaborate apparatus, with a tripod twelve or fifteen feet high, rope and pulley was sometimes seen: the dish was hauled up and tipped up by a string fixed to its edge, and the dirt fell upon a prepared surface below. All this was desperate hard work, but the digger was not afraid of that. The threat to the permanence of his position on the goldfields lay in the poverty of the alluvial ground.

The alluvial was mostly shallow, perhaps because of the lack of any rush of water to carry it far or deep. The working miner could go a certain way with quartz, but the alluvial gave him little chance of making savings which he could himself invest. Hence he was not really working so much for his own account as to sell, or let the storekeeper who financed him sell, to an agent of some company. When the outcrop samples had been taken and dollied—pounded in an iron mortar with an iron pestle and then passed through a series of sieves—it was necessary, if the reef was promising, to test it by cuts and shafts. Often a party would divide and some work for wages in a neighbouring mine, sending half to keep their friends going as they developed the claim. But the unaided miner could go no further. What happened then? A French writer describes a common procedure. 'Intermediaries (generally storekeepers to whom the miners were more or less in debt) came to the main centres to offer new discoveries. Provided they were in a place where the presence of gold had already been indicated, they immediately found a taker. A mining expert . . . despatched to the spot, soon returned with a report almost always conceived in rather vague terms, but almost invariably finishing by a phrase of this kind, which became typical: "I congratulate you upon having had the good fortune to acquire a property which appears to have such a promising future". No more was necessary; a company was immediately formed with a big nominal capital, a very small working capital of ready cash, and the affair was launched on the market. The public, attracted by the promises of the prospectus, sometimes also by an artificial rise skilfully brought about on the stock exchange, bought the shares often above their nominal value, the promoters converted their scrip into good solid money and passed on to begin the same operation again on another mine as little known as the preceding.' [1] In other words, the gold rush was developing into a mining-share boom.

About the middle of 1894 the Department of Mines noted an increasing number of mining companies that relied upon capital to be raised in Europe. Not less than 100 such companies were registered in London in 1894, their nominal capital being £8,415,000, and 73, with a nominal capital of £7,743,000, in the first half of 1895. The excitement extended to the Continent. There were Australian companies as well. But the most characteristic features of the boom were to be found on the spot. Both at Coolgardie and at Kalgoorlie the official stock exchange was supplemented by an 'open call' exchange held in a large hall about eight o'clock at night. In a single night nearly 100,000 shares might be sold in this market of a few hundred working miners. It was not uncommon indeed to see self-appointed auctioneers standing on empty cases at street-corners with a motley crowd filling the street and buying and selling merrily.

Meanwhile the rough mining camps of tents, shan-

1 O. Chemin, *De Paris aux mines d'or de l'Australie Occidentale* (Paris, 1900), pp. 335-6.

ties, houses of hessian and shops of galvanised iron and wood were growing into populous towns. The net immigration into Western Australia was 16,000 in 1894, 18,000 in 1895, 36,000 in 1896, and a large proportion of the immigrants must have been bound for the mining centres.[1] Coolgardie became a municipality in July 1894, Kalgoorlie in May 1895, though the teams and camel caravans on the dusty roadway served as a reminder that they were on the mining frontier. A railway was being rapidly pushed inland and reached both towns before the end of 1896, and before it came camel trains had considerably reduced the early freights and cheapened supplies. Outlying camps—notably Menzies nearly 100 miles north of Coolgardie—were also booming, and the established means of communication were supplemented by a bicycle express service along the tracks made by the camels. Timber mills, brickfields, ice factories flourished, and the mining boom was capped by a land boom. Water was still short and sanitation backward. Amusement also was not very plentiful outside the drinking saloons and the billiard-rooms. There was some trouble with sly-grog-shops, but it was not really serious. Quite apart from the prospector class, whose rough code was in many respects admirable, there was in this frontier population a not inconsiderable nucleus of educated men. There was a certain external differentiation between Coolgardie and its forward younger sister: 'shirt-sleeves and slouch-hats are *de rigueur* at Hannan's; collars for Coolgardie, but flannel shirts at Kalgoorlie'.[2] But fundamentally it was the same society—and whatever its good points, it had

---

[1] Detailed statistics of their distribution are not available: the population of Coolgardie in June 1896 was about 6000, and one would hazard a guess that it was still the larger town.   [2] R. Radclyffe, *op. cit.* p. 34.

grave weaknesses both in expert knowledge and in common honesty. Among the classes represented was the reckless unthinking speculator and the common swindler.

The boom was certain to end in a collapse. For the companies promoted by the means already described demanded results at the earliest possible moment, and that involved the appointment of managers and the installation of crushing plant without a proper opportunity for securing qualified men or considering the capacity and location of the machinery. Good engineers or managers were rare, and even good miners were hard to keep. Good mines, indeed, there were, but one of those which had excited the greatest expectations, the Londonderry, for which a company of £750,000 capital had been floated in London and Paris, proved, when reopened by its new owners, to be a mere blow-out: 'the kernel had been taken and only the worthless shell left.' This sharp disappointment with a rich mine naturally reacted upon mines that had hardly existed except upon paper, the more so because the installation of machinery in some cases exhausted the working capital of the company. By the end of 1896 the great boom was over.

The end of the boom, however, did not mean a decline in yield. On the contrary the total yield of the West Australian mines increased from about 250,000 ounces in 1896 to 600,000 ounces in 1897. In particular, the richness of the Golden Mile at Kalgoorlie only now began to be realised. When the Adelaide syndicate which had first located it was put into liquidation in 1898 it had distributed to its shareholders £905,000 in cash and £3,421,000 in shares. The dividend-paying mines at Kalgoorlie were at first few, but the processes were being steadily improved, and in 1896 tellurides of gold were struck which, though they had to be sent to Fremantle or South Australia for smelting, were exceedingly rich. Kalgoorlie, in short, could afford to wait. In 1898 its population rose to 25,000, in 1899 to 35,000, and its mining stocks began to soar with better reason than before. It had now left Coolgardie far behind. It was, indeed, even less of a poor man's field than at first. Not many miles off, however, at Kanowna, a deep alluvial lead was discovered in October 1897. A rush of 12,000 men followed—the largest alluvial rush in Western Australia—and though there was only room for about a third of them, and the yield after reaching 63,000 ounces in 1898 sharply declined, Kanowna and a few other deep leads to a less extent softened the blows dealt to the independent miner by his unfortunate speculations of the boom and the rise of the great company mines since. There was indeed a fringe of prospectors and miners still advancing into the wilderness and developing the mines they found—particularly northwards of Menzies into the Mt. Margaret field and northwards and north-eastwards of Cue into the Murchison field. In each of those districts water was more readily obtainable by artesian wells, though on the other hand timber for mining purposes tended to be scarce. Numerous small centres with a population of a few scores or hundreds—even 2000 at Cue—grew up, and the output of each district steadily rose to 100,000 ounces or more. But even on these fields the development of most of the mines clearly had to pass at an early stage to those with command of capital.

Now the goldfields regulations of Western Australia were based upon those of Queensland, which bore the influence of the individualist Australian miner's suspicion of capital. The Queensland prohibition of leases

20

for two years after the proclamation of a field was omitted from the Western Australian law. But there remained 'labour conditions' requiring the employment of a certain number of men per acre, subject to exemption in certain cases: the administration was not very strict, but capital pressed for a relaxation of the law. The sharpest clash, however, was on the question of the alluvial miner's rights on the leasehold of a quartz-mining company. So long as alluvial mining was a mere matter of surface dry-blowing the leaseholders made little complaint, but with the discovery of the deep leads the operation of the law, which permitted a dual title, was claimed to be obstructive to leaseholders' operations. A particular case gave point to the difference of view. The Government, by a regulation limiting to ten feet the depth to which alluvial might be worked on a lease, leant to the leaseholders' side. The alluvial miners ignored the regulation, and after the Premier had failed to pacify them, it was agreed to take a test case to the Supreme Court, which decided in their favour. They were, in short, strong enough to force a compromise, which, after consideration of the whole administration of the goldfields by a Royal Commission, was embodied in an amending Act of 1898: miners were to be allowed to work alluvial gold on land under application for lease, but once the lease was granted the lessee's privilege was exclusive: it was, however, provided that the warden might obtain a report upon land likely to contain alluvial and postpone hearing a lease application for six months.

Apart from this issue there had been a tendency to criticise administration as being too much under the influence of the old-established colonists and too unresponsive to the needs of the goldfields. It was true that Western Australia, which only received responsible government in 1890, was governed for the whole of the succeeding decade by the ablest, sturdiest and most respected of its native-born sons, Sir John Forrest. It was also true that during the rush years 1895 and 1896 the administration of the telegraphs, the post-office, the railways and the customs virtually broke down for a time under the strain. Nevertheless the record of achievement to which Sir John Forrest was able to point was considerable. 'In the short space of five or six years, in a country which in its natural condition is absolutely devoid of any permanent water, 400 miles of railway have been completed to most of the important places on the Eastern Goldfields; telegraphs have been erected to every important centre; public buildings have been erected in every township, those in Coolgardie and Kalgoorlie being in many cases finer than those in the metropolis; schools have been opened and erected at all important places; hospitals and qualified medical men supplied at every centre; Warden's Courts have been established; police protection and postal arrangements have been furnished everywhere, roads, water supplies, public batteries, telephones, etc., have been provided. . . . A project for supplying the Coolgardie Goldfields with water is also in full course of being carried out at an estimated cost of £2,500,000.'[1] But the discontent was there, and on one great issue it was very serious. Western Australia had held somewhat aloof from the federation discussions of the 1890's in the eastern colonies. The mining community, however, hailed for the most part from those very colonies, kept up the

---

[1] Refutation by Sir J. Forrest of Statements made in Petition from the Eastern Goldfields: *Minutes and Votes and Proceedings,* Parliament of W. A., 1900 (1st session), No. 3.

connection—partly through a settled habit of paying a Christmas visit, as well as through correspondence and remittances—and clearly desired to share their destiny. At Kalgoorlie particularly it pressed for a referendum on the subject such as was held in the other colonies, and when Forrest was obdurate, for separation of the gold-fields. Such a new colony, equipped with a railway to Esperance Bay and entering the federation on its own account, would place the remnant of Western Australia in an impossible position. A petition to the Queen gave Chamberlain an opportunity of bringing pressure to bear on Forrest, and the West Australian leader gave way. A referendum was held on 31 July 1900, and the goldfields brought the whole of Western Australia with them into the federation. Thus the effects of the gold rushes upon Western Australian political development were decisive.

The peak of the Western Australian gold output was reached in 1903, when it passed the 2,000,000 ounce level, 1,150,000 ounces coming from Kalgoorlie and district. But whilst the reef gold was being extracted by ever-improving methods, alluvial mining, which had never struck deep root in Western Australia, was withering away. The typical miner was a wage-labourer, socialistically inclined, whose wages, fixed by Arbitration Court awards, very probably contributed, as the critics maintained, to the decline of the goldfields and at any rate prevented the capitalist from having his own way. And the prospector—where was he? Some of his kind no doubt settled on the land, for these were years of rapid agricultural development in Western Australia, whose wheat acreage increased tenfold between 1903 and 1914 and whose wheat export outdistanced its export of gold. Some lingered on in odd places, eking out a subsistence from their old calling, but living perhaps chiefly on their memories. Some travelled beyond the confines of Australia, prospecting still. But their work for Australia was done.

This sturdy, self-reliant class of men, first developed in the Victorian rushes of the 'fifties, had since ranged far and wide through the Australian bush and over the tussock-covered mountains and along the rivers of New Zealand. They had been the predominant element, in influence if not in numbers, in all the subsequent rushes. They did not indeed impose institutions of their own framing as the American miners had done in the Rocky Mountain camps, for Victorian institutions were of governmental design, and other Colonial Governments copied the pattern in their statute-books: but though the diggers, unlike their American counterparts, looked to Government to provide the administrative framework, it was of course moulded by their habits and prejudices. Socially these Australasian rushes were more orderly and less picturesque. Technically, their development may well have been slowed down by the diggers' tenacious suspicion of large-scale capitalistic enterprise: but the New Zealand dredges of the 'nineties were a local development. They did less than the American rushes to 'open up the country': the earlier rushes were in country already opened up by the squatters, and hardly anywhere did the gold, as in the Rocky Mountains, prove to be a pointer to even more important deposits of the baser metals. Nevertheless the gold rushes powerfully influenced the Australian character and way of life. The pastoral industry, dominant before the rushes, did not tend to produce a democratic society. There were democratising influences among the small farmers and in the cities: but it was the gold rushes that 'tipped the scales in the land war' between the pastoralist and the small farmer. They were a stimulating, individualising, unifying force.[1] They could not indeed bring New Zealand into the Australian orbit. Though the diggers' influence bound the colony across the Tasman Ocean closely to Australia in the 'sixties, it only touched two provinces, and did not prove as powerful or lasting as that of the pioneers on the land. But on the Australian continent they certainly helped to overcome particularism, for they took no heed of colonial boundaries. Even their prejudices had a lasting effect: their suspicion of capital strengthened the Australian Labour movement, and their dislike of Chinese infiltration gave the initial impetus to the policy of a White Australia.

AUTHORITIES

The most useful general account of gold-mining in New Zealand is the official *Handbook of New Zealand Mines* (Wellington, 1887). The revised edition of 1906 deals with later developments. Vincent Pyke, *History of the Early Gold Discoveries in Otago* (Dunedin, 1887), is authoritative, but disappointing on the side of social life: of this there are interesting sketches in R. Gilkison, *Early Days in Central Otago* (Dunedin, 1930). A. J. Harrop, *The Romance of Westland* (Christchurch, 1923), is a useful account, by a scholar who knows the coast, of the West Coast rush. Of this J. von Haast, *Geology of the Provinces of Canterbury and Westland* (Christchurch, 1879), C. L. Money, *Knocking about in New Zealand* (Melbourne, 1871), R. C. Reid, *Rambles on the Golden Coast* (London, 1886), G. O. Preshaw, *Banking under Difficulties* (Melbourne, 1888), give interesting contemporary sketches. There is a singular dearth of such for the Otago goldfields: but I have been able to make use of notes on contemporary newspapers and Provincial Council records made

[1] D. E. M. Cubis, 'Australian Character in the Making' (Royal Australian Historical Society, *Journal and Proceedings*, xxiv, 1938).

for another purpose some years ago. The account of the origins of the Thames fields must be sought in the Appendices to the Journals of the New Zealand House of Representatives.

The only systematic treatment of the Queensland goldfields is W. Lees's compilation, *The Queensland Goldfields, 1858–1899* (Brisbane, 1899), which is not written primarily as a history and at some points requires to be used with caution, but contains data not available elsewhere. J. T. S. Bird, *Early History of Rockhampton* (Rockhampton, 1904), is especially useful on the Canoona episode. A group of books, E. B. Kennedy, *Four Years in Queensland* (London, 1870); C. H. Allen, *A Visit to Queensland and her Goldfields* (London, 1870); 'An Eight Years' Resident' [E. Thorne], *The Queen of the Colonies* (London, 1876), deal with the early days of Gympie, and the last has some interesting material of a general character: the eight years were 1863–71. On Charters Towers, there is *The North Queensland Register's Mining History of Charters Towers* (Charters Towers, 1897), but it has disappointingly little on the early years. Mulligan's prospecting expeditions are described in R. L. Jack, *Northmost Australia* (2 vols., London, 1921), and there is a little also about the earliest days of the Palmer Rush. The Wardens' Reports, etc., are in the Queensland Parliamentary Papers, but these are not as informative as might be hoped.

J. S. Battye's *History of Western Australia* (Oxford, 1924) is the most scholarly history of any Australian State. It has a fairly full account of the goldfields down to the entrance of Western Australia into the Commonwealth. There is also a very useful history of mineral discoveries in the *Western Australian Year Book for 1902–04* (Perth, 1906). H. P. Woodward, *Mining Handbook to the Colony of Western Australia* (Perth, 1904), is useful on mining methods. The Wardens' Reports mostly confine themselves to actual mining, water supply and communications. The best contemporary book on mining life is D. W. Carnegie, *Spinifex and Sand* (London, 1898). Julius M. Price, *The Land of Gold* (London, 1896), is a good account by a visiting journalist; R. Radclyffe, *Wealth and Wildcats* (London, 1898), is graphic, but not very specific in detail; John Marshall, *Battling for Gold* (Melbourne, 1903), is vague as to dates but generally convincing. Of various works by A. F. Calvert, *The Coolgardie Goldfield* (London, 1894) is the best. O. Chemin, *De Paris aux mines d'or de l'Australie Occidentale* (Paris, 1900), is useful on the mining boom. Sir John W. Kirwan, *My Life's Adventure* (London, 1936), is a book of reminiscences by a very well-informed observer; W. Lambden Owen, *Cossack Gold* (Sydney, 1933), is slighter, but worth reading.

CHAPTER IX

THE DIAMONDS OF KIMBERLEY AND THE GOLD OF THE RAND

THE gold excitement of the mid-nineteenth century infected a few South Africans, and some of them returned to prospect the valleys of their own land. One of these prospectors, P. J. Marais, who had taken part both in the Californian and in the Australian rushes, seems to have discovered gold in the Crocodile valley in October 1853 and exhibited specimens to the wondering burghers of the Transvaal in December. The Volksraad of this simple, conservative pastoral community, whose occupation of the high veld was less than twenty years old and whose claim to independence had been admitted by the British Government less than two years before, must have been torn between hopes of prosperity and fears of an influx of diggers from abroad: the offer of a reward to Marais if he discovered a profitable goldfield seems to have been coupled with a requirement that he should give no information to any foreign Government. But Marais failed to find a payable goldfield and thus extricated the Volksraad from its dilemma.

The belief that the country was gold-bearing, however, was hard to eradicate; and sooner or later it was likely to gain sustenance from the discovery of the ancient gold workings farther north and of the gold barter that had been carried on for hundreds of years with the Arabs and Portuguese on the coast. Hartley,

a hunter of ivory, saw some of the workings and heard
from native guides the secret of the trade with the
Portuguese. In 1866 he invited Karl Mauch, an enterprising young German geologist, to accompany him to
Matabeleland. They made two journeys, in 1866 and
1867: the first was encouraging, the second gave
substance to their hopes. Mauch found gold in quartz
outcrops in various spots in Mashonaland and more
especially on the Tati, in the borderland between the
Bechuana and the Matabele country. He himself had
doubts as to whether the gold could be worked in this
remote district and whether the Matabele would permit
it to be; but the newspaper accounts after the expedition's return to Pretoria in December 1867 said much of
the extent of the 'goldfield' and nothing of the difficulties. The reports attracted attention in London and
brought two shiploads of diggers from Australia to
Durban. They also led the Government of the Transvaal
to seek to annex the country, in the first instance by the
despatch of an envoy to the Bamangwato and Matabele
chiefs, and then by proclamation extending the boundaries of the republic. The British Government, however,
declined to recognise the proclamation: Portugal,
awaking from its sleep, protested: the envoys were unsuccessful: and a petition from the Bamangwato chief
to the High Commissioner at Capetown to 'govern the
gold-diggers in the name of the Queen of England' had
for the time being equally little effect. There was,
therefore, no regular authority at Tati. In any case only
a hundred diggers made their way up in 1868; and
most of them probably did not stay long, for quartz-
working in that remote, dry, provisionless country was
a thankless task. The London capitalists had more
reason to hope for success, and about May 1870

Captain Levert, on behalf of one group which had already brought up machinery, secured from the new Matabele chief, Lobengula, an exclusive concession for the Tati region. A certain amount of work continued to be done at Tati, not only by this company, but by others on sufferance; but it was not until the advent of the railway—the British South Africa Company's railway—twenty-five years later that production became regular and important. The Tati discovery introduced a few experienced prospectors into South Africa, and for a few years prospecting was hopefully carried on in Natal, in the Transvaal, in the Matabele and Mashona country, even in parts of the Cape, but still no gold rush occurred.

No gold rush was indeed destined to occur in South Africa until practically all the phenomena of an alluvial gold rush had been produced by the discovery of diamonds. The history of this rush is so closely intertwined with the history of gold in South Africa that it must be treated at length. The first diamond was found in the Hopetown district of the Cape Colony in 1867 by pure chance. When this stone was known to be a diamond, search was naturally made for others, and in more than one district a stone was picked up. In 1869 attention began to be concentrated on the banks of the lower Vaal, and towards the end of that year some Australian gold-diggers on a prospecting party from Natal initiated the practice of digging for diamonds. They 'shovelled the gravel into cradles . . . picked out the coarser stones by hand, washed away the sand and lighter pebbles, and saved the heavy mineral deposit, hoping to find some grains of gold as well as diamonds above the screens of their cradles'.[1] After some weeks'

[1] Gardner F. Williams, *The Diamond Mines of South Africa* (New York, 1906), i, 125.

unsuccessful work, the diggers turned their attention to a gravel hummock or kopje, pointed out by Koranna natives as having yielded some small surface diamonds. It yielded richly. As Gardner Williams says, 'such a discovery could not long be concealed from visiting traders and roaming prospectors, and before three months had passed some prying eye saw half a tumblerful of the white sparkling crystals in their camp'.[1] The secret was out, and a diamond rush to Klipdrift began.

The South African colonies and states had long been depressed by drought, financial embarrassment and stoppage of railway construction, and a war between the Free State and the Basuto; and men of all classes and types welcomed this new opportunity of adventure and wealth. In June 1870 the diggers were to be numbered in hundreds only: by October there were probably more than 10,000 on the banks of the Vaal, more than half of them whites. The majority came from Cape Colony, but Natal had its full share, and the stolid Boers of the Republics were by no means immune from the fever. The means of transport was the long, low ox-waggon, with its seven to ten yoke of oxen, its convex wooden frame and canvas roof—the South African counterpart of the 'prairie schooner'. The mission station of Pniel on the opposite bank from Klipdrift soon rivalled it in importance, and before the end of the year the white camps of the diggers spread for eighty miles along the tree-fringed river.

The diggers knew they had no legal title to the ground, but, to quote Gardner Williams again, 'their rocky field was so apparently worthless that no farmer had cared to secure it'.[2] At first, as in California in 1848,

[1] Gardner F. Williams, *The Diamond Mines of South Africa* (New York, 1906), i, 126.　　　　　　[2] *Op. cit.* i, 145.

they dug and moved on as they pleased, but the growth of numbers and the superior richness of certain places entailed some limitation, and some time in the course of the year an informal mass meeting chose a committee to institute a system of registered claims. The size was soon settled at thirty feet square—in this following Australian rather than American practice—and certificates were to be granted by the committee; the water's edge remained open to all for washing; no man was allowed more than one claim, save prospectors, who were allowed four; absence for more than three working days entailed forfeiture. Only the regulation that no party should employ more than five natives could be described as peculiarly South African.

The diggers' life resembled that of many another alluvial mining camp in its mixture of races and costumes, its rapidly rising buildings, its lively trade, its crude but vigorous night life, even its oddly incongruous ritual observance of Sunday. In the matter of food supplies the Vaal River diggings compared favourably with most of the American and Australian camps; for not only beef and mutton and game but maize meal were plentiful, and tobacco, butter, eggs and honey were also to be had in more limited quantities. A market was held in the early morning, supplies being commonly sold from the waggons of the farmers who had brought them in. Vegetables and forage, and after a time fuel, were scarce, and general merchandise, having to be brought from the coastal ports in lumbering ox-waggons, was dear.

The early harmony of mining camps was apt to be transient. Here on the Vaal it was soon disturbed by rival claims to political authority. At Klipdrift, north of the river, the first Government to make its claim heard was that of the Transvaal, but it spoiled its chances by ignoring the diggers and granting a twenty-one-year monopoly of the right to search for diamonds along the Vaal. The diggers refused to recognise any such concession and asserted the authority of their own elected committee. Stafford Parker, a sailor who had some years' experience of the native tribes and had been on the spot since the beginning of the search for diamonds, was elected 'President of the Diggers' Republic' and exercised a quasi-magisterial authority in an effective rough-and-ready way. President Pretorius of the Transvaal sought to retrieve his blunder by cancelling the concession, and visited the diamond fields in September, offering them a large measure of autonomy; but his attempts at conciliation did not succeed. South of the Vaal President Brand of the Free State appointed on 29 August a magistrate with gold-digging experience whose authority was judiciously exercised and consequently won more respect. But the Boer Republic and the diggers were not the only parties interested. Certain chiefs of the coloured peoples of the region, more particularly Waterboer at Griquatown, also asserted claims. Waterboer, influenced by his able agent David Arnot, did not pretend to be able to cope personally with the diamond-diggers but requested that he and his people might be taken under British protection and his territory annexed. There was merely an Acting High Commissioner at Capetown at the time, and in any case the question of annexation was obviously one for London; but the appointment of a magistrate under the Cape of Good Hope Punishment Act, which provided for cases outside the colonial borders, was an indication that the authorities at Capetown could not but interest themselves in a territory now swarming with British subjects and claimed by a friendly chief. When the magistrate arrived at Klipdrift on 13 December, 'President' Parker, who had found the Free State claims troublesome even in the bosom of his committee, abdicated in his favour. The British flag had not yet come to Klipdrift, but it was on its way.

Before the political dispute came to a head, however, its venue had shifted. In August an overseer found a fifty-carat diamond on a farm, Jagersfontein, away from the river. Next month some children picked out diamonds from the mud with which another farmhouse was plastered. These discoveries revealed the possibility of dry diamond diggings and, as success was achieved, diverted interest particularly to a saucer-like depression known as Dutoitspan. Permission to dig was obtained, in one case at least reluctantly, from the proprietors of the farms in return for a monthly licence fee. Digging was easier than on the river: there was no question of standing knee-deep in water cradling: but at first claim-holders thought they had exhausted their claims when they came to a bed of limestone a couple of feet or so down. When, however, some enterprising digger took it into his head to sink through the limestone, and found that it soon gave way to yellowish diamond-bearing decomposed rock, the attractions of the dry diggings quite outweighed those of the river. Early in 1871 Klipdrift and Pniel, having grown from mere camps into regular towns, began to decline almost as speedily as they had risen: the rush 'left nothing much behind but empty sardine and canned-meat tins, paper collars, broken pipes and mud walls. . . . The newspapers with their presses and type, the canteen-keepers with their barrels and bottles, the smith with his bellows and anvil, the shoemaker with lapstone and hammer, the clock and

319

watchmaker with all his time-keepers and jewellery, the chemist and druggist with his drugs, the doctors with their instruments, marched off in long processions for the new diggings.'[1] Dutoitspan was the new centre: near it was half a square mile of claims thirty feet square, 'a chaotic mass of irregularly shaped holes of various depths, and endless whitish mounds of various sizes'.[2] There was indeed a new complication, for the ownership of the diamond-bearing farms was bought by capitalist syndicates, but an open clash between the proprietors and the diggers was avoided for the time by the Free State Government, which arranged that there should be a monthly licence fee of ten shillings: five shillings going to the Government, four shillings to the proprietors, one shilling to a committee elected by the diggers of each camp.

The search extended from Dutoitspan to neighbouring farms. Diamonds were found on Bultfontein, then on Vooruitzigt: finally in July 1871 a discovery of surpassing richness was made by Rawstorne, a young man from Colesberg, under an old thorn-tree crowning a grassy knoll about a mile beyond the first Vooruitzigt discovery. Such was the extent of the 'new rush' that within a fortnight claims could only be had by purchase at a price ranging from £20 to £100: within three months the price had been forced up to £2000–£4000. By that time some claim-holders had made fortunes, and a contemporary happens to mention that within twenty days 110 carats of diamonds had been found by 'Mr. Rhodes of Natal'.[3] 'Colesberg kopje' was buzzing with

[1] R. W. Murray, *South African Reminiscences* (Capetown, 1894), pp. 236-7.
[2] C. A. Payton, *The Diamond Diggings of South Africa* (London, 1872), p. 15.
[3] *Ibid.* p. 215. This was probably Herbert Rhodes, though Cecil John, a lad of eighteen, was for a time in charge of his brother's claims.

diamond-diggers. The claims, thirty-one feet square in the first instance, were often subdivided into quarters.[1] On each from six to a dozen men, European and native, might be seen at work. On the veld away from the kopje, as a rule, were the sorting-tables. 'Here', writes an observer of the early months, 'under awnings of various kinds, rugs, blankets, etc., placed on four props round the table, sit men, and many ladies too, with the "scraper" in one hand, and sometimes a horse's, cow's or wildebeest's tail in the other, for flicking the flies away, while their partners, or the more than half naked black labourers, bring down the precious stuff from the claims in carts, wheelbarrows, or very commonly in a bullock's hide sewn to two poles, and sift it there.'[2] Within three months there was a town beside the diggings. A description of the approach from Pniel in November is worth quotation. 'Far off, on a low swell that reached our horizon, appeared a broken crest, faintly white against the sky. . . . Only a white sheen of tents along the ridge. . . . So on, lost and regained alternately, with every glimpse more dingy and more broken, until the pale grey mounds of "sorted stuff" came into view. Then lonely little camps occurred, consisting perhaps of a family waggon with two or three gipsy tents around, and little heaps of whitey soil; the whole encircled with a six-inch ditch, and a fence, may be, of thorns. These are mostly occupied by Boers, who carry their stuff home for wives and children to "sort". Further on are more pretentious dwellings, houses of canvas stretched on wooden framework, with neat

[1] Thirty Boer feet were equivalent to thirty-one British feet: here the claims were first delimited under Free State auspices.

[2] Payton, *op. cit.* p. 23. For another description, by Cecil Rhodes, of methods of working late in 1871 see Basil Williams, *Cecil Rhodes* (London, 1921), p. 28.

windows cut in them, bound with coloured braid or ribands round the edge. . . . The mounds of "sortings" are now close by, thronged with busy men. . . . The roadway grows snowy white. Our wheels sink in "diamondiferous sand", brought from a depth of fifty feet. Piled up on either hand, it narrows the road to the last inch. We seem to be in a cutting, ten feet deep. Above us on each side, the sieves are endlessly at work, throwing a cloud of poisonous dust upon the wind. . . . Here and there, the mound falls back to give a "canteen" place for plying trade. . . . The treasure-bearing sand is borne past us each moment, in screaming bullock dray, and mule cart, and sack and bucket of the Kaffir. It goes to those solitary tents outside. We approach the business quarter. . . . The excavated road becomes a street. Wooden houses show themselves, all hung about with miscellaneous goods. Broadcloth and snowy *puggaries* are seen. Thicker and thicker stand the tents, closer presses the throng. A din of shouts and laughter fills the air. We pass large drinking shops full of people; negroes go by in merry gangs. . . . One more sharp turn, and the market square opens before us, with Main Street on the right . . . as regular as mathematics can make them.'[1] Such was the Kimberley rush in its early months, a compound of the ingredients of any alluvial diggings and of the South African environment.

It was in the early months of the new rush that the political future of the diamond fields was decided. The Orange Free State undoubtedly performed some governmental functions from an early stage of the dry diggings. Its magistrate moved from Pniel to Dutoitspan. It allowed diggers' committees considerable scope, but it at any rate shared responsibility for a sensible attempt

[1] F. Boyle, *To the Cape for Diamonds* (London, 1873), pp. 111-13.

to facilitate the working of claims at the new rush by requiring all claim-holders to leave one-fourth of their claims as a roadway. It was perhaps unfortunate for the Free State that the Griqua title to the diamond fields was first urged in connection with the unsettled banks of the Vaal rather than with the farms of the dry diggings, and that the Transvaal Government showed its ineptitude before its own more prudent line of policy could be developed. But once the Cape Government had appointed its magistrate at Klipdrift, no action by the Free State authorities on the other side of the river was likely to be allowed to prejudge Waterboer's claim to the diamond fields or the consideration by the Imperial Government of his request for incorporation in the British dominions. An attempt by the Free State Government early in 1871 to coerce the diggers at one river camp into the payment of licence fees was firmly resisted not merely by the diggers but by the British magistrate. Moreover Lord Kimberley, the Secretary of State for the Colonies, returned a favourable answer to Waterboer's request—and clearly not so much on account of the strength of his legal case, as in the belief that the influx of diamond-diggers, most of them British subjects, required an acceptable, regularly established government. The fact that Lord Kimberley proposed government as part of the Cape Colony, and Sir Henry Barkly, the new High Commissioner, finding this unpopular both at the Cape and on the diamond fields, decided to proceed nevertheless with the annexation, is not very material from our present point of view. Suffice it to say that the annexation was proclaimed on 17 November 1871 and that President Brand, whilst protesting against it, did not attempt to resist it.

It was thus a British authority that had to preside

over the transition from rush conditions to regular industry, over the evolution of Colesberg kopje into Kimberley. An emigration from Europe to the diamond fields was now beginning, not indeed large in scale, but including men with capital who aided in the differentiation of the diamond-diggings from the common type of alluvial gold rushes. Skilled diamond-buyers began to appear, Jews being very prominent among them. The smaller buyers perambulated the fields : one of the greatest figures of the diamond fields, Barney Barnato, learnt his trade in this manner. There were still storekeepers who bought diamonds, and we hear of one man who 'combined in his own person the various functions of dissenting minister, dentist, watchmaker and jeweller, homœopathic chemist, and diamond buyer'.[1] The Standard Bank of South Africa made advances on diamonds. But it was the development of the large diamond-buyer and the diamond broker that was typical of the coming industrial stage of the diamond diggings.

Already the wealth of the diamond fields was stimulating trade and agriculture all over South Africa. The benefit to neighbouring farmers was obvious; but there was a market also for the sub-tropical products of Natal and the wines and fruit of the Cape. The overseas trade of Capetown and of the eastern ports, East London and Port Elizabeth—the latter particularly so far as the heavier merchandise was concerned—flourished as never before. The waggon-building industry of the Paarl district received a fillip from the demand for transport to and from the fields.

But transitions from a rush to a more settled condition of things were apt to be painful. A psychological and economic reaction after the optimistic speculation

[1] C. A. Payton, *op. cit.* p. 118.

of the rush was unavoidable. Australian experience did
not suggest that the monthly licence system would permanently reconcile the interests of the diggers, the farm
proprietors and the Government. Californian experience
did not suggest that a community with the racial mixture and the social traditions of South Africa would pass
easily through the period now beginning.

The South African custom of leaving heavy manual
labour to natives and confining them to such labour had
not at first been universally observed on the diamond
fields: early writers mention cases—indeed they seem
to have been common on the river diggings—where all
the work on a claim was done by white men according
to the diggers' custom in Australia and America. But
some diggers had brought their native servants with
them and some employed native labour available on the
spot. Moreover South African diamond-diggers had
not to depend for their labour upon enslavement of
Indians or negroes like the mine-owners of Brazil
and Spanish America. Wages might be earned on the
diamond fields—thirty shillings a month with food. As
this news spread to the kraals there ensued a native
diamond rush, harder to parallel than the white man's
rush which had preceded and caused it. 'First', writes
Gardner Williams, 'came the neighbouring Griquas,
Koranas and Batlapins, with Basutos from their
southern reservation, followed by a stream of Zulus,
Mashowas, Makalakas and Hottentots, and Kafirs of a
hundred tribes, ranging east to the Indian Ocean and
far north-west into Namaqua and Bechuana lands and
north-east into Matabeleland and the regions lying
beyond the Limpopo and the Zambesi. The white
diamond-seekers were willing to pay, for a few months'
hunting for little white pebbles, enough to buy a cheap

gun and a bag of powder and balls—most precious of all earthly things in the eyes of a roving African. Then the white camps were lively, humming social resorts, abounding with good food and tempting drink, where black men were welcome and well protected. So the natives swarmed in faster and faster. . . . Some of this swarm could be persuaded to remain at the mines for a year or more and work quite steadily; but most drifted away at the end of a few months, or as soon as they were able to get their coveted guns and powder pouches.'[1] The labour was unskilled, but it was cheap and it was willing. Soon the restriction of Europeans to overseeing and sorting was taken for granted, and even sorting was often done by natives under European supervision.

This influx of natives gave a characteristic colour to the life of the diamond camps. To quote Gardner Williams again, 'no mining camp on earth ever before held such a motley swarm of every dusky shade, in antelope skins and leopard skins and jackal skins and bare skins—with girdles and armlets of white oxtails, and black crane plumes and gorgeous bird feathers, and dirty loin cloths, and ragged breeches, and battered hats and tattered coats. With and without the fire of rum they might dash off at any moment into some wildly whirling reel or savage dance, gabbling in a hundred dialects, whooping with weird cries, and chanting plaintive, gay and passionate strains, now dissonant, now sweet. Whenever a new party of "raw" natives came in from the wilderness, weary, grimy, hungry, shy, trailing along sometimes with bleeding feet and hanging heads, and bodies staggering with faintness, a howl of jeers was a common greeting, and a pelting with rotten fruits and stones was likely to follow

[1] Gardner Williams, *op. cit.* i, 188-9.

the scared troop up the street of the camp, though the natives were not churlish at heart, and might, afterwards, share their last crust with the strangers.'[1] But the control of this native diamond rush obviously set the authorities a difficult problem, and its difficulty was increased in one respect by the British annexation, for the new Government did not debar natives and coloured men from holding a digging licence. The number who actually held such licences must have been small, and Theal states that even under the Free State Government 'those who wore clothing and presented a respectable appearance were not prevented from digging for themselves'.[2] But the place of the native and coloured man in society was a matter that had caused friction for more than a generation past between the imperial authorities and South African public opinion. Moreover, with the employment of natives on sorting, diamond thefts by natives, who disposed of the stones through canteen-keepers of a low type, began to be a subject of complaint; and native claim-holding, it was said, gave facilities for the concealment of diamond-stealing.

A month after the British annexation, on learning that a canteen-keeper had been implicated by the confession of a native in the buying of stolen diamonds, a mob of diggers burnt down a number of low-class canteens. The ringleaders were later brought before the court and bound over to keep the peace; but it was impossible, with a scanty force of police recruited from such material as rush conditions offered, to ignore the

[1] *Op. cit.* p. 218.

[2] G. M. Theal, *History of South Africa from 1795 to 1872*, vol. iv (4th edition, London, 1919), p. 355. These were no doubt 'Cape coloured' people, *i.e.* men of slave, Hottentot and mixed blood.

strong opinion of the camp, voiced by a committee of diggers recognised by the British authorities, against native claim-holding. There was friction also over the enforcement of the farm proprietors' share in the licence fees and the supersession of claim-jumping by the auctioning of vacated claims—which would tell in favour of the man with capital. Despite the imposition of heavy penalties in May 1872 on the sale or purchase of uncut diamonds by unauthorised persons, illicit diamond-buying went on; and in July it provoked riots of a more serious character than those of the previous December. Many canteens were burnt. The British Commissioners appealed to the steadier section of the digging community to assist in the maintenance of order, but they deemed it wise to agree to suspend the issue of licences to natives or other coloured persons except on the production of a certificate from a diggers' committee. Sir Henry Barkly disapproved of this concession, and instead made it necessary for any registered claim-holders in future to secure a certificate from a magistrate or justice of the peace—a less obnoxious method of achieving the diggers' aim. He also prohibited canteen-keepers, under penalty of whipping, imprisonment and expulsion, from dealing in diamonds. Then the claim-holders began to find that illicit diamond-buying was virtually independent of native claim-holding and was inherent in the employment of ignorant, ill-paid, easily led natives in the extraction of a product at once extremely valuable and easily concealed.

The strains and stresses of 1872 were partly due to a factor not to be found on goldfields, a sharp fall in the market price of diamonds, caused, of course, by the diggers' success but attributed by them to conspiracy among the diamond-buyers. The dealers were nervous of new discoveries. '*Without* new fields', wrote Boyle, 'the crowds arriving cannot live; *with* them . . . the present race of diggers horribly fear their dwindling profits will vanish altogether.'[1] There were alarums and excursions, but no discoveries. As hopes and fears dwindled, the population of the diamond fields—estimated by Sir Henry Barkly in September 1872 at 16,000 whites, and 21,000 natives, and often reckoned higher—began to decrease. Moreover as the digging went deeper a number of claim-holders were unable to bear the increased expense of working. In the later months of 1872 the roads which had served to cart the stuff and separate the claims at the Kimberley mine fell in. And at a depth of fifty or sixty feet the 'yellow ground' gave way to a slaty blue breccia composite, which was also diamond-bearing but was best given some weeks to disintegrate by exposure to the air. The smaller men could not afford to pay more or wait longer for their returns. The decline of the small claim-holder was arrested when from about the end of 1874 an improved water supply permitted large numbers of diggers to wash the debris heaps by adaptations of the gold-diggers' cradles and puddling machines. A few months afterwards the population was officially estimated at 15,000 white persons of all classes, 10,000 coloured persons and 20,000 native labourers from the interior. But debris-washing was not a permanent industry.

Whilst the diamond industry was thus painfully changing its character, political conditions naturally remained unsettled. Early in 1873 Richard Southey, who had for many years been Colonial Secretary of the Cape and was as much responsible as any man for the annexation of the diamond fields, was appointed their

[1] F. Boyle, *op. cit.* p. 367.

administrator. A few months later he became lieutenant-
governor of the new Crown Colony of Griqualand West,
with a partly elected legislative council to assist him and
his executive in the government. Southey attacked his
problems with vigour and decision. He tightened up
the liquor and diamond-selling laws. He issued a proclamation against gambling, which, though it never
flourished as it did in the Rocky Mountain mining
camps, had become a pest. He took a strong line with
the farm proprietors, who wished to raise the licence fee
from ten shillings to five pounds and at Kimberley ten
pounds monthly, by arguing that they were quit-rent
tenants only, without right to the minerals and precious
stones. But these measures added a number of vested
interests to the opposition he had to face. The appointment of a commission including four respected diggers
and two officials to report on the mines and their management and the subsequent passage of a new Mining
Ordinance, under which a Mining Board was elected in
July 1874, were followed not by a diminution but by
an increase of political agitation. At various times administrative grievances were put forward, and the mention of such matters as the requirement that diamonds
be purchased at offices only, the restrictions on liquor-
selling, and the fees payable on registered native servants show the composite character of the agitation.
But Southey was probably right in his suggestion that
its real strength lay in the feeling against licences for
coloured persons—and the related matter of illicit diamond-buying—and in the friction between diggers
and proprietors. In the minds of some of the diggers,
however, the objects of the agitation extended a good
deal beyond the remedying of grievances, however important. They sought to impose on members of the

'Defence League and Protection Association' a pledge to pay no taxes to government 'until such time as the League declares by a majority that the people are taxed, ruled and legislated for by themselves under a free and liberal Government'.[1] Moreover, as in the agitation that preceded the Eureka stockade, there was a section— with an English element in it but with an erratic Irish Fenian and a German prominent as leaders—which was willing to use physical force and began drilling with that end in view. The details hardly concern us here, for there was no Kimberley stockade, nor had the agitation important political consequences. Barkly clearly thought Southey too intransigent and was unwilling to offend the Republics by sending an armed force to a region in which they still claimed an interest, but in May 1875 he agreed to Southey's pressing request, and on 30 June 1875 the troops arrived, the agitation evaporated, its leaders being arrested (though not punished) and their association dissolved. About the same time the Government purchased Vooruitzigt farm for £100,000 —an advance of £94,000 on the price paid by De Beers of Port Elizabeth in 1870.

Having bought out the proprietors, the Government was able to grant secure titles for both claims and buildings. Kimberley indeed remained a frontier community. It was a town of canvas and galvanised iron. As yet lacking an abundant supply of pure water, it lacked not only gardens and flowers but sanitation worthy of the name. Its unpaved market-place was still full every morning of ox-waggons laden with foodstuffs, forage, firewood and so forth: indeed all goods still came by ox-waggon across the veld. On the other hand, the farmer-diggers

---

[1] *The Diamond Field*, 25 November 1874, enclosed in Southey to Barkly (26 November) and printed in *Parl. Papers*, 1875, lii [Cmd. 1342], p. 22.

of the early days had largely given place to a cosmopolitan crowd of adventurers, not to say wastrels, from Europe.

A practical digger was still often responsible for the working of a claim, finding superintendence, labour, gear and tools, and receiving a half or three-quarters of the proceeds. But ownership was passing into the hands of capitalists. At first no digger was supposed to hold more than two claims: in 1874 the number was increased to ten: in 1876 the Mining Board removed the restriction altogether. The new owners, however, inherited from the days of individualistic digging a minutely subdivided mine. As the diggings increased in depth the technical problems were met with remarkable ingenuity. After the collapse of the roads the Kimberley mine was surrounded by a massive timber staging connected by ropes with the separate claims in the pit, by this time hundreds of feet deep. 'The din and rattle of the thousands of wheels and the twang of the buckets along the ropes', we are told, 'were something deafening, while the mine itself seemed almost darkened by the thick cobweb of ropes.'[1] But the difference in depth of individual claims and the undermining of the walls of the pit as it deepened caused falls of reef which could not be adequately met by the co-operative machinery of the Mining Board. The accumulation of surface water was another serious problem. Underground working was the real solution, and that required not merely large-scale enterprise but either fully effective co-operation or unified control.

Diamond-mining was now becoming a large-scale industry, drawing its native labour from an increasingly

---

[1] T. Reunert, *Diamonds and Gold in South Africa* (Capetown, etc., 1893), p. 27. There are illustrations in Gardner Williams.

wide field. It was natural that claim-holders should attempt to draw capital from an increasingly wide field also, and that despite the prejudices of diggers of the old school claims should pass from individuals to joint-stock companies. By the beginning of 1881 there were, according to one authority, about a dozen companies operating in the Kimberley mine with a total capital of about £2,500,000, the most successful diggers, however, still holding most of the shares. Then there ensued the speculative boom which the history of gold rushes would lead us to expect. 'The various offices of companies in formation were simply stormed,' says the authority just quoted, 'and those who could not get in at the door from the pressure of the crowd, threw their applications for shares (to which were attached cheques and banknotes) through the windows, trusting to chance that they might be picked up.'[1] The mania spread from the diamond fields themselves throughout South Africa and even attracted some capital from Europe. In six months the number of companies rose to over seventy, their nominal capital to over £8,000,000. Needless to say there was much unsound financing and incompetent management, and more than a little fraud and 'salting' of mines. In June the boom was sharply checked by the decision of the banks to make no more advances on mining securities. It enhanced rather than diminished the technical difficulties, for pressure for dividends led at first to increased output and then to increasingly serious falls of reef. The Mining Board, vainly attempting to cope with these through assessments on claim-holders, went bankrupt in March 1883. Later in that year open-cut working became almost impossible in the Kimberley mine. Its difficulties diverted

[1] J. W. Matthews, *Incwadi Yami* (London, 1887), pp. 246-7.

attention to the other mines, notably De Beers, which improved in richness as it went deeper; but eventually they too were brought by reef falls to an impasse. Underground working clearly required larger capital expenditure, and in view of the jealousies inevitable among large competing companies the technical case for unified working of each mine was by the middle 'eighties increasingly plain.

The increasing dominance of the big men was also visible in the 'eighties in the increased stringency of the law against illicit diamond-buying—which may be regarded as the revenge of the unscrupulous small men upon the dominant class of claim-owners. The very difficulty of suppressing 'I.D.B.' shows that a considerable section of the community was prepared to wink at it. According to Matthews the ultimate destination of the diamonds stolen by the raw Kaffir and passed on to the 'swell native' and from him to the low-class white man was generally some licensed diamond-buyer. Diamond-stealing was not in itself a worse crime than any other kind of stealing. But the rigour of the measures instituted in 1880–82 against it—the special court and special police force, the placing of the *onus probandi* on the holder of uncut diamonds—testifies to the power of the diamond magnates, who attributed to it the fall in the price of diamonds and the increasing embarrassment of the industry. It was an offence not only against morality but against monopoly.

In the early and middle 'eighties the trend towards monopoly in the diamond mines was unmistakable, but it was still a question how far it would go. French banking interests seem to have attempted to bring about an amalgamation of interests in 1885, but they failed. At the end of that year there were still ninety-eight

separate holdings in the mines, a striking contrast with
the 3600 original claims, but complete amalgamation
must have seemed a long way off. In May 1887, however, Cecil Rhodes's company, formed in 1880, succeeded in consolidating all the holdings in De Beers
mine. The strongest claim-holder in the Kimberley
mine was Barnett Isaacs, known as Barney Barnato, who
had made his way by sheer energy, resourcefulness,
financial judgment and self-confidence from the streets
of Whitechapel to wealth and power on the diamond
fields. The two men had not yet come into conflict. The
considerations that led them to conflict belong rather
to the domain of human nature than to the technique of
diamond-mining. But Rhodes's imperialist aims could
obviously be more effectively promoted if he controlled
the entire diamond fields than if he rested content with
a single mine, and when he found that Barnato was determined to run the Kimberley mine in rivalry with De
Beers he took up the challenge with all his strength.
Alfred Beit, the Kimberley representative of the Paris
diamond firm of Porgès & Cie, stood behind Rhodes,
and when his financial resources no longer sufficed, the
Rothschilds were induced to finance him. The competition drove the price of shares in Barnato's company
up, the price of diamonds down. Barnato, being at
bottom a sensible man and realising that he could not
hold his own against such a financial combination
directed by so purposeful a genius, came to terms in
March 1888. To obtain control of the two poorer mines
was a matter of some importance, for they might de-
press the price of diamonds, but not of comparable
difficulty. The vast powers of the new combination, De
Beers Consolidated Mines Ltd., controlled by Rhodes,
Beit and Barnato, do not here concern us; but it is of

some interest and significance to observe how its powers were used in Kimberley.

Its treatment of its native employees derived in part from its position of monopoly. It developed the system of compounds instituted by Barnato's Central Company in 1885. This, of course, greatly facilitated precautions against diamond-stealing, particularly as the area of the compound was covered with fine wire-netting and a covered way constructed from the compound to the mine. The exclusion of liquor and playing-cards put an equally effective check on drunkenness and gambling. The opening of stores within the compounds caused objections from traders; but the construction of hospitals and dispensaries, swimming baths, churches and schools within them showed that their purpose was not merely repressive. The scene in a compound after the day's work was over was graphically described a few years later by a special correspondent of *The Times* (Lady Lugard). 'Perhaps as many as a hundred fires blazed before the open doors of the huts, and round each fire a circle was gathered of natives, dressed and undressed, varying in degrees of duskiness, but all alike composing groups in the warm flame-light with now a face here, an arm or a leg there, thrown into sharp relief that would have defied either painter or sculptor to reproduce. From black and grey and smoke-colour to the high lights of burnished copper, rendered sharper by the white and blue tongues of the blazing wood, no gradation was missing. Large three-legged pots were pushed into the embers and presided over by one or two members of each circle. The remainder, while they waited for their supper, were engaged in chatting, smoking, and playing a game with pebbles upon a sort of chess-board marked out in the earth. . . . Natives from all parts of South Africa live together harmoniously . . . but the custom is for the various tribes to have their separate huts and messing arrangements.'[1] For the white employees De Beers constructed a garden village.

With the arrival of the railway at Kimberley in November 1885, an arrival long delayed by the jealousies of Capetown, Port Elizabeth and East London, the diamond fields ceased to be a mere oasis of material wealth in the midst of the deserted veld. But their civilisation remained peculiar. Kimberley was still a polyglot, multicoloured town of corrugated iron. It still depended for its wealth on a few great pits which reminded a visitor of the craters of a volcano, and on the labours of a multitude of tribesmen who flocked to it, generally for a few months only at a time, from their distant homes over the veld. The output was as great as ever, £3,000,000 or so a year. What had changed profoundly was the economic and social system. On the river diggings, on a few smaller mines in Free State territory, the individual miner still worked away, in somewhat increased numbers after the rationalisation of the Kimberley mines. But the singularly free, if turbulent, society that had been brought to the diamond fields by the first rush had passed away: in its place was a rigorously controlled society, equipped with a scientifically managed industry, watched by a secret police, and dominated by a benevolent autocrat.

The course of events on the diamond fields, far from hampering the search for gold which had begun shortly before their discovery, stimulated it. Many failed to get remunerative claims, many others must have sold their

[1] *The Times* special correspondent, *Letters from South Africa* (London, 1893), p. 17.

claims for want of capital or from sheer restlessness. Some parties, especially of old Australian miners, left the diamond fields in the later months of 1871 for a reported goldfield at Eersteling, near Marabastad in the Northern Transvaal. It had been discovered by a Natal trader-prospector named Button two years previously, but only just disclosed to the Transvaal Government. Button was appointed Gold Commissioner, but after meeting the diggers to discuss regulations, proceeded to England to raise capital for working his reef. Operations continued for some years, but the few score diggers attracted to Eersteling mostly dispersed.

Many returned to the diamond fields, but some continued prospecting. McLachlan, who made the next discovery, was probably one of these. In February 1873 alluvial gold was reported six hours on horseback east of Lydenburg. 'Macmac' was rich in patches; and promising new finds, especially at Pilgrim's Rest, eight miles away, in September, retained a population of perhaps 1500 diggers for some time on these Lydenburg fields. The digging was strenuous: it was reported that many diamond-diggers 'when they see the work go back without putting a spade in the ground'.[1] Natives were employed; but Scully, who 'hired a couple of boys to carry down the wash', himself worked with a pick and shovel and his partner washed the dirt.[2] It suited the men with Californian, Australian and New Zealand experience. The Transvaal President, Burgers, visiting the field in September 1873, appointed a gold commissioner and required the diggers to pay a monthly licence fee; but he recognised their claim to a voice in their own affairs—

---

[1] T. Baines, *The Gold Regions of South East Africa* (London, 1877), p. 161.
[2] W. C. Scully, *Reminiscences of a South African Pioneer* (London, 1913), p. 244.

not only through the machinery of a diggers' committee but through representation in the Volksraad. Later the diggers complained of inadequate police, of postal arrangements, roads, heavy licences and other dues, but such complaints were common form on gold rushes. A peculiarly South African turn was given to events on the goldfield, however, when in 1876 Sekukuni and his Bapedi rose against the Transvaal. The Transvaal Government was weak and mishandled the military operations. It was natural that the diggers, who still numbered 300 or 400, though the fields had passed their peak, and who were nearly all British subjects, should band together for their own defence and appeal to Natal, their chief base of supply, for British support. The Sekukuni war was certainly a factor in the British annexation of the Transvaal in 1877, and so was the prospect of mineral wealth, but the question was a complicated one. The connection between the Lydenburg diggings and the British intervention was not so close and direct as has sometimes been supposed.

Another discovery by an Australian digger, at Blaauwbank near Krugersdorp, late in 1874 had also attracted attention, though being of quartz it was less likely to produce a rush than the alluvial gold near Lydenburg. There seems to have been continuous interest in this discovery during the British annexation, and the British administration engaged men with Australian experience to report on this and other goldfields; but the reports were generally unfavourable and the gold yield was negligible.

The Boer Government to whom independence was restored in 1881 probably connected the Lydenburg diggings with the British annexation. Moreover the operations of prospectors and miners, digging holes on the farms and endangering the farmer's cattle and using his water, were no doubt irksome to the Transvaal Boers. Hence we find the new Government adopting a new gold policy, no longer favouring the individual digger but rather making concessions to capitalists and closing farms to prospectors unless the owner gave his consent. The new policy was applied at the Lydenburg fields, thousands of pounds being paid as compensation to the existing claim-holders. The London financiers interested seem to have burnt their fingers, but the diggers, who had quite possibly received more than they would actually have extracted from their claims, re-sumed prospecting. A discovery of rich patches of alluvial gold in 1882 at 'de Kaap', a bold headland on the eastern slope of the Drakensberg about fifty miles south-east of Lydenburg, again by a digger with Australian and New Zealand experience, gave the signal for a new rush. It was the more opportune because it came at the time when the diamond fields company boom had collapsed and the reef-falls seemed to be making the diamond mines unworkable. Some hundreds of diggers gathered on a plateau known as the Duivel's Kantoor (Devil's Counting-house); when the Government granted a concession to a company they spread farther afield. The next centre of interest was on a group of farms belonging to G. P. Moodie and situated about thirty miles away across the valley below de Kaap. Gold seems to have been discovered there in 1883, but the rush was at its height in 1884, when there was a long dispute between Moodie and a diggers' committee which claimed to exercise authority and turn off those who would not accept it. However, of the thousand or so who gathered at Moodie's only a few appear to have done well: the gold was mostly reef gold and a few stamp-batteries driven by water-wheels were all that could be erected to work it until rough roads were made. From Moodie's prospecting parties moved on. In 1884 Graham Barber discovered in a deep gorge the reef which gave its name to the most famous centre of the Kaap fields, Barberton. The richest reef, however, was about twelve miles away and a thousand feet higher up in the mountains. A sixty-year-old Yorkshireman named Edwin Bray, who had been prospecting in the Transvaal for nearly twenty years, so it is said, chanced to find a nugget, followed up his discovery by months of working on a shaft, abandoned this for lack of dynamite, began again on the open hillside with his pick and almost at once struck a reef which came to be known throughout the mining centres of the world as the Sheba. This took place some time in 1885; early in 1886 a company was formed, though it had no working capital and had to defray the cost of its first battery from the profits of experimental crushings.

So many reefs were discovered in the Barberton region that the concessions policy of the Transvaal Government broke down. A compromise was attempted between the small claim (now 150 feet square in alluvial ground: 150 by 300 on a reef) and the large concession: claim-holders were allowed to hold blocks of twelve claims for a merely nominal monthly payment whilst proving their ground. This expedient encouraged 'shepherding' and speculation, and in 1886 there was a boom in Barberton. The town itself, nestling at the foot of the steep range separating the Transvaal from Swaziland, soon had a population of about 4000, with hotels, stores, banks, Government offices, newspapers, two stock exchanges, churches, a theatre and two music-halls, and canteens by the hundred. There may have

been another 4000 in the surrounding country. Traders
and speculators arrived from Natal and from Kimberley.
Even the European financial centres took a hand. The
nominal capital of the companies' shares nearly reached
£2,000,000; the market value of their shares passed the
£5,000,000 mark. But the boom was short-lived. A
German mining engineer a few years later could point to
Barberton as a shining example of how not to conduct
gold-mining operations. Fees were paid to 'experts' who
merely walked over the ground and kicked a stone here
and there. Batteries were built by streams with insufficient water, dams constructed without regard to
their foundations. Reef companies with claims extensive
enough to command capital insisted on having batteries
and races and ropeways of their own.[1] Yet when crushings were made the yields were found to be unpayable.
Gardner Williams, a genuine expert from America and
the future manager and historian of the diamond mines,
was sent out to report on the reefs by a powerful London
group and impartially damned nearly all. The Barberton
bubble was pricked. There was gold in the Barberton
reefs; there was a fortune in the Sheba, which was
floated on the London market for £600,000 in October
1887; but there is a limit to the bad roads and bad
management that gold mines can stand. One does
indeed get the impression that most of the men who lost
money in Barberton were speculators who deserved to
lose it: there had been no alluvial to inaugurate a poor
man's rush. Alluvial was found near Steynsdorp to the
southward in 1885; and on the strength of rich outcrops
and some alluvial finds there was a scramble for concessions in 1886–87 in the land of the Swazi king. But
the taint of speculation was strong everywhere. There

[1] B. Knochenhauer, *Die Goldfelder in Transvaal* (Berlin, 1890).

was the noise and hurry but less of the honest toil of a genuine gold rush—though amongst it all patient, steady-going miners could be found.

The Barberton boom was merely a foretaste of what was to happen on the Witwatersrand. No single individual discovered the Rand. Prospectors had been active in this region thirty-five miles or so southwards of Pretoria ever since gold had been found at Blaauwbank. The most enterprising of them were the brothers Struben, who had experience of mining at Pilgrim's Rest and elsewhere and some command of capital: it was they who, under pressure, disclosed to the Transvaal Government in June 1885 their belief in the wide extent and depth of the gold-bearing conglomerate or 'banket' of the Rand. At first, however, their belief seemed ill justified by results. For its justification it needed a luckier strike, greater capital and equal faith. The main reef leader was discovered on Langlaagte farm in February or March 1886—precisely when and by whom are controverted points. In July the farm was bought by J. B. Robinson, a prominent figure on the diamond fields, disappointed by the course of events there and on the look-out for a new road to wealth. Apparently Robinson was backed by Alfred Beit, but it was his enterprise rather than Beit's. As soon as they heard the results of Robinson's pannings, Cecil Rhodes and his associate Rudd made their way up, began to acquire properties as Robinson was doing, and offered to amalgamate their interests with his. But Robinson preferred to hold aloof. In any case the really significant fact is not the exact priority of this or that capitalist but the circumstance that the Rand imported its capitalists ready-made from Kimberley. The gold rush to the Rand was from the first dominated not by a crowd of men who wished to make their fortune but by a few who had already made it.

The presence of these influential Kimberley capitalists also affected the policy of the Transvaal Government. The local machinery of landdrosts and veldcornets, which had grown out of the needs of a pastoral population, could be and was applied for such purposes as inspection of work in progress, proclamation of certain farms as goldfields as from 8 September 1886, and issue of mining licences under the existing gold law; but Robinson, Rhodes and the rest intended to make themselves heard on the terms of the gold law, and President Kruger and his Executive were quite willing to hear them. As we have already seen, since 1881 they had tended to favour the capitalist rather than the individual miner. Owners of farms were entitled to a mining lease of one-tenth of their area, and though at first sight this might appear to favour the Boer, in fact it favoured the capitalist who acquired the farm. Though claims might be taken up by diggers at a fee of one pound per month, half of this fee went to the owner of the farm. Though a Diggers' Committee was to be chosen to settle disputes, deal with applications for water-rights and other matters of common interest and represent the diggers in negotiation with the Government, the owners of proclaimed farms had seats on it beside the elected representatives. The provision for the amalgamation of adjoining claims to the number of twelve, the absence of any limitation on the purchase of claims, the emphasis placed on 'protection' rather than on 'jumping', are further indications that the atmosphere was very different from that of the American or Australian gold rushes or of the diamond fields in their early days. Moreover there is this to be said in defence of the policy of the capitalists and of the

Government. The Rand was no shallow, rich alluvial field: it was not even a quickly remunerative quartz reef: it was an immense body of low-grade ore requiring elaborate, large-scale working. It was lucky in having capitalists on the spot from the beginning instead of discovering its need of capital by dint of the trials and errors of smaller men.

At the time of the September proclamation the chief concentration of diggers was in Ferreira's camp of tents, reed huts and waggons. This, however, was found to lie on the main reef and the town of Johannesburg was laid out on a different site. The first 700 'stands' were put up to auction on 18 December. Within three or four months there were three streets lined with buildings, chiefly of unbaked brick or galvanised iron, erected by the mining men or by traders from Capetown, Port Elizabeth, East London, Durban, Kimberley. Within a year the population had risen to 5000 or 6000. The morning market of produce, firewood, etc., brought in by perhaps a hundred ox-waggons testified to the dependence of Johannesburg, like Kimberley before it, on supplies from the veld: the demands of the Diggers' Committee for a sanitary inspector, a district surgeon, a hospital, a telegraph, a water supply, were reminders to the Boer Government of the needs of urban civilisation. The Government indeed acceded to most of these demands and in November 1887 replaced the Diggers' Committee by a Sanitary Committee, whose powers covered a radius of three miles from the Post Office, but it refused to take the further step of erecting a municipality with power to deal with liquor and other licences and levy rates. Whether President Kruger and the Volksraad admitted it or not, however, modern urban civilisation had come to the Transvaal, with its appurtenances of hotels, banks, a stock exchange, newspapers, theatres and music-halls, and—though the actual buildings might be flimsy and soon pulled down—these institutions were not the mere mushroom growths of an ordinary gold-rush town but were as solid and enduring as the reef on which they were based.

The Rand nevertheless could not hope to escape the usual trials of a gold rush. The whole of the reef was not taken up by capitalists from Kimberley. When the fields were proclaimed there were perhaps 3000 prospectors scattered over thirty miles of country. The methods of the prospector were simple, not to say primitive. 'Breaking off a piece of the exposed banket, he pounded it up in a mortar and transferred the powder to his prospecting dish. The tail of gold, if present, was exposed.' [1] Then he estimated the yield per ton and decided whether or not to peg out a claim. Once the claim was pegged, however, the aim of the individual claim-holder and of the small syndicate, conditioned by their lack of capital, was to secure immediate results and sell. Cuttings would be made in the ground to lay bare the reef, and then men would 'sit on their claims waiting for the representative of a wealthy syndicate to come along and relieve them of their untested ground at a stiff price'.[2] The technical competence of the managers even of larger mines was low: they may have 'understood how to manage Kaffirs', but they did not understand how to develop gold mines, and where working capital was available much of it was undoubtedly wasted. There could be no question of a large output almost at once as in an alluvial rush: apparently only some 23,000 ounces were produced in 1887: but once crushings had

[1] Sir Lionel Phillips, *Some Reminiscences* (London [1924]), p. 104.
[2] E. P. Mathers, *The Goldfields Revisited* (Durban, 1887), pp. 267, 293.

begun in May, Johannesburg was ripe for a stock exchange boom. 'Sensational crushings', wrote Mathers, 'are being made from one rich narrow vein of banket for no other purpose than to off-load shares on to a still gullible public, and to refloat companies on the London market for amounts in no way warranted by the work done or the quantity of auriferous ground exposed.'[1]

The spectacular rise in diamond shares caused by Rhodes's amalgamation operations prevented markets in and outside South Africa from concentrating on gold shares. In March 1888 these operations were virtually concluded. The banks called in loans, with the result that gold as well as diamond shares fell sharply. But the set-back was only temporary. By about August the steadily augmenting production of gold—which reached 230,000 ounces in the year 1888—began to be translated into rising share values, and speculators and company-promoters were in their element.

The democratic atmosphere of a gold rush pervaded the Johannesburg Stock Exchange. 'Among the members', wrote a London broker, 'were men who had been store-keepers, canteen-keepers, lawyers, policemen, farmers, ostrich-feather dealers, clerks, bookmakers, one or two defaulting brokers from London, and there were some who were said to have been dealers in old clothes, and a good many of them looked as if that was their natural calling. There were men from Kimberley, too, some of whom were known to have taken the degree of I.D.B.'[2] But this informal,

---

[1] *Op. cit.* pp. 317-18.
[2] E. E. Kennedy, *Waiting for the Boom: A Narrative of Nine Months spent in Johannesburg* (London, 1890). Kennedy's description was of June 1889, but in this particular would apply earlier.

happy-go-lucky assemblage was in fact engaged in a contest for wealth and power and the equality was an illusion.

If there were true equalitarians in South Africa they were the prospectors who spread themselves far and wide over the Transvaal. They made discoveries in widely separated places about this time. Prospecting began at Klerksdorp, some eighty miles south-west of Johannesburg, about the end of 1886: reefs enough were found to justify its participation in the boom and in 1889 it had developed into a town of perhaps 3000 people. Prospecting in the Murchison Range in the far north-east may have been an outgrowth of the former discovery at Eersteling rather than of the Rand; but there seem to have been at least 1000 there in 1889. Yet the soil of the Transvaal remained inhospitable to the individual miner: alluvial discoveries were few and unimportant: companies to exploit the reefs were formed readily enough, but actual exploitation was a different matter. Rhodes's method of operation was more appropriate to the conditions of South African gold-mining. It was in the midst of the boom that the famous Rudd concession of exclusive rights to all metals and minerals in his dominions was granted by Lo Bengula, on 30 October 1888: a few months later, in their application for a charter, the promoters of the British South Africa Company stated that it was one of their objects 'to develop and work mineral and other concessions under the management of one powerful organisation'. There were, of course, other objects in Rhodes's mind: he desired to colonise Lo Bengula's country and to cut off the Transvaal from expansion northward: but it was to the activities of prospectors and to the half-interest it reserved for itself in mining companies arising out of them that the Chartered Company looked for its profits.

Meanwhile a check had been administered to the Rand boom. The companies, even the honest companies, were as a rule too small for the profitable working of low-grade ore; the technical skill of the management was inadequate; and pyritic ore was unexpectedly encountered in the best producing mines. In February 1889 the local banks, which had lent freely on the inflated scrip, called in their loans. The European stock markets were still in confident mood, for gold production was rising every month. But a drought, prolonged through the rainy season of 1889, deprived mining companies of water, sent food prices soaring, forced speculators to unload their shares in order to get the means to live, and drove native labourers away. The apprehension of famine was greater than the facts justified and may have been fostered by mining magnates and storekeepers anxious for a railway, but it sent a shiver through the Rand. Nor was London, with its own heavy load of mining shares, in a position to support Johannesburg. In November 1889 a steady decline in the Rand shares began; and when President Kruger, on a visit early in March 1890, refused the demands for a railway and for a reduction of taxation on mining claims, it was intensified. A depreciation of 30–50 per cent. in the last three months of the year was followed by a further depreciation of 50 or even 75 per cent. in the first three months of 1890. Some of the speculators merely decamped, perhaps after issuing worthless cheques: others returned to their farms or their stores: others, again, were tied to Johannesburg by their overdrafts and struggled through the depression as best they could.

The Rand had passed through the speculative boom, the stock market equivalent of an alluvial rush. The period that followed was one of technical progress and consolidation into a regular industry. The instruments of progress were many and varied. A discovery of coal, made by prospectors sinking for gold late in 1887, within easy reach of the Rand at Boksburg, proved to be the first of a series. Made available in the first instance by a tramway, it reduced the dependence of the Rand on wood fuel, inevitably dear in that treeless region. The advent of the railway from the Cape in September 1892 meant a great reduction in the cost of transport of mining machinery as well as of other supplies. The feverish competition in railway-building that ensued from Natal and Delagoa Bay, important as it was in the economic and political development of South Africa, need not be enlarged upon here: suffice it to say that it tended to lower freight rates further until in 1895 they ranged about a fourth of the rates in 1889. After long research in Scotland and experiment on the spot, the pyritic ores began towards the end of 1890 to be treated by the McArthur-Forrest cyanide process, which extracted about 75 per cent. of the gold. As 1891 wore on, the wealthier companies erected cyaniding plants of their own, paying a royalty to the patentees, whilst smaller mines sent their tailings and pyritic ore to be reduced by companies established for the purpose. A description, comparatively free from technicalities, of the extraction of the gold in 1895 is perhaps worth quoting. 'The ore, as it comes from the mines, is dumped on to grizzleys, which separate the fine stuff from the coarse. The former, passing through the grizzleys, falls directly into a bin, while the latter runs down the grizzleys to a sorting-floor or table. The pay-rock that remains after sorting is delivered to rock-breakers for preliminary crushing. The product of the rock-breakers, falling into the ore-bins, is eventually trammed with the fines to the battery bins. From the latter the ore is fed by automatic feeders into the mortar boxes where it is wet crushed. With few exceptions quick-silver is added in the mortar boxes, and the usual methods of extracting gold by amalgamated copper plates are followed. The pulp on leaving the plates is, in some cases, led over blanket strakes, or on to con-centrators, by which it is relieved of pyrites and black sands. . . . The amalgam obtained from the mortar boxes and plates is subjected to the usual operations of cleansing and retorting, the resulting gold being melted into bars. Concentrates are either treated by chlorina-tion at customs works or cyanided on the spot.'[1] It will be obvious that gold-mining on the Rand had by this time become a highly mechanised industry. Large plants entailed rapid extraction of ore, and although machine drills were as yet considered more costly than manual labour on the reef 'stopes' they were extensively adopted for greater speed. A Rand mine with its tim-bered shaft, its cross-cuts towards and its drives along the reef had left the superficial open-cut working of the early days far behind.

This technical progress enabled large bodies of lower grade ore to be profitably worked, but the investment of capital in such elaborate undertakings was only justi-fiable if the industry was to have a long life. It was before long discovered that the dip of the reef diminished as the depth increased, thus favouring deep working from inclined shafts, which were less expensive than

[1] F. H. Hatch and J. A. Chalmers, *The Gold Mines of the Rand* (London, 1895), pp. 184-5.

vertical shafts. But it remained to be proved whether the reef would eventually peter out and whether working at great depths would pay in any case. In June 1893, after about eight months' work with a diamond drill, a borehole on the Rand Victoria property struck the reef at about 2400 feet and the assay proved it to be payable. Those who had believed in the deep levels had already taken up blocks of claims along the line through which the reef would pass when its dip carried it outside the limits of the original claims. They could now begin sinking their shafts with confidence, and in 1894 a new 'deep level' boom was on the way.

This period of consolidation and new advance strengthened the hold of the big mining companies on the Rand gold industry. They alone could afford the highly-paid mining experts brought, from America particularly, to the Rand, the expensive cyanide or concentration plant of the new era, and *a fortiori* the heavy preliminary expenditure required by the deep-level mines. A Diggers' Committee had long since ceased to be the appropriate organ of the gold-mining community. Its quasi-municipal functions had passed to the Sanitary Committee: in other respects its place had been taken by the Witwatersrand Chamber of Mines, formed late in 1889 and afterwards extended to cover the whole of the Transvaal. This was an organisation of companies—with a minimum subscription of twenty-five guineas—for the compilation and circulation of statistics, the making of representations to the Government on legislative and administrative questions, and the regulation of matters of common interest. Even the Chamber, however, was or soon became only an organ of the real directing group of financial houses. There was Eckstein & Co., the Rand representatives of the great diamond house of Wernher, Beit & Co.; there was Rhodes's Consolidated Goldfields of South Africa; there was Barnato Bros., in which the two Joels were associated with their uncle Barney Barnato; there was J. B. Robinson, who had parted with the richest of the early mines, which bore his own name, but still controlled his Langlaagte Estate; there were Neumann & Co., the Albus, the Farrars.[1] It was difficult to disentangle the interests of these great houses; they were constantly disposing of some and acquiring others; but they were more important than the individual mines they controlled through subsidiary companies with interlocking directorates. New groups grew and others diminished in importance. But their collective domination of the Rand gold industry remained unshaken. The capital of their companies, at first reckoned in tens of thousands of pounds, was now to be reckoned in millions. With the initial advantages that most of them had brought from Kimberley they were in a position to deal with the London financiers on equal terms. They were so strongly entrenched and their operations were so complicated that the control of their shareholders, who hardly knew what they held, was reduced to a shadow. And their power was such as to give them control of any new discoveries virtually on their own terms. Prospectors' licences were cheap: diggers' licences at twenty shillings per month were obtainable by every white person who conformed to the laws of the Transvaal, subject to the rights of the surface owner to a mining lease and a varying number of preference claims: but if the initial discovery escaped

---

[1] There were other groups: a list, with enterprises controlled, is to be found in Mermeix, *Le Transvaal et la Chartered* (Paris, 1897), pp. 246-53. A few mines (some of them Natal enterprises) were not absorbed by any group.

23

the vigilance of the mining houses, the syndicates of peggers who fought one another in the rush for claims could be bought out at leisure, thanks to the great houses' command of the capital essential for development. They might require some time to digest what they swallowed. But the remedy of jumping, traditional on alluvial goldfields, was more likely on the Rand to benefit blackmailing parasites than working diggers. The demand of the companies for indefeasible ownership, which received satisfaction in the amended gold law of 1891, had a large measure of justification in an industry so dependent upon capital.

This great industrial structure was reared upon a base of skilled white and unskilled native labour. The white mine-workers, largely from the declining mines of Cornwall, were of an independent temper. Even the natives were not so much at the beck and call of the companies as might be expected. Their numbers rose from perhaps 35,000 in 1892 to 42,500 in 1894 and 51,000 in 1895, but never seemed equal to the demand. The wages were low by European standards, averaging in 1892 fifty-seven shillings and sixpence a month, with free food and quarters. But it was claimed that inefficiency made labour costs per ton high in comparison with other countries and that the higher the native's wages the shorter the time he remained in the mines. An attempt in 1890–91 to lower wages by agreement among the companies soon broke down in face of competition for labour with the railways and among the mines themselves. Afterwards the Chamber of Mines applied itself rather to improving the supply. The natives, of whom the majority came from Portuguese East Africa, found their own way to the mines. They travelled on foot, generally without clothing or food,

running the gauntlet through strange tribes and un-
friendly farmers. Near the mines the bands would be
met by touts, European or native, tempting them into
the service of some particular company by offers of
wages which the touts had no responsibility for carrying
out. Once engaged in the service of the mines, labourers
were lodged in the company's compound: but the compounds, which seem to have become general in 1890,
could not be as strictly regulated as De Beers' at
Kimberley. Labourers might be lured away by touts
of other companies, and in the absence of De Beers'
company stores were liable to waste their substance in
riotous living, encouraged by keepers of low canteens
near by. Whatever the disadvantages of truck and
'monopoly capitalism' they were outweighed by the
evils of this uncontrolled native gold rush. The
Chamber of Mines began its attempt to replace chaos
by order with the appointment of a Native Labour
Commissioner in 1893. His duties were to obtain
information from the companies regarding demand for
labour, to communicate with native chiefs regarding
its supply, to arrange for passes safeguarding the natives
against molestation, and for shelter and protection on
their journeys, to sanction contracts, to hear and consider native complaints and take measures to meet them.
But the difficulties of his task were immense. His
authority depended on the full co-operation of the
companies and the assistance, or at least the tolerance,
of Government. Neither was entirely absent, but there
were companies which preferred on the whole to go
their own way, and Government officials who were at
any rate not unwilling to obstruct. It proved impossible
to arrange contracts for the introduction of labourers
from Portuguese East Africa: there was no means of

enforcing engagements with the labourers. The Chamber then contemplated direct action by its own Native Labour Department and pressed the Government to make new pass regulations permitting such enforcement. Its efforts were at last rewarded on 18 December 1895.

By that time the relations between the Rand magnates and their organ the Chamber and the Government, always important to the mines, had reached a crisis. Whatever the attitude of the backveld Boer, the Government of the Transvaal clearly had no objection to capitalists as such. Since the restoration of the Republic in 1881 its deliberate policy had been to encourage large-scale rather than small-scale mining enterprise. The views of the Chamber of Mines with regard to the gold law, mining regulations, pass regulations in general prevailed. If there were sometimes unacceptable amendments and often exasperating delays they were perhaps not an unreasonable price to pay for continuing co-operation. But did President Kruger really desire co-operation? The Rand magnates came to have an uneasy feeling that he did not. The President for his part suspected the magnates of a desire to secure an economic and thus a political stranglehold over the Transvaal State, and this he intended to defeat. This may have been one motive of his policy of encouraging industries by the grant of concessions to individuals independent of the mining magnates. It was certainly responsible for the most obnoxious of these, the concession for the manufacture of dynamite. It was natural that the Chamber of Mines should object to the concession to a monopolist of one of their essential supplies. In 1892 it succeeded in demonstrating that the *concessionnaire* was merely importing dynamite under another name; and the Volksraad thereupon cancelled the concession. But next year the Volksraad set up a State monopoly in which the former *concessionnaire* had an interest. The real object of the President, however, in keeping the business in explosives under monopolistic control was not to enrich any individual, nor to pander to the great Nobel Trust, which failed to come to terms with the Chamber but had a large interest in the new monopoly: it was not even to put money into the coffers of the State, but rather to be able at need to manufacture armaments for its arsenals. That was a department of state into which mining magnates must not pry. The concession to the Netherlands Railway Company was undoubtedly also political in its object. The relations between the railway company and the mining industry varied: whilst the Chamber in its annual reports never failed to throw stones at the dynamite monopoly, it was occasionally appreciative of the attitude of the railway company. But the company did not fail to conform to the tendency of monopolies to keep their rates unduly high, whilst to the Government its foreign connections seemed to be a bulwark not only of financial but also of political independence.

Above all the President was determined not to open up a path to control of the State through the grant of political rights. If all the goldfields were to have representation, he told the journalist Mathers in 1887, 'they would have more voices than the Raad. . . . I will provide for this representation. But they must work with me, or otherwise if they were against me in any way they would cause the scheme to be broken off.' [1] This was but a qualified promise, and it was never

[1] E. P. Mathers, *The Gold Fields Revisited* (Durban, 1887), p. 245.

357

followed up. In 1890 an attempt was made to side-track any demand for the franchise. A Second Volks-raad was set up, with power to regulate many matters of importance to the mining community, but sub-ordinate to the other chamber of the legislature: for it aliens might vote after two years' residence. But on the main line of political advance the President strengthened his defences as the fluid conditions of the gold-rush days hardened and a permanent but still rapidly growing community formed on the Rand. The franchise law of 1894 required not only the assumption of Transvaal citizenship but fourteen years' residence as a qualifica-tion for the vote, and even then there was no absolute right. This fourteen years' postponement was but a veiled refusal.

The franchise was not a matter which concerned the magnates primarily. They had means of influencing the Government more effective than a vote, which would only be useful to them if others would use it in accord-ance with their wishes and interests. It was the general community called into being by the gold rush that lacked a voice in the management of its affairs. The ever-expanding, vigorous, bustling city of Johannes-burg did not enjoy municipal self-government. Materially, it was a flourishing city, like the mining centres of the Western United States with which it was often compared. It was indeed less under the influence of gamblers and roughs than they. But whereas they had political liberties and sometimes misused them out of sheer insouciance, it had none. It appeared to care for nothing but making money. But an increasing number of its inhabitants began to think of it as their home. In 1892 some of the traders, professional men, engineers and the like, formed the National Union to

agitate for the franchise and other reforms—the right
to use the English language, for example, in administration, the law courts and education. The franchise law
of 1894 seemed a provocation, and at the same time
Kruger attempted to enforce commando service against
a native chief upon men to whom he thus denied political
rights. The British High Commissioner, Loch, visiting
the Transvaal in June, thought there was a risk of
insurrection on the Rand. The rising temperature had
a profound effect on Cecil Rhodes, who was interested
not merely as a mining magnate but as Premier of the
Cape and projector of a Federal South Africa. If it led
to an explosion, would not the triumphant 'Uitlander'
majority set up a new republic? Undoubtedly the predominant element in the mining community, even in
the National Union, was willing to accept a reformed
republic. Rhodes desired to arrest this drift of British
subjects away from the British flag. He gradually, as
he pondered over the problem, determined to abandon
the policy of co-operation with the Boer Government
and aloofness towards the National Union. If he and his
ally Beit gave financial support to the reform movement
they would surely increase its chances of success, and
might hope that a successful revolution would bring
the Transvaal under the British flag and into a Federated
South Africa. The idea of support from the police of
the British South Africa Company which he had created
soon became a part of Rhodes's plan, but only a sub-
ordinate part. The revolution was to be made on the
Rand itself.

Rhodes, however, had misjudged the situation on
the Rand. He had not lived for years in that community
as he had at Kimberley. He was so intent on his distant
aim of federation that he failed to observe the nature of

the ground under his feet. It is difficult to believe that
he had not exaggerated the risk of an Uitlander
Republic; though the policy of conciliation backed by
bribery might before long have installed a more friendly
Boer Government, a successful armed rising demanded
more unity than actually existed on the Rand. Amongst
the skilled white mine-workers from the English mining
districts and Australia there was little love for the
capitalists, and no such burning sense of grievance as
would have caused these deep-rooted prejudices to be
forgotten for the sake of patriotism or liberty. For the
most part they probably regarded themselves as
sojourners rather than as citizens deprived of their
rights. The politically conscious element among them
compared the coolness of the reformers on the subject
of the ballot with the willingness of the Government
to meet the wishes of the Mine Employees and
Mechanics' Union in regard to working regulations in
the mines.[1] The National Union did not find the support
of the magnates an unmixed advantage. Moreover
Rhodes's policy of keeping the flag issue in the background until the revolution actually took place did not
succeed. His belief that the British flag would and
must be the symbol of the revolution became known
at Johannesburg and caused consternation among the
reformers. Many Americans and South Africans had
accorded their support only on the understanding that
the objective was a reformed republic.[2] In the end
Rhodes was persuaded that the revolution must at least

[1] The best statement I have come across of their point of view is in E. B.
Rose, *The Truth about the Transvaal* (London, 1902), pp. 27 ff.

[2] On the Reform Committee there were thirty-four men from the British
Isles, eighteen South Africans, eight Americans, two Germans, an Australian,
a Swiss, a Hollander and a Turk: A. P. Hillier, *Raid and Reform* (London,
1898), p. 89.

be postponed, but, as all the world knows, Jameson, disgusted with the hesitations of the reformers, sought, on 29 December, to force an outbreak by riding to the Rand with his B.S.A. police. The Rand revolution had degenerated into the Jameson Raid. There was no chance of seizing the arsenal at Pretoria, an essential part of the plan of revolution. The Reform Committee constituted themselves a Provisional Government, but there was a half-heartedness about their actions, natural in view of their unpreparedness and the division in their counsels. Jameson was obliged to surrender before he reached the Rand: the Reformers, disappointed also in their hope that the High Commissioner might intervene in their favour and hardly in a position to fight, found President Kruger disposed to press home without much scruple the advantage he had won. Rhodes and the mining magnates had ignominiously failed to overthrow the Boer Government.

On the other hand, though individuals among them were imprisoned and the Chamber of Mines split, the mining magnates as a body could not be displaced from the control of the gold industry. The Chamber continued to make representations on behalf of the industry to the Government, and some at least received satisfaction. The Government in 1897 actually appointed an Industrial Commission to consider its grievances. The Commission recommended a reduction in import duties on foodstuffs and in railway rates, a modification and possible abolition after further enquiry of the dynamite monopoly, a labour agreement with neighbouring States: the Volksraad whittled down these recommendations, but they were not wholly ineffectual. Moreover, with support from the Commission, the pass regulations framed just before the Raid were stiffened so as to make it less profitable for touts to infringe them; the law against the sale of liquor to natives was strengthened; a gold theft law adapted from the I.D.B. law of Griqualand West was passed. But the underlying struggle for power between the leaders of the mining community and President Kruger had not ceased; it had merely merged into a struggle for control of all South Africa, in which the British Government rather than the Rand magnates had become the chief protagonist against Kruger, in which the rights of the British subjects on the Rand rather than the interests of the gold industry were the central points at issue.

Politics tended to push purely industrial questions into the background in this period, but the development of the gold industry continued. Political rather than technical considerations predominated on the stock market. But the deep-level production which, in anticipation, had caused a boom in 1894–95, in realisation caused shares to advance steadily in 1898, when gold production exceeded 3,500,000 ounces, and a nominal capital of over £40,000,000 was invested in the industry. The level of mining and metallurgical skill on the Rand was now as high as anywhere in the world, and technical efficiency steadily increased. It was on the welfare side that the principal shortcomings of the gold industry were to be found. The recruitment of native labourers, though on a larger scale than before and under somewhat more effective control, still offered too much scope for the unscrupulous labour agent and tout. Robbery on the way back to the kraals still continued. Above all, the natives at the mines continued to be exploited by unscrupulous sellers of liquor. The week-end was the occasion of such orgies and tribal fights that perhaps a fifth of the native workmen were habitually unfit for work on Mondays. The canteen-keepers, using mine police boys and perhaps even compound managers for their unscrupulous purposes, snapped their fingers at the prohibition law passed in 1896. 'The former canteens', writes Rose, 'were reopened, ostensibly as Kafir truck stores, eating-houses, etc. Trap-doors were constructed for passing out the stuff to the boys in such a manner that the vendor could not be seen, whilst others were provided leading into double walls, underground cellars or adjacent premises, into which disappeared both stock and vendors on the approach of the detectives appointed to cope with the trade. In addition, elaborate electric-bell installations and signals were fitted up to enable those on the watch outside to give timely warning. . . . The illicit dealers openly boasted of their interest in the nefarious traffic and of their enormous gains. . . . They engaged newly arrived young Russian Jews, at what would appear to them princely remuneration, agreeing in the event of the latter being trapped and prosecuted, to pay the fines, or, if they were sent to prison . . . a lump sum on release as compensation.'[1] It is impossible to escape the conclusion that the real safeguards of the canteen-keepers lay not in their bells and trap-doors but in the laxity of public opinion and, in particular, the corruption of the police. Smuts, appointed State Attorney in June 1898, was given control of the detective service in November; but Rose maintains that it was not until the *Transvaal Leader* in 1899 had given a lead to the community by Vigilance Committee methods and organised a series of unofficial raids on the canteens that this crying abuse was really dealt with. The white mine-workers, largely employed

---

[1] *The Truth about the Transvaal* (London, 1902), pp. 48-9.

on a contract basis, were better able to look after themselves than the unfortunate natives; but they too suffered from the lack of proper attention to the healthfulness of working conditions underground.

It is outside the province of this book to discuss the outbreak or course of the Anglo-Boer War of 1899–1902. Naturally, it sharply interrupted the progress of the gold industry. Some few mines never entirely discontinued working; some were worked by the Boer Government; and all were virtually undamaged when they fell into British hands in May 1900. Only gradually, however, did they come into production again. The dynamite, railway and tariff grievances of the mining community could now be remedied. The engineers were as ready as before to keep in the van of technical progress, whilst under the stimulus of Milner, a keen social reformer, more attention was given to problems of health and welfare. Prospectors ranged far afield. The stock markets looked forward to an immense expansion of the industry. But the skilled white miners of the years preceding the war were dispersed, and above all the native labourers, the foundation on which the whole superstructure of the industry had been raised, did not return in the required force. In December 1902 there were only 50,000 of them: in August 1899 there had been 100,000, and even that number had been considered insufficient. During the war they had found employment as mule- and ox-drivers, trench-diggers and general labourers: after its conclusion they were absorbed in repatriation and restoration work in the country, on the railways or at the ports. A *modus vivendi* reached by Milner with the Government of Mozambique in December 1901 reopened the Portuguese territories to recruitment under the auspices of the mine-owners through their Native Labour Association, but the conviction gradually grew that labour for the mines must be imported from outside South Africa, and as East and Central Africa and India were found to be inadequate or impossible, that it must come from China.

Many of the mining magnates came to this conclusion before 1902 was out, and in the early months of 1903 Milner did likewise—though his view was that the Chinese must come for a limited period, to ease the transition to an economy in which white labour took a greater part, and certainly not to introduce a new pattern into the already sufficiently varied texture of South African society. The advocates of Chinese immigration realised that public opinion must be prepared for it; and 1903 was a year of propaganda and hot controversy in which they gradually got the upper hand. A Labour Commission which sat from July to November came with two dissentients to the conclusion that there was an actual shortage of 129,000 native labourers in the Transvaal mining industry, and a prospective need in the next five years of a further 196,000. A resolution in favour of Chinese immigration was passed by the Transvaal Legislative Council on 30 December by 22 to 4; and though representative institutions had not yet been restored, a petition with 45,000 signatures showed clearly that the Legislative Council on this matter represented majority opinion and not merely capitalist opinion on the Rand. A Labour Importation Ordinance was passed on 10 February 1904. The terms of the Ordinance had been most carefully designed to secure that the Chinese should come voluntarily and under responsible control; that they should work only on unskilled labour on the Witwatersrand and on three-year contracts; that they should be properly accommodated on the journey and at the mines; that on the expiration of their contracts (which were, however, renewable for a second term) they should return to China. At the end of June the first Chinese arrived: a year later there were some 41,000 at the mines.

The main object of the introduction of the Chinese was achieved. It set the wheels of the mining industry revolving again at full speed ahead. The number not only of white but of native employees increased. The return of the natives may have been due to crop failures and retrenchment on public works, but it showed that the mines still had plenty of work to offer them. On the other hand, outrages committed by stray Chinese at distant stores and farms revived local opposition; and the whole system excited intense opposition in Great Britain, particularly on the part of the increasingly vocal working-class movement. There was no 'Chinese slavery'. 'The majority of them', wrote a miners' M.P. who came out to see for himself, 'were of good physique, active and strong. The dining-rooms, dormitories, wash-houses, were all on a large scale, clean, orderly, well ventilated and well arranged. Of wholesome, nutritious food there was ample supply. . . . Many of the white miners with whom I talked, some of them well known to me, declared that the Chinamen were well treated, much better, they averred, than the Kafirs. . . . They may, in their leisure, travel at will over the whole mining premises, which, in some instances, extend over several hundred acres.' [1] If the word 'indenture' excited prejudice in England, the thing itself was doubt-

[1] Thomas Burt, *A Visit to the Transvaal* (Newcastle-on-Tyne, 1905), pp. 58-9. The fact that Burt was opposed to the system gives additional weight to these statements.

less endured philosophically by the coolie, long accustomed to such a system. The compounds, if they were a restraint on freedom, were a safeguard of a minimum standard of living and a canalisation of racial prejudice which, if allowed free scope, might have been dangerous. There were no outrages on the Rand such as there had been in California or at Lambing Flat. If there were no women, it was because the Chinese had not taken advantage of provisions in the Labour Ordinance for their bringing wives and young children. As for the charges of immorality, they are common form in that type of politico-racial controversy. Nevertheless, the measure was justifiable only as a temporary expedient, and the right of Great Britain to say that it should stop, as the Liberal Government said that it should after its return to power, had been earned by the sacrifices of the Anglo-Boer war.

The British Government prohibited the issue of further licences to introduce Chinese. The responsibility for the decision to repatriate the Chinese at the mines as their contracts expired rested with the new self-governing colony of the Transvaal. The repatriation, which began in July 1907, did not cause as severe a crisis as the gold industry expected. There were already 90,000 native labourers at the mines, and within two years there were 160,000: the number of Chinese had never risen much above 50,000. Recruitment in the Portuguese territories improved, partly perhaps because of Sir J. B. Robinson's competition with the Native Labour Association, but no doubt also because of better regulation of recruitment and working conditions. For under the post-war administration labour agents and compound managers were brought under control; housing, food, hospital accommodation and medical supervision in the compounds were markedly improved; the pass law was made simpler, less burdensome, less humiliating; the illicit liquor traffic, though not entirely eliminated, was checked. Meanwhile larger plants, the spread of re-grinding of the ore after amalgamation by tube-mills, and various labour-saving devices brought quantities of lower grade ore into the field of profitable working and thus assured long-continued expansion.

Not that the gold industry was immune from troubles. The Chinese experiment and the economy drive which followed it—and no doubt also the increasingly socialistic trend of thought in the working-class world— made the white mine-workers more anti-capitalist than before. There was a prolonged strike, with some dangerous rioting, in June and July 1913; and from January to March 1922, when the decline in the price of gold after war-time inflation led to new economy measures and to fears of a wholesale displacement of white labour by natives, these experiences were repeated in more violent form. The old rivalry between the mining industry and the Boers reappeared with the advent of a united self-governing South Africa, and the old railway rate grievance came to the front again. Despite continued progress in the technique of stoping and of crushing, the peak of gold production seemed to be approaching. But world conditions came to the rescue of the Rand, and with the rise in the price of gold consequent upon the currency depreciations of 1931–33 that peak has receded again into the distance.

In South Africa there was no decline as the gold rush passed into an industrial stage, but rather an uneven, intermittent advance in activity. For this reason it is hard to say when the period of the gold rush ended and the industrial stage, marked still by much of the hectic excitement and adventurous spirit of a rush, began. For the same reason it is difficult to treat of the character and influence of the gold rush apart from those of the gold industry. The prospector and individual miner played a less important part than in America or Australia: it was their work of course which first revealed the location of the gold, but since 1885 the characteristic of the South African gold industry has not been the wide dispersion of the individual miner but the concentration in a few hands of a single great reef. This may have made for technical progress: though of course the professional mining engineers were at first brought in from outside, they gained by their experience and interchange of ideas on the Rand itself, and their essential part in the industry was a further point of contrast with the amateurish, if ingenious, methods of the early gold industry of California and Victoria. The skill of the mining engineers and, at a lower technical level, of the European mine-workers showed that a gold industry resting upon unskilled native labour as its foundation need not be as unprogressive as that of eighteenth-century Brazil had been, but there had been such rapid technical progress in the world as a whole that this comparison, and perhaps even the comparison with California and Victoria, is hardly fair. The fact remains, however, that the gold of the Rand never could have been developed by the small-scale individual enterprise of earlier generations.

The effects of the Rand gold upon South Africa have been profound. It has not opened up new territory to settlement upon the American scale: but it has been the foundation of the railway and industrial development of South Africa. After the diamonds of Kimberley had first

tempted the railway out into the veld came the gold
which transformed South Africa from a widely scattered
group of pastoral and agricultural communities into a
modern nation-state. Even on agriculture the effect of
the gold has been far-reaching, providing as it has done
an important local market and thereby—often through
a transference of ownership from custom-loving Boers
to commercial companies—increasing its output and
efficiency. Furthermore, Kimberley initiated and the
Rand immensely developed the process of industrialisa-
tion and urbanisation of the South African Bantu.
Though many Bantu came to live permanently in the
towns, the average native still spent part of the year at
his kraal and only part at the mines, and the compound
system partially insulated him from urban influences.
But the effects of the 'native gold rush' were very far-
reaching, none the less so because the 'colour bar'
against skilled native labour, applied in the beginning
when the native had no skill, has been raised and
hardened since he began to acquire it. The gold mines
have hastened the onset of the most difficult problem
confronting the South African nation, the adaptation of
European and African to the requirements and potentialities of an industrialising, urbanising society.

Yet the Rand and its gold have always had something of an exotic character. The modern industrial
society, with the great gold industry at its centre employing some 300,000 natives and some 43,000 white South
Africans, has not grown out of the slow-moving pastoral
society which existed before it appeared on the veld:
rather it has been superimposed upon it. The gold rushes
spread the democratic civilisation of the American
frontier over the Rocky Mountains: they democratised
the pastoral society of Australia: but they left the Boer

as he was before. Wealth and energy came to South Africa in abounding measure as a result of the discoveries of diamonds and gold, but democratising tendencies were evanescent in a society founded upon caste and in an industry demanding large-scale operation. They withered away amid the dust-storms and shanties of Kimberley, and the society of the rushes—of Kimberley first and then of the Rand—took shape, progressive indeed, but dominated by a highly concentrated financial power, a new source of divisions in an already deeply riven community.

AUTHORITIES

Of the general histories of South Africa only three have much material on our subject. G. M. Theal, *History of South Africa since 1795* (various editions), a narrative history of the older type, stops short of the Rand but is interesting on the diamond fields and the earlier gold rushes. Professor E. A. Walker's *History of South Africa* (London, 1928 and 1935) is the ripe fruit of modern scholarship and is particularly valuable as relating the history of the diamond and gold fields at every point to the general history of the country. *The Cambridge History of the British Empire*, vol. viii: South Africa (Cambridge, 1936) has, in addition to narrative chapters by various hands, a valuable chapter on economic development by Arnold Plant.

The standard work of Gardner F. Williams, *The Diamond Mines of South Africa* (New York, 1902 and 1906) is perhaps the most satisfying book on any of the rushes, and is full of first-hand information not only on the technical but on every other aspect of the diamond mines. Of contemporary accounts of the early days the most useful are C. A. Payton, *The Diamond Diggings of South Africa* (London, 1872) and F. Boyle, *To the Cape for Diamonds* (London, 1873). J. W. Matthews, M.D., *Incwadi Yami* (London, 1887) and R. W. Murray, *South African Reminiscences* (Capetown, 1894), are full of good material: the former is especially good on illicit diamond-buying and on the company boom of 1880–81. Louis Cohen, *Reminiscences of Kimberley* (London, 1911) is written in a sensational journalistic style and is more successful in conveying atmosphere than precise facts. J. Angove, *In the Early Days* (Kimberley, 1910) is quiet and matter-of-fact. G. T. Amphlett, *History of the Standard Bank of South Africa* (Glasgow, 1914) is useful on the financial side. Basil Williams, *Cecil Rhodes* (London, 1921) is the best life of the leading figure of the fields. On the political side, the *Parliamentary Papers* from 1871 on are essential; A. F. Lindley, *Adamantia* (London, 1873) is an interesting commentary from the opposite angle; C. W. de Kiewiet, *British Colonial Policy and the South African Republics, 1848–1872* (London, 1927) and *The Imperial Factor in South Africa* (Cambridge, 1937), and J. A. I. Agar-Hamilton, *The Road to the North* (London, 1937) are scholarly modern works.

There is no work on the goldfields comparable to Gardner Williams. The best is Owen Letcher, *The Gold Mines of Southern Africa* (Johannesburg and London, 1936), a work of serious journalism rather than of scholarship. Accounts of Mauch's journeys are to be found in Petermann's *Geographische Mittheilungen* (Gotha, 1867–70) and in 'Bamang-Wato', *To Ophir Direct* (London, 1868); and the facts about the early fields are collected by the traveller T. Baines in *The Gold Regions of South East Africa* (London, 1877). There are some interesting details in W. C. Scully, *Reminiscences of a South African Pioneer* (London, 1913), and H. W. Struben, *Recollections* (Capetown, 1920). The best material on de Kaap is in E. P. Mathers's two contemporary books, *A Glimpse of the Gold Fields* (Durban, 1884) and *The Gold Fields Revisited* (Durban, 1887), and in B. Knochenhauer's pamphlet, *Die Goldfelder in Transvaal* (Berlin, 1890). On the pre-history of the Rand gold rush there are two modern works of painstaking research, G. S. Preller, *Argonauts of the Rand* (Pretoria, 1935), and James Gray, *Payable Gold* (Johannesburg, etc., 1937): there is some interesting detail (about J. B. Robinson) in the Majority Special Number of *South Africa* (1 January 1910) and in the reminiscences of Hans Sauer, *Ex Africa* (London, 1937), W. P. Taylor, *African Treasures* (London, 1932) and Sir Lionel Phillips,

Some Reminiscences (London, [1924]). But contemporary detail, apart from Mathers, is singularly deficient. The *Reports* of the Witwatersrand Chamber of Mines only begin in 1889. H. Dupont, *Les Mines d'or de l'Afrique du Sud* (Paris, 1890) is particularly valuable for its connected account of the boom. Most accounts of the Rand in the 'nineties are chiefly interested either in technical matters, like F. H. Hatch and J. A. Chalmers, *The Gold Mines of the Rand* (London, 1895), or in politics, like Mermeix [Gabriel Terrail], *Le Transvaal et la Chartered* (Paris, 1897), and J. P. Fitzpatrick, *The Transvaal from Within* (London, 1899), but are sometimes useful on other aspects. Amid the spate of works produced by the Anglo-Boer war, E. B. Rose, *The Truth about the Transvaal* (London, 1902) and D. Blackburn and W. W. Caddell, *Secret Service in South Africa* (London, 1911) are of great interest for our purpose. On the labour problem after the war see *Report of the S.A. Native Affairs Commission, 1903–5*; L. S. Amery, *The Times History of the War in South Africa*, vol. vi (London, 1909); *The Milner Papers, 1899–1905* (ed. Cecil Headlam, London, 1933), and L. von Praagh, *The Transvaal and its Mines* (London and Johannesburg, 1906). Valuable modern surveys are *Report of the Economic and Wage Commission* (U.G. 14, 1926); D. M. Goodfellow, *A Modern Economic History of South Africa* (London, 1931); R. I. Lovell, *The Struggle for South Africa* (New York, 1934).

CHAPTER X

ALASKA AND THE KLONDIKE

THE British Columbian miners who went up to Cassiar in and after 1873 mostly went by way of the coastal region of Alaska. The Russians, who had discovered Alaska in 1741 and exploited it for its furs, had sold it in 1867 to the United States. There was an annexation boom in the capital, Sitka, but it had no economic foundation. What economic foundation other than the fur trade could Alaska find? Its timber and fish were not commodities of which the Western States were short. It rested with the prospectors to find an answer. Gold had been discovered in small quantities under the Russian régime, and the prospectors now at work in the north made other strikes within a few years of the American occupation. None was of any importance, however, until 1880, when on the strength of an explorer's report a quartz-millowner and a merchant of Sitka fitted out a French Canadian, Juneau, and an American, Harris, for a prospecting expedition. In August these two men made some promising discoveries, particularly on Douglas Island; and their account and the specimens they brought back to Sitka caused a small rush. Juneau, on the mainland, became the centre of a district containing perhaps 1500 miners. Its output in the years 1881–83 was probably not more than $500,000 in value. But a quartz outcrop near by, discovered in November 1880 by another French Canadian, Pierre

Erussard (French Pete), passed into the hands of a builder and contractor from San Francisco, John Treadwell, who with the aid of San Francisco capitalists made it for a generation one of the most productive and progressive gold mines in the world.

Once the Treadwell company had erected its large stamp-mill and asserted its rights against the surface miners it was in a position to give regular employment to 200 or 300 men. But regular employment was not the desire of the prospector's heart: the effect of this discovery was rather to encourage him in his dreams of wealth. Its most direct stimulus to prospecting was doubtless along the coast; but the more enterprising miners were beginning to cross the coast divide into the vast basin of the Yukon River. The first trader-prospector, Harper, arrived in 1873 by way of the Mackenzie River system and the Porcupine, an old fur-traders' route. But later parties came over the passes, their rocky path being smoothed by the influence of the United States naval commander with the coastal Indians. There was merely a trickle at first, but the discovery of coarse gold in the autumn of 1886 on a Yukon tributary known as Forty-Mile Creek enlarged it into a small stream. Next summer there were 200 or 300 miners in the district and they won 4000 or 5000 ounces of gold. An ounce a day was about the minimum of a payable claim. Various gulches on this creek continued productive for some years, and there were further discoveries on the Sixty Mile, within fairly easy reach, in 1892, and on Birch Creek, some 200 miles further down the Yukon, in 1893. As the placers up the river were showing signs of exhaustion, there was a decided shift of population in 1894 down to Circle City, the river base of supplies for Birch Creek.

By this time, though the mining population of the Yukon was still to be reckoned in hundreds only, the camps had developed a marked individuality. For supplies they depended on what they could pack on their own or Indians' backs over the steep Chilkoot pass and then float down the Yukon on boats built by themselves, supplemented by what could be brought up the river on sternwheel wood-burning steamers. Permanent inhabitants had of course to rely on the latter, and until 1890 the steamer was so small that it could only bring up provisions for 100: the rest had to make their way out, poling their way up the river or steaming down on the chance of catching a revenue cutter or trading vessel bound for the States. With the advent of a larger steamer provisions were sufficient for all who wished to winter in the country, though they were generally 'bespoke'. They consisted chiefly of bacon and dry brown beans and flour, from which the miners baked bread with sour-dough yeast. The steamers and the stores were controlled by two large companies, who paid the store-keepers on commission: they in their turn 'grub-staked' or gave credit to many of the miners, thus encouraging them to stay and prospect further. The mining camps proper did not lie very far from the bases of supply: but outlying places were reached by packing or dog-freighting from roadhouse to roadhouse. A summer trail might be 'a continuous bed of black, soft, stinking, sticky mud'.[1] The going was better in winter. Dressed in his *parka*, a big shirt coming down to the knees with a fur-trimmed hood attached, the old miner cared little for the cold until his mercury bottle froze up; and his howling, ravenous 'huskies' made good time with his sled over the snow. It was more difficult to adapt himself

[1] J. E. Spurr, *Through the Yukon Gold Diggings* (Boston, 1900), p. 168.

to the summer mosquitoes and black flies: but though these were almost maddening in the swampy country near Circle City, they were not troublesome in all the mining districts.

The miners' triumph of adaptation to the conditions was, however, in the extraction of the gold itself. The season of low water in which river bars could be worked was short. The gold in the gulches was in ground frozen as hard as iron at a depth of eighteen inches under the thick coating of moss. Miners had learnt at Cassiar to burn off the moss; but even so the work was extremely hard in the short three months of summer, and though the long hours of daylight permitted two or three shifts, only shallow rich deposits could be profitably worked. In the winter of 1887–88 one miner seems to have had the happy thought of building a fire on the ground at the bottom of a frozen creek claim. A few years later the practice of 'drifting' or 'fire-setting'—thawing the ground by nightly fires until bedrock was reached and then working along the 'pay-streak'—became general on the Yukon.[1] 'By morning, if the amount of fuel has been properly gauged, nothing remains but the dying embers and the hot ashes; the smoke and gases have all escaped.'[2] Drifting, at the rate of a foot or so a day, was carried on throughout the winter, the pay dirt being constantly tested by the pan. In the summer the resultant dumps were put through sluice-boxes and the gold was finally panned out. Thus mining could go on most of the year and the range of profitable digging greatly increased.

[1] Similar methods were used in Siberia, but there is no trace of Siberian influence.

[2] W. B. Haskell, *Two Years in the Klondike and Alaskan Goldfields* (Hartford, 1898), p. 206. There is a full account of this method in H. A. Innis, *Settlement on the Mining Frontier* (Toronto, 1936), pp. 199-204.

Forty Mile and Circle City were the centres of social life. A few score log-cabins, saloons and dance-halls, stores and warehouses, barber's, baker's and black-smith's shops stood in wide straggling thoroughfares at Circle City, all higgledy-piggledy at Forty Mile. Wood shavings and tree stumps bore testimony to their recent origin in the primeval forest, empty tins to the distant urban civilisation which they fed with gold and by which they in return were fed. Drinking, gambling and prostitution flourished. Yet there was a true communal spirit, represented in Circle City particularly by the Order of Yukon Pioneers, which held weekly lodge meetings and made levies for sickness, for widowhood, and for sending 'outside' those who had been broken by hard work and privation. Nor were the miners in-dividually without taste or intelligence. There is testi-mony to the popularity of Shakespeare, and of books of science and philosophy, on the Sixty Mile, and one of the finest flowers of Western literature was cherished by one rough old miner in his cabin. 'Andy', says the United States Senator who tells the story, 'looked round complacently on the dirty floor, the two small bunks, the grimed window constructed of old ale-bottles, and the dark blackened rafters above. On a small shelf were some books. . . . They included six volumes of Gibbon. "Who left these here?" said I to Andy. "Who left them here?" he answered sharply; "why, no one. I've had 'em for two or three years. Take 'em everywhere, and read 'em nearly every night when I get time. I'll bet I know more about Caesar, Hadrian, Attila, Belisarius and all the others than you do—or most anyone else.' "[1]

The boundary between Alaska and Canada split the

[1] Jeremiah Lynch, *Three Years in the Klondike* (London, 1904), p. 80. The miner was Hunker, discoverer of one of the Klondike creeks.

Yukon basin in two. Some of the mining camps were on the Canadian, some on the Alaskan side of the line; but most of the miners were Americans, though often of foreign origin. The United States, mainly perhaps for fear of the expense, had left Alaska practically without law or government until 1884, and even then limited itself to administering justice in the coastal districts. The Canadian Government had jurisdiction at Forty Mile but, taking the advice of its surveyor Ogilvie, left the miners alone at first. Thus the camps depended for regulation of mining and for the maintenance of law and order upon the American system of miners' meetings. Claims varied from 300 to 1320 feet in length and extended 'from rim rock to rim rock': there was no pressure of population, and large claims were now allowed, indeed encouraged, by United States law.[1] They had to be recorded with an officer appointed by popular vote, and had to be worked—though they might be worked by proxy—in the month of July under penalty of forfeiture. Serious crime was rare. The penalty of being sent down the river in a boat—or on a log if no boat was available—was a severe deterrent.

Amongst the early Yukon miners this system worked smoothly. But as the population grew more mixed there came to be a feeling that the meetings were too much influenced by the saloon-keepers and loungers; that the verdict in mining disputes might depend upon a suitor's popularity, which in turn might depend upon the number of treats he gave when near the saloon. Merchants complained that they could not collect their debts. Moreover the Canadian Government had no desire to see the whole Yukon basin insensibly pass

[1] The 20 acre claims permissible under the Act of 1872 seem to have been usually 1320 by 66 feet. On the law see above, p. 195.

under American control. So in 1894 it sent up Inspector
Constantine of the North West Mounted Police, and
next year established him at Forty Mile as Agent with
wide powers and twenty police to back him. The
Mounted Police—though they left their mounts behind—were a body of men admirably adapted to the
conditions of the mining frontier. 'We allowed them as
large an amount of licence as was at all compatible with
decency and the maintenance of law and order; but
when a man overstepped this limit, we lost no time in
"dropping on him", and so the people—naturally inclined to be peaceful and law-abiding . . . —came to
have a very wholesome respect for us.'[1] All testimony
bears out this statement of one of the original party.
Their functions extended from the mere maintenance
of order (and the suppression of miners' meetings) to
the collection of mining dues, though the liquor traffic
was as yet unregulated and there was need of more legal
machinery. In United States territory, at Circle City,
the miners' meetings still functioned, exercising powers
more extensive than the Canadian representatives of law
and order.

It was in Canadian territory that the first great gold
discovery in the Yukon region was made. An experienced Nova Scotian prospector named Henderson,
grub-staked by a storekeeper on the Sixty Mile, found
enough to stimulate others. Then, on or about 16
August 1896, an Indian, Skookum Jim, discovered
'Bonanza Creek'. He and another Indian and their
white brother-in-law, all hunters rather than miners,
washed out about eighty ounces in eight days after they
had duly recorded their claim. The brown-coloured

[1] M. H. E. Hayne and H. West Taylor [ed.], *The Pioneers of the Klondyke*
London, 1897), p. 79.

creek, seldom more than eight yards wide, flowed through a marshy valley, bordered by hills covered with stunted spruce, into the Throndiuck (corrupted into Klondike) River, a tributary of the Yukon. The news caused great excitement at Forty Mile, which was depressed, and everyone hurried first up the river to stake a claim and then down again to record it: Eldorado, a tributary of Bonanza Creek, and Hunker Creek near by, were also found to be rich: all could find 500-foot claims, and hastily staked them.[1] Lower down the Yukon at Circle City, which was prosperous, there was scepticism initially, but when news arrived first of a $65 and then of a $212 pan, a midwinter rush by dog-team followed the late summer rush by boat.

Ladue, the trader who had grub-staked Henderson, had located the town site of Dawson, at the mouth of the Klondike, before the winter set in ; and log cabins rose there rapidly. The miners too had to build cabins and bring up supplies to their claims, so it was winter before they could test them even by drifting and panning. Some panned out enough gold inside their cabins with melted snow to pay current wages of fifteen dollars per man per day. Nevertheless the spring 'clean up' was a dazzling revelation. Four or five claim-holders cleared about $100,000 each, and the total yield to be divided among a few hundred probably amounted to $2,500,000. For once a high proportion of those who had joined in the rush and worked their claims did really well.

The Klondike discovery had of course been reported to the Dominion Government at Ottawa, and news also percolated to the coast through the trips made by dog-

[1] There was a preliminary recording of claims through the machinery of a miners' meeting: the later resurvey left certain fractions unclaimed: *Information respecting the Yukon District* (Ottawa, 1897), pp. 58-9.

teams carrying light express and mails at one dollar a letter. An influx consequently began early in the spring of 1897 and by midsummer there were 3000 or 4000 people in and about the new town of Dawson. The great rush was, however, inaugurated by the arrival in mid-July, at San Francisco and Seattle respectively, of the steamers of the two Yukon trading companies, the Alaska Commercial Company and the North American Transportation and Trading Company. They brought gold from the spring clean-up valued at over $1,500,000. The news, which was of course immediately flashed all over the world, was the more welcome because the United States was in the grip of the great silver depression. Late as the season was, about 10,000 people started north from San Francisco, from Seattle and Tacoma, from Victoria and Vancouver. If one heavily laden steamer may be taken as typical, the majority were men of the working class, 'men from the Washington ranches, miners from Montana, steamboat men from Puget Sound, and clerks and tradesmen and labourers from the different Pacific Coast States and cities'.[1] But they were soon diversified by such men as a house-builder from Brooklyn, a contractor from Boston, the business manager of a New York paper.[2] The majority failed to get through to Klondike before the season closed; but during the winter newspapers, steamship and railroad companies diffused far and wide publicity about the Klondike, and indeed propaganda in favour of the rush. Next spring the rush was resumed with new intensity. According to the sober estimate of

[1] R. C. Kirk, *Twelve Months in the Klondike* (London, 1899), pp. 13-14. Kirk left San Francisco on 1 August.

[2] Tappan Adney, *The Klondike Stampede* (New York and London), p. 28. Adney left Victoria in the middle of August.

Professor Innis, 100,000 people set out: the vast majority were undoubtedly Americans, but Canada, Great Britain, France, Italy, Greece, Northern Europe, Australia, South Africa contributed their quota. It was commoner, however, to travel hopefully than to arrive. The outbreak in April of the Spanish-American War took the edge off the propaganda drive and gave young men a new outlet for their adventurous spirit; and, besides, the Klondike was more difficult to reach than the scene of any of the other great rushes. The safest estimate of the number who reached it is 35,000 or 40,000.

There were many possible routes to the Klondike. Thousands went up the Yukon by steamer: the two old companies more than doubled their services, and new companies appeared, bringing river steamers up in sections on the deck of other steamers and putting them together at the Bering Sea port of St. Michael. There were fifty-six steamboat arrivals at Dawson between 8 June and 1 September 1898.[1] Hundreds, if not thousands, assembled at Edmonton to make the dangerous journey via the Peace River, the Mackenzie, the Peel and the Porcupine or by some variant route.[2] At one time in the spring of 1898 there were estimated to be nearly 5000 people camped at Glenora on the Stikine, intending to take the route that had once been surveyed for a telegraph to Europe, by way of Teslin Lake.[3] But the old route over the coast divide and down the Yukon was the most popular. At the head of the Lynn Canal, however, there was an alternative pass to

[1] Tappan Adney, *The Klondike Stampede*, p. 383.
[2] Elizabeth Page, *Wild Horses and Gold* (New York, 1932); *The Golden Grindstone: the Adventures of George M. Mitchell recorded by Angus Graham* (London, 1935).
[3] Hamlin Garland, *The Trail of the Goldseekers* (New York, 1899); Hon. Stratford Tollemache, *Reminiscences of the Yukon* (London, 1912).

the Chilkoot, the White Pass. It was well advertised as a good trail for horses, and within the month of August 1897 the mushroom port of Skagway, with 1000 tents and frame buildings, sprang up at the water's edge. In the first instance the trail seems to have been well cut, but it was quite unfit to cope with the traffic of a gold rush. Horses and men alike were 'green'. The soft soil was so torn up that horses had frequently to be pulled out of the mire by ropes and poles. Outfits were large, and men seldom attempted to pack through to Lake Bennett in a single journey: they preferred to pack goods about three miles at a time and then return for another load: hence blocks were frequent along the narrow trail. Those on the trail sought to improve it by stopping traffic whilst gangs spent days 'corduroying' bogs by laying logs across the surface, blasting out slippery rocks, and making log bridges. But it remained a trail of dead horses and stranded men. Virtually all those who reached Dawson before the break-up of the ice in the spring of '98 crossed by the Chilkoot. Skagway made it its business to take toll of the stranded thousands through its saloons, gambling dens and dance-halls. It was in Alaskan territory, and there was no restraint from the law. The town was in fact controlled by a strong-willed gangster from the mining towns of Colorado, Soapy Smith. Almost the only persons who were safe, wrote an officer of the North West Mounted Police, 'were the members of our force. . . . At night the crash of bands, shouts of "Murder!" and cries for help mingled with the cracked voices of the singers in the variety halls.'[1] Soapy Smith himself was a confidence trickster, not a gunman; but

[1] S. B. Steele, *Forty Years in Canada* (London, 1915), p. 296. The N.W.M.P. had an office, but of course no jurisdiction, in the town.

the gunmen outnumbered his own immediate gang, and even though he disapproved of their violence, he would not betray their confidence and hand them over to justice. Though he raised funds for a church and a unit for the Spanish-American War, the municipal motto of Skagway still seemed to the gold-rush immigrant to be 'your money or your life'.[1]

As the spring drew near, the rush, which had been frozen in by the winter, moved on again. A toll-road practicable for waggons and horse-sleds had been constructed over the White Pass to Lake Bennett, and freights fell from 50 to 15 cents a pound. Over the steep Chilkoot Pass, ascended by the gold-seekers in a continuous thin black line, there was first a whim or endless cable for loaded sleds, then an aerial tramway, taking up loads in swinging buckets. At the summits were police posts, seeing to it that each traveller took in 1000 pounds of supplies. The lakes, Bennett and Lindeman, were scenes of feverish boat-building. At Lake Lindeman it was estimated that 10,000 people were assembled: 'on a promontory of flat shore was a huge conglomeration of white tents looking like a flock of scagulls on a beach'. At Lake Bennett several stern-wheel passenger steamers, sent up in sections, were being put together. As soon as the ice broke, a long procession of canoes, sailboats and scows—barges capable of carrying up to ten or fifteen tons—set off across the lakes and down the river, shooting dangerously through or packing laboriously round Miles Canyon and the White Horse Rapids.[2] Then at last in

---

[1] W. R. Collier, *The Reign of Soapy Smith* (New York, 1935), *passim.* Soapy Smith was shot in July 1898 and the gang was then broken up.

[2] Later a horse-tramway was built to relieve those who could afford to pay 3 cents a pound from these unpleasant alternatives.

May and June 1898 the great Klondike rush came to
Dawson. Despite the exposure to the winter and a
catastrophic avalanche on the Chilkoot in April, the
actual loss of life does not appear to have been heavy;
but the number who turned back from loss of faith or
money must have been considerable: those who had
arrived at their destination must have felt that they had
earned a profitable claim.

Meanwhile the Klondike had passed through its
second season. Output rose to perhaps half a million
ounces. Most of it came from Bonanza and Eldorado
creeks; but in June 1897 gold was reported on two
new creeks, Dominion and Sulphur, and before long
miles of claims were pegged out on them and on their
tributaries. Moreover gold was found on the bench or
hillside on Eldorado creek by an old Californian miner,
and though the richness of this particular claim was not
at once apparent, a rich bench discovery in the early
autumn gave a fierce impetus to prospecting. It was
impossible to sink to bedrock in summer; it was in
autumn and winter, when there was no fear that 'the
seepage from the thawing earth would fill a prospect-
hole as fast as it was dug', that the real value of a claim
was revealed. During the winter of 1897–98 the Klondike experienced a severe scarcity. The transportation
companies had anticipated an influx but underestimated
its extent: moreover Circle City felt itself neglected and
a miners' committee there, armed with rifles, took what
it deemed necessary from the steamers, paying the
companies' agents. On 30 September a Government
notice advised an immediate move from Dawson to
the trading post at Fort Yukon of all those then un-
supplied: it seems doubtful if many went there, but a
number went out to the coast by the usual route. Never-

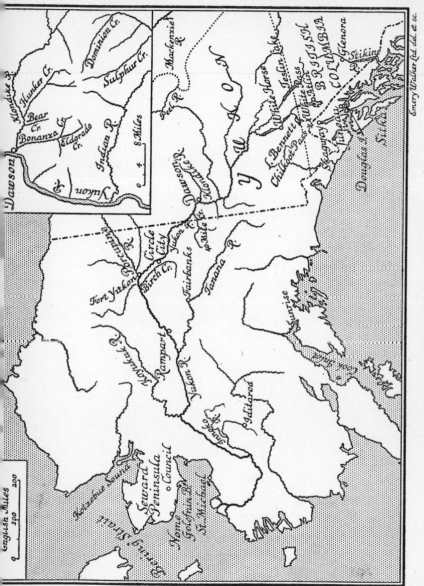

ALASKA AND THE YUKON

Emery Walker Ltd. del. et sc.

theless 5000 or 6000 people wintered in the Klondike, and though there was always enough beans and bacon, many could not afford to pay for flour, which rose as high as $100 a 50-pound sack. The newcomers in Dawson probably suffered more than the established miners on the creeks, unless indeed they came in flush of supplies and could part with some of them for a share in a claim.

When the 1898 rush arrived, the scarcity, which had caused anxiety outside and even Congressional measures of relief, had already abated. Restaurant meals of bacon, beans and coffee cost two and a half dollars; but as the summer proceeded these prices were halved and flour fell to ten dollars a sack. The police had seen to it that the newcomers brought ample supplies. They found a town superficially untidy, with its scattered cabins and its piles of tin cans, but an orderly, law-abiding community. Saloons, indeed, were 'wide open' and did not pay a licence, and gambling flourished. But the Mounted Police saw to it that the gambling-halls were well and honestly conducted. Places of business and amusement were closed on Sundays. The carrying of firearms was prohibited. Serious crime was almost non-existent, and when offences against the law occurred they were punished, and promptly punished. Questionable characters, deterred to some extent, perhaps, by the climatic conditions and the isolation of the district, were kept under surveillance and advised to go out, whilst those who did not follow the advice had but a short career. The firm yet tactful and informal authority of the police won the admiring respect of American observers, who doubtless noted the absence of the political undercurrents apt to interfere with the course of justice in the Western States. Over the border at

Circle City there was indeed an undesirable element, largely composed of emigrants from Dawson, who bore the police no goodwill, but they could do little harm. In the course of 1898 the Canadian Government put the coping-stone on these arrangements for law and order, and a judge of the Supreme Court of the North West Territories arrived in Dawson City.

The young and energetic Canadian Minister of the Interior, Clifford Sifton, devoted much attention to the problems of the Klondike gold rush. Though he had lived in the West all his life, he did not believe that Government should merely stand by and let events take their course. He sought to choose a commissioner and officials of vigour and initiative, but he also adopted a positive policy. He sought to derive some revenue from the goldfields by a royalty—20 per cent. was first proposed—and by the reservation of alternate claims for the Government, for disposal at public auction or other-wise, and to restrict the length of claims to 100 feet.[1] More particularly he sought to improve communications, and to secure as much trade as possible for Canada. In the early months of the rush United States customs officials placed considerable difficulties in the way of Canadian goods and personal outfits for the Klondike; and arrangements for bonding, made by Sifton personally at Washington, were held up by pressure from the Pacific Coast states. This confirmed Sifton in the view, formed on a visit to the passes in October 1897, of the desirability of an all-Canadian route to the Klondike. Late in January he signed a contract for a light railway, to be completed by 1 September, from the Stikine River, on which Canada had

[1] Bench claims were largely located under these regulations and were thus sometimes 100, sometimes 250 feet square.

treaty rights of navigation, to the Yukon River system
at Lake Teslin. The contractors were an experienced
firm, but the project derived too much from purely
temporary difficulties. It was defeated by the Opposition majority in the Senate, so that the effort expended
upon it was wasted. Nor was Sifton's mining policy
much more fortunate. As a result of the criticisms of
his own Commissioner, the size of claims was extended
to 250 feet, the basic rate of royalty reduced to 10 per
cent. The reservation of claims, criticised on the fields
as penalising old miners for the benefit of capitalists if
they were sold and hindering co-operation if they were
not, was not dropped but turned out to be of merely
theoretical interest.

For when the great rush came to Klondike the extension of the goldfields was already virtually over.
Dawson was filled to overflowing with the newcomers—
the *cheechakos*. There was feverish building in the town
and a fringe of house-boats, sometimes three or four
deep, extended for two miles along the river-bank. At
a moderate estimate there were not far short of 20,000
there at midsummer. But the objective of the gold rush
was, after all, the mines. The number of claims on
record increased from some 5000 in January to over
17,000 in September 1898. The bench deposits revealed in that season were found to extend for miles
along the so-called White Channel, and similar benches
were found this summer on other creeks. But there were
no new discoveries comparable in importance with the
new accession of population. Thousands, after a few
days or weeks in Dawson, left for the camps in American
territory or for home. Of the rest there were many,
miners with Californian or Australian experience, capable of intelligent prospecting for bench claims. Other

experienced men took up part of a claim, usually thirty or forty feet square, as a 'lay': that is, they mined this area, paying as a rule half the gold to the owner of the claim. This was more satisfactory to the individualistic miner than wage-work; but many were willing to accept the latter, which at eight to ten dollars a day was not unremunerative despite the high cost of living. Many, on the other hand, took to prospecting farther out, with little result. *Cheechakos* with capital found that they could buy claims on the market, through a mining exchange, and with more confidence than in most other rushes. Ten days were allowed for examination of the properties purchased and of the titles to them before payment was required. The men with grit but with neither capital nor experience soon settled down to employment in the stores, restaurants and saloons, in sawing or hauling lumber, gathering fuel or packing; or gained experience by stripping and sluicing on the claims. Many, however, lingered aimlessly on in Dawson, taking part perhaps in some futile little rush, until they were imprisoned for the winter by the ice.

For the fortunate owners of claims 1898 was a year of great activity—though methods were reckless and hasty and costs high. There was now a well-beaten trail from Dawson to the diggings on the creeks. 'Pack-horses and mules loaded with sacks and boxes plodded along in single file towards the mines, or were returning empty to town. Stampeders, in squads of three and five, with coats off, and mining pans and shovels on their backs, picked their way from tussock to tussock, following the winding trail in and out among the trees in the valley of Lower Bonanza. . . . Now and then one overtook a miner leading one or more dogs with little canvas side-pouches stuffed out with cans of provisions, going to his claim. . . . Dams of crib-work filled with stones, flumes and sluice-boxes lay across our path; heaps of tailings glistened in the sunlight beside yawning holes with windlasses tumbled in . . . the whole creek, where work had been done, was ripped and gutted.'[1]

Meanwhile Dawson was being furnished with the appurtenances of modern civilisation, even while the men struck one observer (who had visited Kalgoorlie) as 'absolutely the roughest, raggedest and most unkempt lot I have seen anywhere'.[2] Doctors flourished on malarial and typhoid fevers, lawyers on mining business. Two banks came on the scene, and with them silver currency to supplement the gold dust in which all transactions had so far been carried out. An assay office was in operation before the season was over. Three newspapers provided the community with a focus for its public spirit in the absence of free municipal and governmental institutions. Public spirit was not indeed the most conspicuous feature of the town, with its large floating population. It had not found time to construct a sewerage system. The wooden side walks, where they existed, were not continuous and no one recognised a responsibility for keeping them in repair. The danger of fire in a wooden town was generally admitted, but despite much talk and the arrival of some fire-fighting equipment, there was no organised fire department when the first great fire occurred in the early morning of 14 October.

In such a gold-rush community, with vested interests offended by Government policy and disgruntled newcomers disappointed in their hopes of remunerative claims, criticism of even an active and well-intentioned

---

[1] Tappan Adney, *op. cit.* pp. 403-4.
[2] Julius M. Price, *From Euston to Klondike* (London, 1898), p. 170.

administration was natural. Three-fourths perhaps of the inhabitants were Americans or 'foreigners who had lingered in the United States long enough to imbibe American ideas'. They were far from being mere grievance-mongers, and indeed it seems that Englishmen and Australian and South African miners were the loudest in their complaints. But it is worth remembering that American miners were not accustomed to being ruled by paid permanent officials or to paying a percentage of their gold to the Government. They were accustomed to private enterprise or informal communal action in the matter of roads and the delimitation and recording of claims. The *malaise* which was evident in 1898–99 was probably in large measure due to a feeling that the goldfields administration had bitten off more than it could chew. It was also alleged that the administration was corrupt. A deputation was sent to Ottawa to urge upon the Government the grievances of the miners. The Minister was convinced that the principal officials were honest. But the Commissioner had only accepted his appointment for a year. Sifton chose as the new commissioner William Ogilvie, already well known to old Yukon miners, and entrusted him with the powers of a Royal Commissioner to investigate the charges against the administration. Ogilvie's appointment was welcomed on the Yukon. The charges, on examination, boiled down to very little. There had been muddle in the Gold Commissioner's office, laxity and pretty clearly some corruption in its lower ranks, but nothing that could not be met by certain changes in personnel, which were duly made.[1] The royalty was leniently administered, and in 1899 the exemption limit

[1] The Gold Commissioner (Fawcett) and the Commissioner of the Yukon Territory (Walsh) were independent officials.

was raised to $5000. In perspective it is impossible to judge very harshly the administration of a gold rush by a Government which had no experienced mining officials on whom to draw.

The winter of 1898–99 marked the transition to a more settled period on the Klondike. Restlessness and lack of employment found vent in various 'stampedes', the reports which caused them being sometimes put about by unscrupulous road-house keepers who were finding trade dull. But a great part of the population was content to live and labour in its cabins on the creeks or to live and amuse itself in Dawson. 'After midnight', one of the latter group relates, 'those who had cabins went to them over the ice trail reluctantly and shiveringly, those who had not slept on and under the billiard-tables, leaving narrow passages along the sides through which men could walk.'[1] The authorities provided wood-cutting for those who needed sustenance. Climatic conditions on the Yukon, however, were not such as to tempt those who had not capital or permanent employment or the adventurous urge of the true prospector to stay. Next year many thousands must have left for the coast or for the new placer camps of Atlin, on one of the Upper Yukon lakes, or Nome. The Klondike rush was over: its future lay in the more efficient exploitation of the claims already taken up. The escape of steam from the exhaust of a small steam scraper suggested the use of steam rather than wood fires for thawing frozen earth. In 1899 a few claim-owners began to drive 'steam points'— hollow steel rods with narrow orifices[2]—into the gravel, allowing them to remain perhaps ten hours and then

---

[1] Jeremiah Lynch, *Three Years in the Klondike* (London, 1904), p. 61.

[2] According to Rickard, *Through the Yukon and Alaska* (San Francisco, 1909), p. 215, a rifle barrel was used for the first experiments.

removing the loosened dirt. Even in its early days this process was at least twice as efficient as fire-setting, which moreover was making heavy inroads on the available fuel. Moreover steam-pointing, at any rate when supplemented by steam-pumping, was not hampered like fire-setting by the wet ground in summer. Now winter drifting, though it had the advantage of giving the individual miner more continuous work, was a relatively expensive method of working out a claim. In shallow claims, with bedrock at a depth of ten or fifteen feet, it paid better to clear the timber and moss in autumn, to thaw the glacial 'muck' in spring with the aid of channels of water, and then to remove the gravel by open-cut working. The new process of steam-pointing also enabled claim-owners to concentrate on the summer season and turn off their wage-workers in the winter. It was hard on the wage-earning miner but it might make the difference between profitable and unprofitable working of a claim. It was part, in short, of the transition to large-scale systematic working of the less rich claims usually found in the aftermath of a gold rush. Only on the less accessible creeks did fire-setting by individual miners hold its own.

The age of machinery was coming to the Klondike. The reduction of costs which it brought was usually dependent on improved communications, and this is also characteristic of the period beginning in 1899. In place of the abandoned Teslin Lake project, the construction of a railway from Skagway over the White Pass was begun in the early summer of 1898, 4000 men being employed. Even before the end of that season it had materially reduced the cost and difficulty of freighting over the pass: by July 1899 it reached Lake Bennett, a year later White Horse, at the foot of the rapids.

There it connected with steamboats to Dawson. The railway freight of 4½ cents a pound contrasted with 40 cents or even $1 by the transport it had superseded. Horses also appeared at the Klondike in numbers in 1899, having previously been limited by the high cost of winter fodder. At first they were used on pack-trails only, but an effort was made to convert these into waggon-roads. The grant of a right-of-way for a tramway in 1899 was more troublesome than helpful, but the construction of a road along the top of the ridge, with branches to the creeks, was a real improvement, and in 1900–1901 a waggon road up Bonanza Creek was built. Whereas in 1899 the appearance of a waggon at the creeks was something like a miracle, in 1901 daily stage-coaches ran from Dawson—though even then a stage-coach journey was interspersed with long walks whilst the coach 'ploughed its way through bogs or up impossible mountain-sides'.[1] It was officially estimated that the freight rate to the creeks in 1903 was about a sixth of what it had been in 1899.

Railways, roads, telegraphs made the Klondike a less isolated community. Improved methods and cheaper transport kept it prosperous for some years. There was still a certain influx in the spring, and miners unemployed in winter by the reversion to summer working could often find work wood-cutting. But improvement in methods could not avert the exhaustion of rich pay-streaks. Though figures vary according to the season chosen, it is clear that the years 1899–1901 were the most productive, yielding about two and a half million ounces of gold in all. Afterwards the yield steadily declined until in 1906 it was only a quarter of what it had

---

[1] Sir H. A. Miers to Mrs. Miers (10 September 1901)—one of a series of letters very courteously shown me by Sir H. A. Miers.

been at the peak. Exhaustion was first evident in the
rich creek claims, and the first effect was a diversion of
enterprise to the bench and hillside claims, which had
often been hampered by the difficulty of getting water
to them. The exodus of miners to other rushes in Alaska,
which was marked from 1903, testified, however, to the
downward trend on the Klondike as a whole. It could
only be reversed by re-working large areas by large-scale
capitalistic methods. Klondike claims had not yet been
worked to any serious extent by imported capital. The
high rate of interest—8 to 10 per cent. a month in 1898
and 60 per cent. per annum even in 1901—was a severe
deterrent to borrowing on the spot, and the big English
syndicates or companies that acquired claims usually
came to grief. The large claim-owners were mostly
men who had acquired their experience and made their
money on the spot: a few years before they had been
'rough prospectors or adventurers, prize fighters,
gamblers, hotel clerks, doctors, anything and everything': even in the days of his wealth one of them, after
entertaining visitors at a champagne dinner, 'slept on
rugs on the floor of his log cabin alongside a safe containing thousands of pounds worth of gold dust and
nuggets'.[1] Had there been a Cecil Rhodes on the Klondike, he might have risen to the new opportunity; but
the most famous of the Klondike claim-owners, Alex.
McDonald, before he died had lost his money in wildcat
schemes. The first man to think in terms of really large-
scale enterprise was a visiting mining engineer, A. N. C.
Treadgold. He saw that a large and steady supply of
water would permit the profitable re-working of many
claims by hydraulicking, and in June 1901 secured
from the Dominion Government, with two associates,

[1] Sir H. A. Miers to Mrs. Miers (5 and 10 September 1901).

an extensive grant of water rights for this purpose. So strong was the local opposition to his powers of impounding water and taking up abandoned claims, so deep-rooted the prejudice of the miner-prospector against the foreign capitalist, that a Royal Commission was appointed to investigate this and other concessions, and Treadgold withdrew. But it was a case of *reculer pour mieux sauter*. He had already secured options on a good deal of ground: with the aid of the Guggenheims and Pierpont Morgan he organised in 1906 the Yukon Gold Company, which proceeded to acquire more claims and options and to bring water seventy miles in flume and ditch and pipe from the Twelve Mile River. Small individualistic enterprise had by 1907 virtually disappeared from Bonanza, Bear and Hunker Creeks, though it held out on others.

The Twelve Mile ditch was completed in 1909. Another form of mining enterprise had not had to await the completion of the ditch. From 1901 dredges of the bucket-elevator type developed in New Zealand and California had appeared on the Klondike. 'The barge is constructed at the bottom of a pit, excavated by the use of scrapers and horses, to a depth sufficiently below the expected water-level to ensure flotation and afford room for movement. Then the machinery is placed in position on the barge. As water is admitted, the dredge floats, and when it starts to work it digs its own way, filling the pit behind as it advances in the course of digging.'[1] If necessary the ground was thawed ahead of the dredge by steam. Thus the hastily mined Klondike creeks were forced to yield up what was left of their gold. The completion of the ditch enabled the company to use cheaper power-driven dredges, and at the same time to work out

[1] T. A. Rickard, *Through the Yukon and Alaska*, p. 220.

the bench and hill claims by hydraulic mining. Another large company operated power-driven dredges from 1910 in the valley of the Klondike River itself. There were smaller companies also at work, but the individual miner was thrown deeper and deeper into the shade.

The Yukon region fought a good rearguard action against the decline of its gold industry. The trend of gold production was upward for some years after 1908: by 1914 it had risen from $2,800,000 to $5,300,000. But the trend of population was downwards. Prospectors went out constantly into the wilderness but found nothing to compensate for the Klondike's decline. Climatic conditions and distance limited the growth of other industries, and in more than one respect the fixed capital that the gold-rush period had left behind proved a handicap. Freights by railway and steamboat remained high—monopolistic arrangements perhaps contributing. Retail business was hampered by these, by direct importation by the large companies, by the rates necessitated by municipal government in Dawson, which indeed caused some traders to move out to the creeks. The Klondike rush could not reveal as other rushes could the capacity of the region for carrying a large population at a high level of civilisation, and decline was the more inexorable when it came. The discoverers found gold in an almost uninhabited wilderness. The gold rush made this wilderness an outpost of modern civilisation, and an outpost it is still.

One must look elsewhere for the chief effects of the Klondike rush. The Pacific Coast, the port of Seattle and the State of Washington most of all, but British Columbia and its ports likewise, felt the stimulus to its shipping and to a wide diversity of outfitting industries. The rush was undoubtedly one factor in the great development of Western Canada then beginning, which endowed it with two (too many) new transcontinental railways and filled the prairies with agricultural settlers. Klondike gold played perhaps a more than proportionate part in the creation of that atmosphere of optimism which led Canada so far forward in the first decade and a half of the twentieth century. Nor must the effect in the scattered towns of South-East Alaska be overlooked: it was not by a mere coincidence that Alaska received a criminal code in 1899, a civil code and a municipal government law in 1900. Alaska was gradually becoming more than a name on the map.

Moreover the Klondike rush was only the most spectacular episode in an intensive search for gold extending throughout and beyond the great Yukon basin. Prospectors had been advancing up the coast. In 1896, it was estimated, 1500 men rushed to 'Sunrise City' on Cook Inlet, where payable gold had been discovered the previous summer; and about 300 wintered there and made good wages. Prospectors also went down the river. As early as 1893 a Russian-Indian half-breed found gold on Little Minnook Creek near the lower ramparts of the Yukon: he worked it at first himself with Indian labour, but in 1897 the secret was discovered by miners moving up on river steamers to the Klondike, and a number of them, frozen in for the winter, founded 'Rampart City' and made some new discoveries. The population rose to perhaps 1000, but the life of the district was short. 'Go out on the creeks', wrote a visitor a few years later, 'and see the hills denuded of their timber, the stream-beds punched with innumerable holes, filled or filling up, the cabins and sluice-boxes rotting into the moss, here and there a broken pick and shovel, here and there a rusting boiler,

and take notice that this region has been "developed".[1]
Eskimos found gold in 1897 in the country behind
Golofnin Bay: next spring American miners arrived
and founded 'Council City'. In the same year unscrupulous steamboat companies took some hundreds of
gold-seekers on a bootless errand to remote Kotzebue
Sound, in which many lost their lives.

In July 1898 a discovery of real importance was
made near Cape Nome on Seward Peninsula, a barren
waste with a few hundred Eskimo and perhaps a score
of white inhabitants, by five men—one of them a
Swedish missionary—who had sailed north on a prospecting expedition from Golofnin Bay. Before winter
set in, 7000 acres of rich placer ground had been staked
out by not more than forty men, who had organised a
mining district with rules to suit themselves. The secret
was not kept long. A few hundreds came up even
during the winter from the nearest Alaskan camps, and
in the summer of 1899 2000 or 3000 from as far afield
as Dawson. Finding no vacant ground they began
claim-jumping, maintaining that many claim-holders
were ineligible as aliens and in any case had not complied with the law requiring an actual discovery of gold
on each claim. Anarchy was only averted by the
presence of a small detachment of United States troops.

The situation was suddenly relieved by the discovery
of shallow alluvial gold on the beach. By early August
1500 men were washing it out with rockers made of
condensed-milk boxes and copper plating from the
sheathing of boats and coffee urns: some, who had no
copper, bottomed their rockers with silver coins. There
was no formal regulation of the size of claims. Fifteen

---

[1] Hudson Stuck, *Ten Thousand Miles with a Dog Sled* (New York, 1914).
He was there in 1909.

or twenty-five feet would be marked out along the beach and held by common consent until worked out. Before the short summer season was over, Nome beach yielded between one and two million dollars' worth of gold, and the creeks a few hundred thousand dollars more.

The Pacific Coast heard the news that fall, and next spring every old hulk on the coast was pressed into service to bring up 18,000 or 20,000 men. Accommodation was shamelessly reserved twice over: bribery of stewards was sometimes necessary to get decent food. At last they reached the distant strand. 'It was indeed a "white city", tents, tents, tents extending along the shore almost as far as the eye could see. Scattered in the denser and more congested part of the town were large frame and galvanised-iron structures, the warehouses and stores of the large companies; and there was the much talked-of tundra, upon which the multitude were encamped, extending back almost from the edge of the sea three or four miles to the high rolling hills, which bore an occasional streak of snow. Not a tree, not a bit of foliage, nothing green, was in evidence. . . . There is not even the semblance of a harbour. It is a mere shallow roadstead open to the clear sweep and attack of the Bering Sea.'[1] On shore was a scene of haste, waste and filth. Feverish building was going on, but the 'bar-room miner' was more in evidence than the prospector. There were no mountain passes to deter the riff-raff. Swindling company promoters and manufacturers of 'gold-mining machines' had free scope for their talents. But most of the beach had been taken up already: the only hope of a new claim was to go out into the wilderness. The majority of the newcomers returned

[1] Lanier McKee, *The Land of Nome* (New York, 1902), pp. 27-8.

whilst they could. Of the 5000 or 6000 who wintered in Nome many were without work and dependent on the charity of the saloon-keepers and gamblers who had hoped to grow rich at their expense.

Originally there was no authority at Nome but that of the miners themselves. Cosmopolitan though the camp was, the American frontier tradition was sufficiently strong for it to organise during the summer of 1899 a city government with 'a mayor, councilmen, a police force, a fire department with town well, a board of health, a hospital corps and charitable organisations'; and theft and disorderly conduct were punished by fine and imprisonment.[1] But its authority had no sanction behind it. In the summer of 1900 many property-holders resisted its collection of assessments for municipal purposes, and law and order might have collapsed altogether had it not been for the troops. In July a federal judge arrived. He, however, was the nominee of a North Dakota political boss, Alexander McKenzie, who accompanied him. McKenzie was interested in a mining corporation and was seeking through influence at Washington to amend the United States mining laws so as to make it illegal for aliens to locate or hold mining claims in Alaska. Taking advantage of the looseness and ambiguity of the mining laws as they actually existed and of the complaisance of the judge, McKenzie got himself appointed, without even the formality of regular legal proceedings, receiver of a number of mines, with permission to operate them and hold the proceeds. Doubtless he hoped, even if his schemes at Washington

---

[1] F. C. Schrader and A. H. Brooks, *Preliminary Report on the Cape Nome Gold Region* (U.S. Geological Survey, Washington, 1900), pp. 45-6. See also A. H. Brooks in *The Gold Placers of Parts of Seward Peninsula* (U.S. Geological Survey Bulletin no. 328, 1908): House Documents, vol. 32, no. 723: 60th Congress, 1st session.

went wrong, to hold the fort during the winter and then decamp if necessary.

Such was the state of law and order at Nome at the height of the rush. Fortunately the injured claim-holders managed to appeal to San Francisco before the ice closed in. McKenzie was taken off to San Francisco in judicial cold storage and punished with that salutary absence of severity which such an important political occasion demanded.[1] The judge, deaf for some months to the sirens of federal justice, finally listened to them in August 1901 and was removed from office a few months later: his district attorney and others even received short terms of imprisonment for contempt of court.

Whilst this comedy was being played out, Nome and the Seward Peninsula—for other creeks and beaches, less rich and extensive than Nome's, were discovered farther afield—were settling down to a steady gold production of rather over $4,000,000 a year. About 2500 people wintered each year at Nome, and some thousands more came in each spring. At first the original creeks were the most productive, the yield being increased and costs diminished by large-scale operations of a few companies, one of which as early as 1900 had begun to construct without rock ballast or grading a narrow-gauge railway across the tundra. On the beach itself storms reconcentrated the sand and a poor man could still hope to make a living by rocker and long-tom. The discovery of a 'second beach line' inland led to great activity in prospecting the tundra, and late in the

---

[1] He was sentenced to a year's imprisonment but pardoned by President McKinley after three months. On this affair, see McKee, *op. cit.*, Rickard, *Through the Yukon and Alaska*, and H. W. Clark, *History of Alaska* (New York, 1930), pp. 111-13.

fall of 1904 the rich third beach line was located. Its exploitation, largely by steam-points, brought the gold yield of Seward Peninsula to some 400,000 ounces in 1906. But although the camp was prosperous there was no repetition of the scenes of 1900. After 1907, despite ditches, dredges and various mechanical aids, decline set in.

Meanwhile a new gold-mining centre had arisen on the Tanana, a great tributary of the Yukon. The discovery was made, in a wide shallow valley covered with moss, by an Italian prospector, Felix Pedro, in July 1902. It was kept a close secret that season by the few men in the vicinity. But early in 1903 a Japanese revealed the news at Dawson, and the now declining Klondike camps sent some hundreds down the river. The first results were disappointing, for the gold was deep. A number of the miners impatiently went down the river on boats and rafts, condemning the new rush so vehemently as to induce suppliers to divert their goods elsewhere. The consequence was that those who wintered at the new centre of Fairbanks, on a slough of the Tanana, went very short, although the toll that they levied on the ptarmigan, the rabbits and the roving herds of cariboo saved them from starvation. Soon afterwards a rich new creek, Cleary Creek, was discovered; and experienced miners arrived from Dawson and bought up the claims. Capital was required, for steam-pointing was the most appropriate method of extracting the pay-dirt. But the trend of production was sharply upward—$35,000 in 1903, $350,000 in 1904, $3,750,000 in 1905, about $9,000,000, that is to say about half a million ounces, in each of the years 1906–9. It was in the years 1904–5, apparently, that Fairbanks as a town was at its liveliest, with saloons, dance-halls, houses of prostitution flourishing. An armed escort had to be organised to collect the gold from the creeks. By 1910 it was a steady-going place: the local choral society was 'lamenting the customary dearth of tenors for its production of *The Messiah*'.[1]

Fairbanks was not a 'poor man's diggings'. Much of the mining was done with capital borrowed at 2 per cent. a month; but the actual extraction was largely in the hands of 'lay men', who paid the claim-owners from 25 to 50 per cent. of the gross output. Neither system conduced to economical exploitation: it made for concentration on the richest gravels, and when the work was done the ground was so gutted as to make the recovery of the remaining gold difficult and expensive. The wage-earning miners struck in 1907 and again in 1908: with the wage system had come its characteristic social disorder.

The trend of events in Alaska was now against the old-style Yukon miner. In 1906 gold was discovered in the upper valley of the Innoko, a rolling country with here and there a group of mountains 3000 or 4000 feet high. This did not come to much, but on Christmas Day 1908 two prospectors found gold in a twelve-foot hole on another branch of the Innoko. Next summer there were some hundreds on the spot. In 1910 there was a regular rush of 2000 or 3000, half perhaps from Fairbanks, and the new town of Iditarod City was founded, ten miles or so from the mines. The gold output was not more than half a million dollars. Next year it was much larger, $3,000,000 from Iditarod and the Innoko jointly. But Iditarod City was overgrown, poorly supplied, disgruntled because the claims were in the hands of a fortunate few. In 1912 many of them were

---

[1] Hudson Stuck, *op. cit.* p. 252.

passing into the hands of the Yukon Gold Company, and the population was markedly on the decline. The prospector was in fact being driven farther and farther out, and though he continued to range over Alaska, to join in new stampedes from time to time, and in some places—as on the Koyukuk[1]—to settle down to a modest, hard-earned living, his great days were over.

In the old days the law had been his friend. The Californian gold camps of 1848–49, left to regulate themselves, had evolved the small claim system as the best method of giving all comers a reasonable chance of success. When Congress in 1866 stepped in and passed a mining law, the wisdom of mining camp regulation was still not denied in general, though it was regarded as inapplicable to capitalistic lode or reef mining. But the emphasis, especially after the placer mining law of 1872, was upon the advantages of large-scale exploitation as against wasteful individualistic mining. Not only were claims of 20 acres, or of 160 acres for an 'association', permitted: they might be staked under a power of attorney. No proper precautions were taken in regard to such powers of attorney; and unscrupulous first comers would serve themselves by appropriating large areas, perhaps staking a claim for a lawyer so as to be assured of his services if their proceedings left any loophole for litigation. The provision that 'assessment work' should be done in order to hold a claim was as much honoured in the breach as in the observance. The looseness of the provisions in regard to staking opened another door to fraud. In the Nome and Fairbanks rushes the 'mining district' system survived merely to cloak naked monopoly. When in 1912 Congress at last modified the law, requiring powers of attorney to be written and not

[1] On the Koyukuk see R. M. Marshall, *Arctic Village* (New York, 1933).

more than two in number and putting the burden of proof of assessment work upon the claim-holder, the American mining frontier had already reached the limit of its extension. The prospector retired to the back of the stage on which he had played so prominent a part; and indeed the play was played out.

Authorities

The most authoritative work on the Klondike is Professor H. A. Innis's *Settlement on the Mining Frontier* (Toronto, 1936)—part of vol. ix of *Canadian Frontiers of Settlement*: written by a distinguished economic historian, it deals comprehensively and suggestively with the economic aspects and is useful on the social, political and technical side as well. Of the early Yukon prospectors there is a good contemporary account in G. M. Dawson, *Report on an Exploration in the Yukon* (Montreal, 1888). The Canadian Government published a useful pamphlet of *Information respecting the Yukon District* (Ottawa, 1897), but little else. Its policy is examined in J. W. Dafoe, *Clifford Sifton in relation to his Times* (Toronto, 1931). The gold rush and the period just preceding it are well portrayed in M. H. E. Hayne and H. West Taylor, *Pioneers of the Klondike* (London, 1897), and W. B. Haskell, *Two Years in the Klondike and Alaskan Goldfields* (Hartford, 1898), the latter a work of considerable descriptive skill. These two writers did not take part in the rush of 1897–98 like Tappan Adney, author of *The Klondike Stampede* (New York, 1900). Other intelligent and interesting contemporary accounts are R. C. Kirk, *Twelve Months in the Klondike* (London, 1899), and Angelo Heilprin, *Alaska and the Klondike* (New York, 1899); Heilprin, however, was only there for a few weeks. A. N. C. Treadgold's *Report on the Goldfields of the Klondike* (Toronto, 1899) is useful especially on the technical side, and has additional interest in view of the author's later activities. Jeremiah Lynch, *Three Years in the Klondike* (London, 1904) is valuable as one of the few books with some detail on the years after 1898. A little later come interesting accounts from J. S. McLain, *Alaska and the Klondike* (New York, 1905); an official publication, *The Yukon Territory: its History and Resources* (Ottawa, 1909); and more particularly T. A. Rickard, *Through the Yukon and Alaska* (San Francisco, 1909). W. Ogilvie, *Early Days on the Yukon* (London, 1913) adds some interesting details but is a little disappointing. E. Salin, *Die wirtschaftliche Entwicklung von Alaska und Yukon Territory* (Tübingen, 1914) is a systematic and scholarly study.

On Alaska, H. H. Bancroft, *History of Alaska* (*Works*, vol. xxxiii) (San Francisco, 1886), based on Russian as well as English authorities, is still the best account of the period before 1885. H. W. Clark, *History of Alaska* (New York, 1930) is a valuable short account of the later period, but is not always accurate. Jeannette P. Nichols, *Alaska* (Cleveland, 1924) is both lively and scholarly but virtually confines itself to the political side. An earlier work deserving of mention is Miner W. Bruce, *Alaska: its History and Resources . . .* (Seattle, 1895, and New York and London, 1899). On Nome there is a good deal of information in E. McElwaine, *The Truth about Alaska* (Chicago, 1901), and Lanier McKee, *The Land of Nome* (New York, 1902), and in McLain and Rickard. On Fairbanks there is little except in Rickard and in the publications of the United States Geological Survey, especially its annual *Mineral Resources of Alaska*. Archdeacon Hudson Stuck's *Ten Thousand Miles with a Dog Sled* (New York, 1914) is a travel book above the average, but has only occasional glimpses of the goldfields.

CHAPTER XI

CONCLUSION

THE energetic peoples of Europe began to embark upon their great outward movement over the oceans in the fifteenth and sixteenth centuries. The first of the gold rushes took place in the eighteenth century, but the second half of the nineteenth century was the age of the gold rushes proper. Great though the earlier expansion was in its significance, the numbers taking part in it were not large. The Spaniards and Portuguese could only exploit the gold or silver that they found by the forced labour of Indians and slaves; and indeed they had no thought of exploiting it otherwise, for they regarded themselves as the natural superiors of the Africans and Americans, they despised manual labour, and they did not appreciate the disadvantages of the crude and wasteful methods of the labour they employed. In New Granada and in Brazil a considerable class must have acquired some rough-and-ready skill in prospecting, but their technique was backward by comparison with that of German or Cornish miners and they showed no particular desire or capacity to improve it. By the time the Minas Geraes rushes occurred, the numbers involved were large, but they were swollen by slaves and the technique of the gold industry still made no noteworthy advance. Moreover the Governments of Spain and Portugal, though they allowed considerable freedom to prospectors, pertinaciously attempted to regulate the gold industry so as to raise a revenue from it and to exclude foreigners from the gold regions. These narrow fiscal and national considerations could not avail to prevent the development of the gold industry, but they did hamper it: they could not prevent the gold from ultimately finding its way into the markets of the world but they did limit the influence of the gold rushes to the colonial and metropolitan territories concerned.

In Siberia there was less freedom of prospecting at first, though before long it became adequate for its purpose; and even more than in New Granada and Brazil the vast areas and the inhospitable character of the country made individual prospecting virtually impossible. Freedom of exploitation was also limited, not by fiscal and national considerations alone but also by a social and economic system, based on serfdom, which inclined the Government towards a policy of concessions to capitalists. The actual exploitation of the gold was not by serfs except in the Urals; but even in Eastern Siberia the habits of mind of the concessionnaire were those of the serf-owner. Government regulation might mitigate the lot of the labourer, but it could not give him the incentives of a free man nor could it give the concessionnaire technical knowledge. Foreign technicians had given the gold industry some of its initial impetus, and in the end foreign experts and foreign capital had to be called in to get the industry out of its rut.

Whatever significance the Siberian gold rushes might have had for the world, they became mainly of local importance when the great Californian gold discovery occurred. The Californian gold rush was the first of a new type, directly affecting all that followed it. In all these rushes freedom of prospecting could be taken for granted, and exploitation by free labour also, though in South Africa there was unskilled native labour at the bottom. All the resources of modern ocean transport were available for all who cared to go, though they might have a hard journey when they reached their port of destination: and the news of the discoveries was diffused as widely as the nineteenth-century newspaper could spread it. In these circumstances it is worth making again the point that the participants in the American gold rushes were mainly Americans, in the Australasian rushes, after the first, mainly Australians, even in the Kimberley and Rand rushes largely South Africans. The remoteness of the Yukon and Alaska and the temporary character of the gold rushes to such inhospitable territories make them something of a special case. Only in Victoria, after 1852, was the gold rush predominantly composed of immigrants in the usual sense of the term; and even there the emigration from the British Isles in 1852–54 was under a quarter of a million, whereas over a million people left the British Isles in those three years. The importance of the gold rushes in the great international migrations of the nineteenth century can easily be exaggerated.

In the history of mining, however, the nineteenth-century gold rushes were of great importance. They had an initial bias in favour of individualistic, small-scale exploitation. The individual miner had at first no special skill, but he was quick to assimilate all that could be learnt and his natural ingenuity soon developed the art he had acquired. This individualism conduced perhaps to rapid rather than scientific exploitation, though with surface alluvial (placer) deposits it was probably as effective a method as could have been applied. In the later stages and deeper workings technical conditions told strongly in favour of large-scale, capitalistic exploitation. The individual miner, in Australia particularly, fought stubbornly against this tendency but it was ultimately victorious. The ultimate result of free mining enterprise was, in short, a capitalistic gold industry, though this industry was technically progressive and its workmen were highly skilled: it was very different from the large-scale operations of Siberia and Brazil and *a fortiori* of ancient times. It applied to the mining of gold the methods of the industrial revolution.

The Californian and Victorian gold rushes were also important to the world through the sheer volume of gold they produced. They raised the annual output of gold to six or seven times what it had previously been. Though some of this gold was absorbed in the arts and industry or drained off to the East, the stimulus to trade, to shipping and to manufacture was marked, and it gave the initial impetus to the industrial enterprise and widely diffused prosperity of the period of rising prices which lasted until 1873. By that time, since 1866 in fact, a marked downward trend in gold production had set in, but it only amounted to about a third by comparison with the figures of 1852 and 1853: gold was still being produced in quantities many times greater than before the Californian discovery. France and Germany adopted a gold standard: the United States, after financing its civil war with 'greenbacks', made them convertible into gold: the world, in short, found new uses for the gold that was being won in the Western United States and in Australasia. The upward trend in gold production was resumed in the 'nineties: in 1913 it was three times what it had been in 1853 and in twenty years the world's stock increased by half. Gold provided the metallic basis for a great credit expansion which vastly increased the productivity of world economy.

Adequate treatment of the technical and financial effects of the gold rushes would, however, require a book in itself; nor is it the proper conclusion of a study of the gold rushes. Scenes and characters differed from rush to rush, but all had this in common. They were adventures, adventures of the common man. The frontier settlers of the Mississippi Valley and the prairies, the men who drove their flocks and herds out into the Australian bush, the high veld of South Africa, the pampas of South America, had something of the spirit of adventure in them too: so had most of the millions of emigrants who left the Old World in the nineteenth century for the New World of the West and of the South. But it was upon the gold-seekers that there descended most of the spirit of the Conquistadores and the Elizabethans—not their lust for conquest, indeed, but their zest for the unknown, their carelessness of consequence. They were as typical of the nineteenth century as those other adventurers of the sixteenth, though they plundered Mother Nature rather than their fellow-men. Moreover only a few hundred could conquer with Cortes or Pizarro or sail with Drake. In the gold rushes tens of thousands of men took part, and though many faltered or fell by the wayside, the best of them evolved a new type of self-reliant character, a new free, careless social life. With all its faults it had a fine savour of the spirit of adventure, which is the salt of history.

INDEX

417   27

THE END

SIBERIA

English Miles

0   100   200   300   400   500

WESTERN UNITED STATES AND BRITISH COLUMBIA

English Miles
50 0 100 200 300

Queen Charlotte Islands

BRITISH COLUMBIA

Quesnel
Cariboo Mts.
ROCKY
Lillooet
Fraser R.
Thompson R.
Harrison L.
Yale
Hope
Kootenay L.
New Westminster
Victoria
Bellingham
Rossland
Colville
Coeur d'Alène
Fort Benton
Missouri River
NORTH DAKOTA
WASHINGTON
Lewiston
Orofino
Bitter Root Mts.
MONTANA
SOUTH DAKOTA
Portland
Wallula
Columbia R.
Walla Walla
Umatilla
Helena
Butte
Virginia City
Bannack
Deadwood
Black Hills
Salmon R.
OREGON
IDAHO
Idaho City
Boise
Wood
WYOMING
NEBRASKA
Rogue R.
Owyhee Mts.
Snake River
Sweetwater
South Pass
Platte R.
Klamath R.
Humboldt R.
Great Salt Lake
Black Hawk
S. Platte R.
KANSAS
Trinity R.
Salt Lake City
Denver
Leadville
Pike's Peak
Smoky Hill R.
NEVADA
Nevada City
Virginia City
Carson City
Austin
White Pine
UTAH
Aspen
Cripple Creek
Silver Cliff
COLORADO
Arkansas R.
Sacramento
Stockton
Tonopah
Goldfield
San Juan Mts.
San Francisco
S. Joaquin R.
Monterey
CALIFORNIA
Kern R.
Colorado River
Santa Fé
Los Angeles
Colorado Desert
ARIZONA
NEW MEXICO
Longitude 120° West
Gila River

W. P. Morrell: The Gold Rushes

Emery Walker Ltd. del. et sc.

SOUTH AFRICA

English Miles

0   50   100   150   200

MATABELELAND

BECHUANALAND

PROTECTORATE

TRANSVAAL

oBulawayo

Tati

Limpopo R.

Marabastad o

Murchison Range

Crocodile R.

Lydenburg o

Pilgrim's Rest

De Kaapsche Hoop

Witwatersrand

oPretoria

Steynsdorp o

Barberton

Delagoa Bay

Krugersdorp

Boksburg

Johannesburg

SWAZI LAND

Vaal R.

Klerksdorp

ORANGE FREE STATE

Pniel

Klip Drift

Kimberley

GRIQUALAND

Griquatown o

WEST

BASUTO LAND

NATAL

Orange R.

Hopetown

Durban

Orange R.

CAPE COLONY

East London

Capetown

Paarl

Port Elizabeth

Longitude 32° East

W.P.Morrell: The Gold Rushes

Emery Walker Ltd. del. et sc.

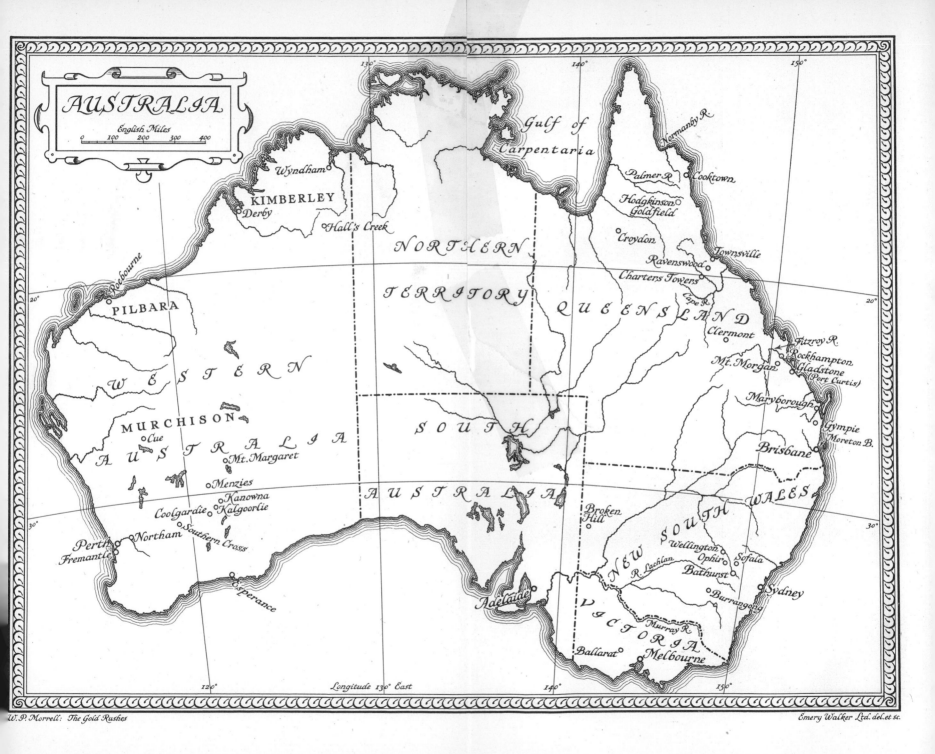

Emery Walker Ltd. del.et sc.